28074.

5.00

MEASUREMENT OF RADIANT ENERGY

MEASUREMENT OF RADIANT ENERGY

EDITED BY

W. E. FORSYTHE

Incandescent Lamp Department, General Electric Company

CONTRIBUTORS

Charles G. Abbot   George R. Harrison
Elliot Q. Adams   Herbert E. Ives
Loyal B. Aldrich   Loyd A. Jones
Ernest F. Barker   Lewis R. Koller
Bentley T. Barnes   Henry F. Kurtz
William W. Coblentz   A. Herman Pfund
Paul H. Dike   Bartholomew J. Spence
Gustave Fassin   Donald C. Stockbarger
William E. Forsythe   A. Hadley Taylor
Kasson S. Gibson   Willibald Weniger
Archie G. Worthing

Prepared under the Direction of

A. C. Hardy, Herbert E. Ives *and* W. E. Forsythe

Constituting a Committee on Methods of Measurement of Radiation of the Division of Physical Sciences, National Research Council.

First Edition
Third Impression

McGRAW-HILL BOOK COMPANY, Inc.

NEW YORK AND LONDON

1937

THE MAPLE PRESS COMPANY, YORK, PA.

To the memory of

CHARLES ELWOOD MENDENHALL

one of the pioneers in this field

PREFACE

This book was written as the result of a discussion with Dr. F. K. Richtmyer regarding the need for collecting certain information pertaining to radiant energy and methods of measuring it. As a result of this discussion, a committee of the Division of Physical Science of the National Research Council was appointed by Dr. Richtmyer, who was then Chairman of the Division, to look into the feasibility of such an undertaking. This committee was made up as follows:

> Dr. Arthur C. Hardy, Professor of Physics,
> Massachusetts Institute of Technology,
> Cambridge, Mass.

> Dr. Herbert E. Ives, Research Physicist,
> Bell Telephone Laboratories, New York City.

> Dr. William E. Forsythe, Physicist,
> Incandescent Lamp Department, General
> Electric Company, Cleveland, Ohio.

After discussing the matter, the committee prepared an outline of what they thought such a book should contain and then decided that in order that the book might be more representative of the judgment of the authors in this field, men of wide experience in different positions of the field should be asked to write the various parts. The following is a list of the names of the men who participated in the preparation of this book and the subject of the part or parts they have written.

1. Charles G. Abbot, D.Sc., Secretary, Smithsonian Institution. Christiansen Filters, The Sun as a Source of Radiation, Spectral Radiant Intensity of Heavenly Bodies.

2. Elliot Q. Adams, Ph.D., Physical Chemist, Incandescent Lamp Department, General Electric Company, Cleveland, Ohio. Prism Materials, Analysis of Radiation by Selective Reflection.

3. Loyal B. Aldrich, A.M., Assistant Director of Astrophysical Observatory, Smithsonian Institution. The Wadsworth Mounting for a Constant-deviation Spectrometer, The Bolometer, The Solar Constant.

4. Ernest F. Barker, Ph.D., Professor of Physics, University of Michigan. Instruments for Infrared Spectroradiometry.

5. Bentley T. Barnes, Ph.D., Physicist, Incandescent Lamp Department, General Electric Company, Cleveland, Ohio. The Spectrometer as an Optical Instrument, Selective Receivers and Filters, Double Monochromators.

6. William W. Coblentz, Ph.D., Chief of Radiometry Section, National Bureau of Standards. Thermopile Construction and Use.

7. Paul H. Dike, Ph.D., Chief of Physics Division, Leeds & Northrup Company. Galvanometers.

8. Gustave Fassin, Ph.D., Physicist, Bausch & Lomb Optical Company. Spectrometer and Spectrograph Slits.

9. William E. Forsythe, Ph.D., Physicist, Incandescent Lamp Department, General Electric Company, Cleveland, Ohio. Fundamental Concepts and Radiation Laws, Optical and Radiation Pyrometry, Photometry, The Luminosity of Radiant Energy.

10. Kasson S. Gibson, Ph.D., Chief, Colorimetry Section, National Bureau of Standards. Spectrophotometry.

11. George R. Harrison, Ph.D., Professor of Physics, Massachusetts Institute of Technology. Densitometers and Microphotometers.

12. Herbert E. Ives, Sc.D., Physicist, Bell Telephone Laboratories. Photometry.

13. Loyd A. Jones, Sc.D., Physicist, Kodak Research Laboratories. Photographic Methods of Measuring Radiant Energy.

14. Lewis R. Koller, Ph.D., Research Physicist, General Electric Company, Schenectady, N.Y. The Measurement of Spectral Radiation by Means of the Photoelectric Tube.

15. Henry F. Kurtz, B.S., Physicist, Bausch & Lomb Optical Company. The Spectrometer.

16. A. Herman Pfund, Ph.D., Professor of Physics, Johns Hopkins University. Blackening Radiation Receivers, Amplifying Galvanometer Deflections.

17. Bartholomew J. Spence, Ph.D., Professor of Physics, Northwestern University. The Vane Radiometer, The Radiomicrometer.

18. Donald C. Stockbarger, Sc.D., Associate Professor of Physics, Massachusetts Institute of Technology. Filter Radiometry.

19. A. Hadley Taylor, B.S. in E.E., Physicist, Lighting Research Laboratory, General Electric Company, Cleveland, Ohio. A Photoelectric Tube Galvanometer Amplifier.

20. Willibald Weniger, Ph.D., Professor of Physics, Oregon State Agricultural College, Corvallis, Ore. Slit-width Correction.

21. Archie G. Worthing, Ph.D., Professor of Physics, University of Pittsburgh. Sources of Radiation.

After the material was collected, some of the manuscripts were considered to be too long and were shortened. Again, some of the authors did not discuss certain points that the editor thought should be discussed. Such material has been added, either by the author at the request of the editor, or by the editor. There was some overlapping of the material presented by the different authors and wherever possible such duplicated sections have been combined and placed where they seemed to belong.

The name of the author follows each chapter heading where the author wrote the entire chapter; or each section heading where an author has written but a part of the chapter. However, no attempt has been made to indicate the writer of either the various paragraphs that have been transferred from one part of the book to another, or the parts added by the editor.

The material prepared naturally divides itself into five parts: fundamental concepts and the laws of radiation, sources of radiation, the analysis of the radiation, the different methods used for measuring radiation, and finally a consideration of some special problems in radiant-energy measurements.

Several questions are considered such as just what do the different radiation laws represent, just what results do they give, how should radiant energy be specified, what sources should be used for different purposes, and what method of analysis should be used for a particular purpose.

In general, the nomenclature and standards adopted by the Illuminating Engineering Society have been followed. A number of the workers in the field of radiant-energy measurements met at Washington, D.C., on April 29, 1936, and discussed terms to use. A report of their discussion was published in the August, 1936, issue of the Review of Scientific Instruments. The terms and symbols adopted by that group have been used in the book.

In Chapter VIII, Dr. L. A. Jones has used the nomenclature and symbols of photography, which differ somewhat from the Illuminating Engineering Society symbols and nomenclature.

An extended list of references is given at the end of each chapter. These references are to books on the subject and to articles published in the technical magazines that deal with the various phases of the work. Some of the illustrations have been copied from papers which have appeared in the different scientific magazines. Reference has been given to the source of each illustration and the editor and contributors want to express their appreciation for the privilege of reproducing these figures in this book.

The Division of Physical Science of the National Research Council has assumed the responsibility of having this book published and has taken care of certain of the expenses incidental to the work of the committee and to the preparation of the manuscripts. The committee wishes to express its appreciation for this help and its obligation to the authors for their time and for the care they have given to the preparation of their manuscripts; and the committee is especially grateful for the patience the authors have displayed in making the different changes and additions when requested to do so. Without the cooperation of the different contributors and the help of the Division of Physical Science of the National Research Council, this book could not have been prepared and published. Also, thanks are due to Dr. F. K. Richtmyer, who read and constructively criticized practically all of the manuscripts before they were submitted to the publisher. Dr. E. Q. Adams, Dr. B. T. Barnes, and Miss M. A. Easley, colleagues of the editor, have been a great help, not only in the preparation of certain parts of the book, but also in the editing and arranging of the different manuscripts and in preparing the index which appears at the end of the book.

W. E. FORSYTHE.

CLEVELAND, OHIO,
  April, 1937.

CONTENTS

xi

CHAPTER XIII

CHAPTER XIV

MEASUREMENT OF RADIANT ENERGY

CHAPTER I

FUNDAMENTAL CONCEPTS AND RADIATION LAWS

W. E. FORSYTHE*

Radiation is the transfer of energy by either emitted waves or particles, *e.g.*, α, β, and γ rays from radioactive substances, cosmic rays, xrays, sound, and radiant heat. Radiant energy is the type of energy which travels in the form of electromagnetic waves. Since the discussion in this book is limited almost entirely to radiant energy, the word radiation, unless otherwise indicated, will be understood to refer to this type, which starts from some material substance excited by heat, electrical discharge, or other means, and ends when it is finally absorbed by some material substance.

No definite statement can be made concerning the first attempt to measure the total radiation from a source. Spectral radiation measurements were begun sometime in the 150-year interval between Newton, who, about 1665, showed that radiation from the sun could be separated into a spectrum, and Herschel, who found that there was considerable energy beyond the limits of the red end of the visible spectrum. The measurement of radiation is one of the tasks of the physicist that has many pitfalls. Some of these can be avoided and the difficulty of making accurate radiation measurements can be greatly reduced if certain precautions are taken. Methods of avoiding some of the pitfalls, of overcoming some of the difficulties, and of increasing the accuracy of radiation measurements will be outlined in this book.

Whenever electromagnetic waves fall upon any material substance, they are in general, partly reflected, partly transmitted,

* *Physicist, Incandescent Lamp Department, General Electric Company.*

1

and partly absorbed. The part that is absorbed either makes
some more or less permanent change in the structure of the
absorbing substance or is transformed into heat, warming the
absorber. As will be more fully described later, methods have
been devised for the construction of receivers that are very efficient in absorbing radiation. Some of the better receivers
absorb and convert into heat between 99 and 100 per cent of the
radiation that falls upon them, and are so built that very accurate
measurements can be made of the resultant change in their
temperature and this change of temperature used as a measure
of the amount of radiant energy falling upon the receiver.

Symbols. In the physics of radiation certain terms and
symbols are employed which it would be well for all writers to
use in the same sense. The Illuminating Engineering Society[1]
has published a list of definitions of terms used in illuminating
engineering. It is intended in this book to follow as far as practicable the terms defined and symbols given in that report. In
Table 1 are given some symbols, the quantity to which each refers,
the name and value of the term used. Many of these have been
taken from the table in the report of the Illuminating Engineering
Society.

Radiation laws of the blackbody:
Stefan-Boltzmann law for total radiation:

$$W = \sigma T^4 \tag{1}$$

Planck radiation law for spectral radiation:

$$J_\lambda = \frac{A c_1 \lambda^{-5}}{e^{\frac{c_2}{\lambda T}} - 1} \tag{2}$$

Wien displacement law:

$$J_\lambda = A c_1 \lambda^{-5} F(\lambda T) \tag{3}$$

Wien radiation law:*

$$J_\lambda = A c_1 \lambda^{-5} e^{-\frac{c_2}{\lambda T}} \tag{4}$$

* The Wien law gives results that are accurate to better than one per
cent for values of λT less than 0.3 cm deg. To attain this same accuracy
with the Rayleigh-Jeans law λT must exceed 77 cm deg.

TABLE 1

	Symbol	Quantity	Name of unit	Abbreviation, size of unit, etc.
1	A	Area...................	square centimeter	cm²
2	A		angstrom unit	10^{-8} cm
3	B	Brightness..............	candle/cm², lambert	candle/cm², lumen/cm²
4	$\mathcal{B}$ or $N^{\ddagger}$	Steradiancy²............	watt/(cm² steradian)	
5	b	Wien displacement constants..................	....	0.2884 cm deg.
	b_1	....		1.300×10^{-11} watt/(cm³ deg.⁵)
6	°C	(Temperature)..........	degree centigrade	
7	c	Velocity of light.........		2.99776×10^{10} cm/sec.
8	c_1	First radiation constant..		1.177×10^{-12} w cm²*
9	c_2	Second radiation constant.		1.4320 cm deg.
10	d	Differential operator		
11	E	Illumination.............	phot., foot-candle, lux	ph, ft.-c., lx (or mc.)
12	$\mathcal{E}$ or $H^{\ddagger}$	Irradiancy²..............	watt/cm²	
13	e	Base of natural logs......	a numeric	2.718+
14	e	Charge of electron.......		4.8029×10^{-10} e.s.u.
15	e_t	Total emissivity..........	a numeric	
16	e_λ	spectral emissivity........	a numeric	
17	F	Luminous flux...........	lumen	lu
18	°F	(Temperature)..........	degree Fahrenheit	⁵⁄₉ degrees centigrade
19	h	Planck quantum..........		6.6608×10^{-27} erg sec.
20	I	Luminous intensity.......	candle	candle
21	J	Radiant intensity........	watt/steradian	
22	J_λ	Spectral radiant intensity.	watt/(steradian cm)	
23	K_λ	Spectral luminosity.......	lumen/watt	F_λ/Φ_λ
24	°K	(Absolute temp.).........	degree Kelvin	
25	k	Boltzmann constant......		1.371×10^{-16} erg/deg.
26	lu	(Luminous flux)..........	lumen	
27	mμ	(Length)................	millimicron	10^{-6} mm
28	n	Index of refraction.......	a numeric	
29	∫	Integral.................	operator	
30	T	Temperature.............	degree Kelvin, etc.	°K, °C, °F,
31	t	Time....................	second, etc.	sec., min., hr.,
32	U	Radiant energy..........	erg	
33	u	Radiant-energy density...	erg/cm³, etc.	
34	V	Volume.................	cubic centimeter	cm³
35	W	Radiant flux per unit area, radiancy².............	watt/cm²	
36	W_λ	Spectral radiant flux per unit area, spectral radiance²..................	watt/(cm² unit of wavelength)	
37	w	(Power).................	watt	
38	α	Absorptance	a numeric	
39	Δ	Difference...............	operator	
40	θ	Angle from normal.......	degree, radian	deg., rad.
41	κ	Extinction coefficient.....	a numeric	
42	λ	Wavelength.............	cm, etc.†	
43	μ	(Length)................	micron	0.001 mm
44	ν	Frequency...............	reciprocal second	1/sec.
45	π	Ratio of circumference of circle to diameter........	a numeric	3.1416 −
46	ρ	Reflectivity.............	a numeric	
47	Σ	Summation..............	operator	
48	σ	Stefan-Boltzmann constant	....	5.735×10^{-12} w/ (cm² deg.⁴)
49	τ	Transmittance...........	a numeric	
50	Φ or $P^{\ddagger}$	Radiant flux............	watt	w
51	ϕ	Azimuth angle..........	degree	°
52	ω	Solid angle.............	steradian	

* This value of the constant gives the normal intensity—that is, the energy per second for the wavelength and wavelength interval considered, per centimeter squared per unit solid angle around the normal.   (All dimensions in centimeters.)

The numerical value of all constants are taken from summaries prepared by Prof. Birge.[13] All radiation constants as given are based upon degrees Kelvin.   The abbreviation deg. unless otherwise noted refers to degrees Kelvin.

† See Table 2.

‡ These English letters are to be suggested for these terms in the report of the Color Committee of the Optical Society of America.

Rayleigh-Jeans radiation law:

$$J_\lambda = A c \lambda^{-5}\left(\frac{\lambda T}{c_2}\right) \tag{5}$$

Principal corollaries of Wien displacement law: *

$$\lambda_m T = b \tag{6}$$
$$J_m = A T^5 b_1 \tag{7}$$

Definitions. There are some terms that are used in this field that should be specifically defined: *Radiant energy* (U) is energy traveling in the form of electromagnetic waves. *Radiant flux*, sometimes called radiance[2] $(\Phi = dU/dt)$, is the time rate of flow of radiant energy.

Radiant-energy density $(u = dU/dV)$ is the radiant energy per unit volume. This can be calculated from the radiant intensity, the distance from the source, and the velocity of light. *Radiant intensity*,† sometimes called steradiance[2] $(J = d\Phi/d\omega)$, is the solid-angular derivative of the emitted flux and is measured by the energy falling in unit time upon the area subtended by unit solid angle about the direction considered at any distance from the source. *Radiant-flux density*, sometimes called radiancy[2] $(W = d\Phi/dA)$, is the incident or transmitted radiant energy per unit area and unit time. The radiation from a source is often specified by giving for a specified distance from the source the radiant-flux density. This quantity is the solid-angular integral of the radiant intensity for the solid angle that this unit area subtends. This follows directly from the inverse-square law, since the solid angle subtended by the unit area varies inversely as the square of the distance, and the intercepted flux likewise varies inversely as the square of the distance.

Steradiancy[2] $(\mathcal{B} = dW/d\omega)$ is the radiant flux per unit solid angle per square centimeter of the source.‡

---

* These laws show how the maximum intensity and the wavelength λ_m at which it occurs are related, and how the maximum intensity shifts with the temperature.

† This and the following definitions apply only to a uniform point source. If they are extended to larger sources or to sources variable in time or direction, the element of space, time, etc., must be taken small.

‡ For a blackbody the radiant flux in an actual unit solid angle, one steradian, around the normal is 0.92 J_0 where J_0 is the normal intensity.

For a blackbody of area A, several of these quantities are connected by the following equation:

$$dU_\lambda d\lambda = \Phi_\lambda d\lambda dt = A W_\lambda d\lambda dt = \pi J_\lambda d\lambda dt = \frac{\pi A c_1 \lambda^{-5}}{e^{\frac{c_2}{\lambda T}} - 1} d\lambda dt \quad (8)$$

BLACKBODY

The standard for all radiators is the blackbody, which is very simply defined as a body that absorbs all the radiation which falls upon it, i.e., it neither reflects nor transmits any of the incident radiation. It can be shown[3] that such a body will radiate more energy for any and all wavelength intervals than any other body of the same temperature and area provided the radiation is due to the temperature alone. From this definition, using thermodynamic reasoning and certain very plausible assumptions, it can be shown that such a body will radiate an amount of energy that depends upon the temperature alone and also that the radiated energy is distributed among different wavelength intervals according to a definite law.

Blackbody Laws.[4] Thus, there are two fundamental laws which show how the blackbody radiates its energy. The first, which is called the Stefan-Boltzmann law, tells how the total radiant flux from a unit area of a blackbody varies with the temperature.

Stefan-Boltzmann Law:

$$W = \sigma T^4 \quad (1)$$

σ is a constant which will be discussed later. The other law shows how the radiant flux is distributed among the different wavelength intervals. It required three attempts to obtain what is now regarded as the proper form of this law. Wien's first attempt gave his displacement law which shows the form of the equation.

Wien Displacement Law:[5]

$$J_\lambda = A c_1 \lambda^{-5} F(\lambda T) \quad (3)$$

The principal corollaries of this law are

$$\lambda_m T = b \quad (6)$$

$$\frac{J_m}{A T^5} = b_1 \quad (7)$$

which show how the maximum intensity of the radiation and the wavelength at which it occurs are related to the temperature. λ_m is the wavelength of maximum intensity J_m; and b and b_1 are constants. Wien then attempted to find the form of the $F(\lambda T)$ with the final results:

Wien Radiation Law:[6]

$$J_\lambda = A c_1 \lambda^{-5} e^{-\frac{c_2}{\lambda T}} \qquad (4)$$

This law fitted the experimental facts for short wavelengths and low temperatures but did not fit for long wavelengths and high temperatures (Fig. 1), *i.e.*, for large values of λT. For λ expressed in centimeters and T in degrees Kelvin, this equation gives results that are accurate to within 1 per cent, if the value of λT does not exceed 0.3 cm deg.

A formula developed by Rayleigh and Jeans was found satisfactory for long wavelengths and high temperatures, but did not hold at all for short wavelengths.

Rayleigh-Jeans Radiation Law:[7]

$$J_\lambda = A c \lambda^{-4} T \qquad (5)$$

This law gives results that are accurate to within 1 per cent only if the product λT is greater than 77 cm deg.

Planck next attacked the problem and by the introduction of the quantum hypothesis developed his well-known law.

Planck Radiation Law:[8]

$$J_\lambda = \frac{A c_1 \lambda^{-5}}{e^{\frac{c_2}{\lambda T}} - 1} \qquad (2)$$

This law has been found to fit the experimental data well within the experimental error (Fig. 1). The Wien equation is generally used in calculation within the visible spectrum (optical pyrometry), since within this range sufficiently accurate results are obtained.

The Stefan-Boltzmann law and the Wien displacement law are derivable by the thermodynamic reasoning based upon the Carnot cycle with radiation as the working substance. Since Kelvin in his derivation of the thermodynamic temperature scale showed that the scale is independent of the working substance, the scale given by the perfect-gas thermometer and either of these radiation laws must be identical. Considered in this light, either of these laws may be taken as theoretically exact, and used as a measure of the temperature in determinations of the relative radiant intensity of a blackbody.

There are two conditions that the Planck radiation law must fulfill. It must give the Stefan-Boltzmann law by integration

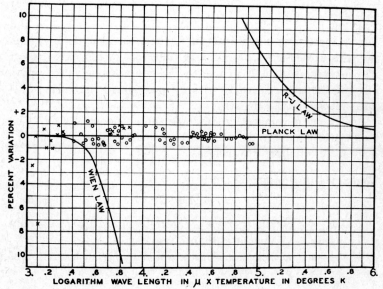

Fig. 1.—Experimental tests of Planck's radiation law. x, Coblentz's points; o, data by Rubens and Michel (only about half of their points shown). For comparison the variations of the Wien law and also of the Rayleigh-Jeans law from the Planck law are shown.

from $\lambda = 0$ to $\lambda = \infty$ and it must satisfy all the requirements of the Wien displacement law. If it had not fulfilled these conditions, it probably would never have been published. This law has been tested by measurements, on experimental blackbodies, of the intensity of the radiation for a wide range of temperatures (300°K to 1700°K) and a wide range of wavelengths (0.5μ to 52μ). These various tests[9] show that the law represents the experimental facts to a very high accuracy. The better experimental values agree with the calculated values practically within ±1 per cent, and show no definite trend one way or the other.

The data plotted in Fig. 1 show the extent of the recorded tests of the spectral radiation laws in terms of the product λT. For reference, the variation of the Wien and the Rayleigh-Jeans laws from the Planck law has been plotted. This shows that there has been no test in the range of the agreement between the Planck and the Rayleigh-Jeans laws. Also there have been no direct tests known to the author that show the validity of the Planck law for small values of λT (less than 1,000μ deg.).

The relative spectral intensity of the radiation for various temperatures and for various wavelength intervals, obtained by

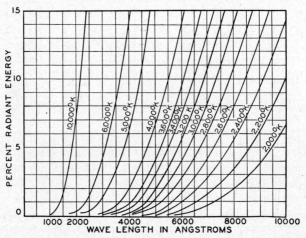

Fig. 2.—Percentage of radiant energy emitted in spectral region between wavelengths zero and λ in angstroms as shown for a blackbody at the various temperatures shown.

calculation using Planck's equation, has been published in the Miscellaneous Papers of the Bureau of Standards.[10] These data are very valuable when one has occasion to calculate a blackbody distribution for almost any temperature. Holladay,[11] by expressing the integral of the Planck equation showing the amount of energy from $\lambda = 0$ to any value of λ, as a function of λT, has developed a method of calculating the percentage of energy radiated by a blackbody at any temperature for wavelengths shorter than any selected value or by taking differences for any selected wavelengths interval. Figure 2 taken from the same paper[11] gives curves for obtaining the percentage of the radiation shorter than a selected wavelength for a range of temperatures.

Expanding the exponential part of the Planck equation into series and evaluating these series for small and for large values of the product λT gives the Wien law for small values of λT and the Rayleigh-Jeans law for large values. If the laws are written in the forms that thus result, it is easy to calculate relative values for the three radiation laws.

Planck:

$$J_\lambda \propto c_1 \lambda^{-5} \frac{1}{e^{\frac{c_2}{\lambda T}} - 1} \tag{2}$$

Wien:

$$J_\lambda \propto c_1 \lambda^{-5} \frac{1}{e^{\frac{c_2}{\lambda T}}} \tag{4}$$

Rayleigh-Jeans:

$$J_\lambda \propto c_1 \lambda^{-5} \frac{1}{\frac{c_2}{\lambda T}} \tag{5}$$

A table of exponential functions will show readily for what value of $c_2/\lambda T$, i.e., for the product λT, either the Wien or the Rayleigh-Jeans law gives results that agree with the Planck law to within 1 per cent.

It is tedious to calculate intensities from the Planck equation. A simple method is to calculate the value of the ratio of the Planck to the Wien law for a series of values of the variable λT, and from such values obtain factors to correct results obtained from the Wien equation, which is much easier to handle.

$$\frac{(J_\lambda)_P}{(J_\lambda)_W} = \frac{e^{\frac{c_2}{\lambda T}}}{e^{\frac{c_2}{\lambda T}} - 1} \tag{9}$$

The ratio of intensities for the Planck and the Wien equations obtained by calculation from this relation is shown in Table 2 for a range of values of λT.

In Table 3 and Fig. 3 are shown values of the specific spectral radiant intensities calculated by using the Planck, Wien, and Rayleigh-Jeans equations for different temperatures and different wavelengths. This shows that the Rayleigh-Jeans law does not

TABLE 2.   RATIO OF VALUES OF PLANCK TO WIEN LAW FOR A NUMBER OF
VALUES OF λT

$\lambda T (\mu^\circ K)$ $(J_\lambda)_P/(J_\lambda)_W$

2,000.. 1.0008

2,500.. 1.0033

3,000.. 1.0085

4,000.. 1.0287

5,000.. 1.0604

give accurate results except for extreme temperatures or wavelengths almost entirely outside of any practical limits.

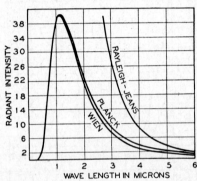

FIG. 3.—Comparison of values calculated from Planck, Wien, and Rayleigh-Jeans for a temperature of 2500°K and for various wavelengths.

TABLE 3.   SPECTRAL STERADIANCY AS CALCULATED BY THE WIEN, PLANCK AND RAYLEIGH-JEANS LAWS FOR VARIOUS VALUES OF λ AND T

(λ IN μ, ω IN STERADIANS, ϕ IN WATTS, $d\lambda = 0.1\mu$)

Wavelength	2μ	6μ	2μ	20μ	154μ	200μ
T..........	1600°K	1600	5000	5000	5000	5000
λT (cm deg.)	0.32	0.96	1	10	77	100
Planck......	4.24×10^{-1}	4.40×10^{-2}	$1.154\times10^{+1}$	2.390×10^{-3}	7.24×10^{-7}	2.549×10^{-7}
Wien.......	4.20	3.42	0.879	0.319	0.133	0.0364
Rayleigh-Jeans	82.4	10.16	2.569	2.569	7.31	2.569

As the Planck equation is written, it gives spectral intensities for unit area for different temperatures as shown in Fig. 4. It may be necessary at times to find the spectral radiant intensity of a blackbody at different temperatures for a definite wattage output, *i.e.*, for equal areas under the curves of spectral intensity against wavelength.   Since the total radiant flux of a blackbody at a definite temperature T is given by $\sigma A T^4$, the Planck equation for any temperature T will give the spectral intensities for a definite flux Φ if it is multiplied by $\Phi(\sigma A T^4)^{-1}$ (Fig. 5).

Lambert Cosine Law.[12]   An adequate discussion of the constants of the above equations requires the introduction of the

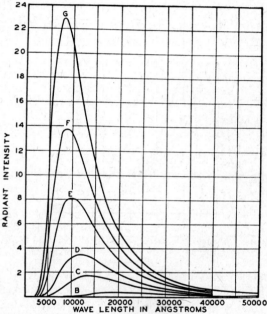

Fig. 4.—Spectral distribution of the radiation from a blackbody of unit area as given by Planck's equation for the following temperatures.

$$B = 1500°K$$
$$C = 2150°K$$
$$D = 2500°K$$
$$E = 2970°K$$
$$F = 3300°K$$
$$G = 3655°K$$

Lambert cosine law of radiation.   This law states that the brightness of a blackbody is independent of the direction from which it is observed.   This theorem is generalized in the statement that the radiation from a blackbody for all wavelength intervals varies as the cosine of the angle of emission.

Radiation Constants.[13]   The constant σ, of the Stefan-Boltzmann law, has been found to have a value of

$$5.735 \times 10^{-12} \text{ watt/cm}^2 \text{ deg.}^4$$

The use of this value of σ in the Stefan-Boltzmann equation will give the total energy radiated per second toward one side (*i.e.*, per solid angle 2π) for a blackbody 1 cm^2 in area for the absolute temperature T expressed in degrees Kelvin. The normal intensity *i.e.*, the intensity perpendicular to the blackbody per unit solid angle, is given by dividing this value by π. (The constant π

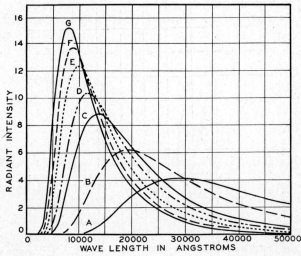

FIG. 5.—Spectral distribution of the radiation from a blackbody as calculated by Planck's equation for various temperatures. The wattage output in this case was kept constant and equal to that from a blackbody of unit area at temperature 3300°K.

Temperature, °K	Area, cm^2
$A = 1000$	118.6
$B = 1500$	23.4
$C = 2150$	5.55
$D = 2500$	3.04
$E = 2970$	1.52
$F = 3300$	1.00
$G = 3655$	0.66

is obtained by integrating the Lambert cosine law.*[14]) The constant, c_2, of the Wien-Planck equation as measured has the value 14,320μ deg. and c_1 has the value 1.177×10^{-12} watts cm^2 per unit solid angle.

The use of the constant σ or c_2 as given follows directly and causes but little trouble. The only care needed is to express c_2 in the units of the wavelengths times the absolute temperature

* This is for a plane blackbody, for a spherical blackbody, the constant of integration is equal to the solid angle, the total radiation to one side (solid angle 2π) is $2\pi J_0$ where J_0 is the normal intensity.

used. The value of c_1 given, presupposes, however, that all lengths are in centimeters, a condition almost never met in practice. For the general case c_1 may be written in symbolic form as follows:

$$c_1 = \text{const.} \times \frac{(\text{wavelength})^5 \text{ power}}{\text{area} \times \text{wavelength interval}} \qquad (10)$$

where the value of the constant depends upon the solid angle considered as well as the other units, for example, for spectral radiation to one side (solid angle 2π and Lambert's cosine law) of a blackbody 1 cm in area for the wavelength expressed in microns and the wavelength interval equal to 0.1μ ($c_2 = 14{,}320\mu$ deg.)

$$c_1 = 3.697 \times 10^{+3} \frac{\mu^5 \times \text{watts}}{\text{cm}^2 \times 0.1\mu} \qquad (11)$$

For the wavelength expressed in angstroms, $d\lambda = 100\text{A}$ and other conditions unchanged ($c_2 = 1.432 \times 10^8 \text{A } °\text{K}$),

$$c_1 = 3.697 \times 10^{22} \times \frac{\text{A}^5 \times \text{watts}}{\text{cm}^2 \times 100\text{A}} \qquad (12)$$

If all the lengths are in centimeters, $d\lambda = 1$ cm with other conditions the same ($c_2 = 1.432$ cm $°\text{K}$)

$$c_1 = 3.697 \times 10^{-12} \text{ cm}^2 \text{ watts} \qquad (13)$$

and per unit solid angle the constant c_1 has the value given in Table 1. If the radiant flux is given in other units than watts, the numeric of the constant will be changed proportionally.

Using the above values of c_1 and c_2 in the Planck equation, one may compute the specific spectral intensity, the spectral steradiancy (*i.e.*, the energy radiated per second per unit solid angle perpendicular to the surface, at the wavelength and for the wavelength interval considered, by a blackbody 1 cm² in area). To obtain the total spectral radiant flux to one side (*i.e.*, solid angle 2π) for the same wavelength interval, multiply this value by π.

Units. Since radiant flux is a flow of energy, its value may be expressed in any of the units of power, or as the amount of energy, expressed in any energy unit, per unit time. The intensity of the radiation from the sun, commonly called the solar constant, is generally given as the energy, expressed in calories, that falls in 1 min. upon a square centimeter at the earth's mean distance and normal to the sun's rays.   Abbot's[15] value of the solar constant is 1.94 cal./(cm² min.).   No definite rule can be given for the choice of one unit over another, but in general the problem itself will influence the decision.   However, units must be given, and it must also be remembered that it is energy flow that is being measured.   Ergs, joules, calories, or B.t.u. per second, watts, or even horsepower (all per some unit area) may be used, but most physicists will probably prefer to use the area in square centimeters, and the power in watts or some multiple thereof or in calories per second.   The engineer may prefer to use watts per square meter, or B.t.u. per square foot per second.

Units of Wavelength.   Spectral-radiant-energy measurements necessitate some statement as to the unit of wavelength to be used. This is necessary since four different sets of units are in use, with the values shown in Table 4.

TABLE 4.   WAVELENGTH UNITS

Name	Symbol	Value
Micron.....................	μ	$1\mu = 10^{-3}$ mm
Millimicron................	$m\mu$	$1\ m\mu = 10^{-6}$ mm
Angstrom..................	A	$1A = 10^{-7}$ mm
X-unit.....................	XU	$1\ XU = 10^{-10}$ mm

It was formerly thought satisfactory to express wavelength in microns, but if this unit is used, the wavelengths of the entire visible and ultraviolet spectrum are expressed by fractions.   To avoid the use of fractions, many authors express wavelengths in millimicrons.   Using this unit, the wavelengths of the visible spectrum are expressed by three figures before the decimal point. For most work in radiation measurements, wavelengths expressed by three figures seem to be accurate enough, but some workers express wavelengths in angstrom units in all cases; hence it seems impossible to get unity of action even among workers in radiation measurements.   The spectroscopist uses angstrom units for all of his work except in the xray region, where the unit XU (XU = 0.001A) is often used.   Whatever units are used to express wavelength, care must be taken when absolute calculations are to be made, since the numerics of the constants, as for instance c_1 and c_2 of the Planck equation, are given for a definite unit of wavelength. For calculations of absolute values, the wavelength must, of course, be expressed in centimeters if the c.g.s. values of the constants are used.

Radiant-energy Measurements. Radiant-energy measurement naturally divides itself into two classes: the first is the measurement of the total radiant energy or flux (*i.e.*, for all wavelengths) from the source, and the other is the measurement of the radiant energy or flux, for various wavelength intervals. The first measurement is easier since the radiation need not be separated into different wavelength intervals—a single measurement with relatively insensitive instruments suffices—but for accurate results the receiver must have the same absorption for radiant energy of all wavelengths present. For spectral-radiant-energy measurements, the absorption of the receiver may be included in the instrument calibration for any particular wavelength. In measuring spectral radiant energy there are two problems: the analysis, *i.e.*, separating the radiant energy into different wavelength intervals, and the measurement of the energy or power within these intervals. The latter procedure may be difficult because the amount of energy is generally small. The radiant energy must be separated into wavelength intervals in such a manner that it is possible to measure the energy for the particular wavelength interval without too great error due to stray radiation. Certain corrections must be made for the instruments involved; these will be given in detail in a later chapter.

Calibration of Radiant-energy-measuring Devices. In measuring radiation, either total or for a definite spectral interval, one must decide whether comparative or absolute values are desired. For many types of work, only comparative values of the radiation intensity are needed; while at other times absolute values are required. When absolute values are required, some method of calibrating the energy-measuring device must be used. The calibration of an energy- or power-measuring device consists in finding the response of the instrument when a known amount of radiation falls upon it. The best method of doing this is to expose the measuring device to the radiation from the standard radiator, *i.e.*, a blackbody at a definite temperature, and

N85
Method

to compare the reading of the instrument with the known amount of energy or power radiated by the standard radiator. The linearity of the relation between the response of the measuring device and the energy or power measured can be tested by making use of the inverse-square law to reduce by a known ratio the amount of energy falling upon the receiver.

The setting up and operating of a blackbody is a painstaking and tedious operation that not many laboratories are equipped to undertake. The National Bureau of Standards[16] is therefore prepared to furnish incandescent lamps calibrated by specifying the amount of radiation per square centimeter at a definite distance in a definite direction from the lamp. Such lamps make very satisfactory sources against which to calibrate energy- or power-measuring devices which have the same sensitivity for all wavelengths emitted by the lamps.

There are several indirect methods of calibrating energy-measuring devices that have been found satisfactory when standard sources are not available. One very good method is to use an incandescent lamp as a source and to assume that the total energy radiated in a particular direction will bear the same ratio to the mean energy radiated as will the candlepower in the same direction to the mean spherical candlepower. This latter ratio can be readily measured in many laboratories. The total energy input of the lamp must be corrected for end loss, gas loss, base loss, etc., in order to obtain the amount radiated. To obtain a calibration for spectral measurements, relative intensities within the visible spectrum for some lamp or other source of known luminous intensity may be measured, and a summation taken of the product of this relative energy and the relative luminosity, wavelength for wavelength. The candlepower of the lamp or other source, in the definite direction, divided by this sum gives the calibration constant.

Geometric Considerations. The amount of radiation that passes from one surface to another as, for instance, from a source being studied to the receiver for making the measurements, depends upon the distance between the two surfaces, the size of the two surfaces, and their respective orientations with respect to the line joining them. Thus, for the general case, the amount of radiation falling upon a receiver from a source depends upon five geometric parameters. (It is assumed here that the receiver, the intervening medium, and the source are isotropic.) The receiver is generally mounted perpendicular to the line joining the two surfaces, and calibrated to give the amount of energy falling upon it per unit time and per unit area.   This eliminates the orientation and size of the receiver, and reduces the variables to three.   These three variables—the distance to the source, its area, and its orientation—must be considered in giving the results of measurements of radiation, either for all wavelengths or for various wavelength intervals.

Specifying Radiation from a Source.   The radiant energy from a source may be specified in several ways: The entire radiation from the source or the entire radiation for unit area of the source may be given.   The radiation within a certain cone about a certain direction may be given and that, too, either for the entire source or for a unit area.   The radiant flux from the source is often given by stating the amount of energy that in unit time passes through or falls upon a unit area in a definite direction from the source (generally along the normal) and at a definite distance.

Spectral Specification of Radiation.   When one is giving results of spectral radiation measurements, for sources of spectrally continuous radiation, care must be taken to give not only the wavelength but also the wavelength interval to which the measurements correspond.   This is because the amount of energy depends upon the wavelength interval; but it might also be noted that it is thermodynamically[17] impossible to have finite energy except in a finite wavelength interval.   Results for continuous spectra are, in general, given per 100A or per 50A at a definite wavelength; but other wavelength intervals may be used. This is equally important when calculating energy distributions from the blackbody equation and the emissivities of the different sources used.   If the distributions of energy are calculated from the Planck equation, written as follows,

$$J_\lambda d\lambda dt = \frac{A c_1 \lambda^{-5}}{e^{\frac{c_2}{\lambda T}} - 1} d\lambda dt \qquad (14)$$

little trouble will be experienced since the equation thus written gives the energy radiated per time dt at wavelength λ for a wavelength interval $d\lambda$ for a blackbody of area A operated at a temperature T.   (Using the appropriate* values of c_1 and c_2, of course.)

The area under the curve, Fig. 6, obtained from this equation must equal the energy for the solid angle ω considered.   If the area is obtained by summing the ordinates from the above equation, $d\lambda$ will be evident from the number of ordinates used; *i.e.*, if the calculations are made for every 10A, $d\lambda$ will be 10A.   This method is self-corrective since if $d\lambda$ is made, say one-tenth as large, that is, $d\lambda = 1A$, ten times as many ordinates will be

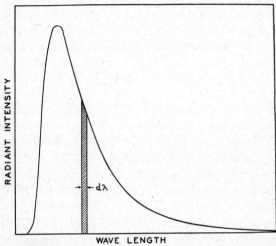

FIG. 6.—Spectral distribution of the radiation from a blackbody.   The cross-hatch part shows the intensity for a wavelength interval equal to $d\lambda$.

summed, and thus the same area obtained (except for the error due to approximating the real curve with a stair-step curve, of course).

Effects of Material Objects on Radiation.   The field of radiant-energy measurements includes not only the study of sources of radiation, as described above, but the measurement of the alterations produced in the radiation by bodies on which it falls, or through which it passes, *i.e.*, of the reflection, the absorption, and the transmission of material objects.   Since these magnitudes are ratios, only relative calibration of the measuring devices is needed.   (It is universally assumed, and is usually true, that the reflection, absorption, and transmission are inde-

*See p. 13.

pendent of the intensity of the radiation used in making measurements.)   Care must be taken that the radiation used in the measurement does not cause a very large change in the temperature of the sample, as these factors generally depend upon the temperature of the substance.   For objects of more than a few wavelengths' thickness, the reflection depends only upon the surface conditions; whereas the absorption and transmission vary with the thickness.

Bouguer-Lambert Law of Absorption.[18]   From the assumption that the transmission of any body is independent of the intensity of the radiation, it follows that each unit of thickness in a homogeneous medium will reduce the intensity of monochromatic radiation in the same ratio.   Expressed mathematically,

$$J_\lambda = J_{\lambda_0} e^{-kx} \tag{15}$$

wherein x is distance along the path of the radiation, J_λ and J_{λ_0} the radiant intensity at distances x and 0, respectively, and k is called the absorption coefficient[19] and, as given, is the negative logarithm of the fraction transmitted by a layer of thickness 1 cm within the material.   For convenience common logs are often used.   This equation is the Bouguer-Lambert law of absorption (not to be confused with the Lambert cosine law).   In the theory of absorbing media, it is customary to take as the unit of distance $\lambda/2\pi$, and to use the symbol κ for the extinction coefficient calculated from the amplitude.

$$J_\lambda = J_{\lambda_0} e^{-\frac{4\pi\kappa x}{\lambda}} \tag{16}$$

wherein the distance x and the wavelength λ are to be in the same units.   This gives

$$\kappa = \frac{k\lambda}{4\pi} \tag{17}$$

Beer's Law of Absorption.[20]   When the absorbing medium is a solution (whether solid, liquid, or gaseous) and the absorbing molecules are far enough apart not to affect one another; and if the process of dilution does not produce changes in the character of the solvent (assumed nonabsorbing, or appropriate correction made), the gradient of the radiant flux density will be proportional to the concentration of the absorbing substance:

$$J_\lambda = J_{\lambda_0} e^{-c\beta x} \tag{18}$$

wherein c is concentration, x is distance, and β the specific absorption coefficient. This equation is known as Beer's law. If the concentrations are in gram-molecular units, the coefficient is known as the molecular (or molar) extinction coefficient.

The transmission of an absorbing body bounded by a medium of different index of refraction is the product of the transmissions of the two surfaces and of the transmittance (i.e., internal transmission) given by the Bouguer-Lambert law. For most substances the absorption of the surface can be neglected, and the transmission of the surface is the complement of the reflection.

In making calculations for absorbing glasses of various thicknesses, allowance for the transmission (i.e., for the reflection) of the surfaces must be made before applying the Bouguer-Lambert or the Beer's law.

Thus, the transmission in the visible of a 1-mm thickness of clear glass or quartz is of the order of 92 per cent, but the transmission of a 2-mm thickness would not be appreciably less, since in neither case does kx differ appreciably from zero.

The absorptance α is a property of a given body, whereas the extinction coefficient is a characteristic of the material. The absorptance may be calculated from the reflectance *at both surfaces*, the absorption coefficient and the dimensions of the body considered. If, as usually happens, the absorption coefficient varies with wavelength, total absorptance α will then be a weighted mean value of α_λ

$$\alpha = \frac{\int J_{\lambda i} \alpha_\lambda d\lambda}{\int J_{\lambda i} d\lambda} \tag{19}$$

where $J_{\lambda i}$ is the spectral radiant intensity.

RADIATION FROM NON-BLACKBODIES

Drude Law. It does not seem possible to write any general law to describe the radiation of non-blackbodies, certainly not in terms of the parameters, wavelength, and temperature. Drude[21] derived a law for the spectral emissivity of a metal in terms of its resistivity ρ in ohm centimeters and the wavelength λ in centimeters.

$$e_\lambda = 0.365\sqrt{\frac{\rho}{\lambda}} \qquad (20)$$

which has been found to hold within a few per cent for wavelength regions longer than about 20,000A. Within the range of this law the total radiation from a metal whose resistivity ρ varies directly as the temperature can be written:

$$W = KT^5 \qquad (21)$$

Probably the reason for the failure of the law of Drude for short wavelengths is that the resistivity ρ depends upon the frequency for frequencies corresponding to wavelengths shorter than 20,000A.

Emissivity. It is customary to give the total radiant flux from non-blackbodies by the use of equations similar to the Stefan-Boltzmann law

$$W = e_t\sigma T^4 \qquad (22)$$

where e_t is the factor that it has been found necessary to introduce so that this equation will represent the facts. The factor e_t is ordinarily a function of the temperature and is called the total emissivity of the substance under consideration. To describe the spectral radiation, the Planck law (or the Wien law within the proper range) is used and a factor e_λ, which is called the spectral emissivity, introduced. The factor e_λ will most certainly be a function of the wavelength and of the temperature and will probably depend upon the direction of observation, since the radiation from non-blackbodies does not, in general, follow the Lambert cosine law. It may also be necessary to consider both the angle of altitude and azimuth, since the radiation may depend upon the orientation of the substance, particularly for non-isotropic substances. This latter variation is generally neglected since most substances are macroscopically isotropic, and e_λ given for various wavelengths and various temperatures, for radiant flux normal to the surface, and the variation of the radiation from the Lambert cosine law of radiation also given. Thus, to specify completely the radiant flux from a non-blackbody at all temperatures and all wavelengths requires a double infinity of factors, since these factors may vary with both the temperature and the wavelength, and requires in addition some statement as to the departure from Lambert's cosine law.

Kirchhoff Law. There is an interesting relation that exists between the radiant flux from any substance and its absorptance for radiation. This relation is the basis for the statement that good absorbers of radiation are also good radiators. If Φ represents the radiant flux from any radiator at a particular temperature and α its absorptance for blackbody radiation of the same temperature, then the Kirchhoff law says that

$$\frac{\Phi}{\alpha} = \Phi_{bb} \qquad (23)$$

Stated in words, the Kirchhoff law is: At a given temperature, the quotient obtained by dividing the radiant flux by the absorptance of any body is the same for all bodies and is equal to the radiant flux from a blackbody at the same temperature. This statement is true for any small wavelength interval; for the total radiation, it is true only if the incident radiation is from a blackbody at the same temperature.

Equation (22) gives:

$$\Phi = e_t \sigma A T^4$$

as the radiant flux from any substance where e_t is the total emissivity. From this relation and Eq. (23), Eq. (24) may be written.

$$\frac{e_t \sigma A T^4}{\alpha} = \sigma A T^4 \qquad (24)$$

or

$$e_t = \alpha \qquad (25)$$

i.e., the total emissivity of any radiator is equal to its absorption factor for blackbody radiation of the same temperature.

Let a certain amount of energy fall upon a surface of some substance. Part is reflected, part transmitted, and the remainder is absorbed. If this substance is of such a character that none of the radiation is transmitted, the incident radiation then is equal to the sum of the part absorbed and the part reflected. Written in the form of an equation, if Φ is the incident radiant flux,

$$\Phi = \rho\Phi + \alpha\Phi \qquad (26)$$

or

$$1 = \rho + \alpha \tag{27}$$

where ρ is the reflectivity and α the absorptance of the material. These same relations hold for any wavelength interval also. If the substance is not opaque, the amount transmitted must be included. From this it follows that the reflectivity plus the absorptance of any opaque substance is equal to unity; and since the absorptance is equal to the emissivity, the emissivity plus the reflectivity is again equal to unity. This last relation

$$e_\lambda = 1 - \rho_\lambda \tag{28}$$

has been used to measure the emissivity of different substances, since, in many instances, it is much easier to measure the reflectivity than the emissivity. This method assumes that the surface has been so prepared that the reflectivity is characteristic of the substance and not of the condition of the surface. The same statement can be made concerning the emissivity, since the emissivity is a function of the substance considered. Reflectivity is generally given for a definite condition of the surface, *i.e.*, a surface that has been well polished or prepared in some equally definite manner.

Brightness and Radiation Temperatures.[22] Measurements are often made of the radiant flux of non-blackbodies with an optical or radiation pyrometer, and the results converted into temperatures as if the radiant flux were that from a blackbody. Since non-blackbodies always radiate less energy at any temperature and for any wavelength interval than a blackbody of the same size and temperature, these temperatures are less than true temperatures. These quasi-blackbody brightness and radiation temperatures are called simply brightness or radiation temperatures. The brightness temperature depends upon the wavelength used in measuring the brightness with an optical pyrometer, and thus the wavelength should be given when giving brightness temperatures of non-blackbodies.

Color Temperature.[23] It has been found experimentally that most metals, when heated, radiate in such a manner that their radiation can be color-matched rather closely with that of a blackbody at some temperature. Thus the color temperature of any non-blackbody has been defined as the temperature at which

it is necessary to operate a blackbody so that its radiation
will match in integral color that of the source studied. As
defined, color temperature applies only to matching within the
visible spectrum.

References

1. I.E.S. Report of Committee on Nomenclature and Standards (1932)
   I.E.S., Trans. **28**, 263 (1933).
*2. F. K. RICHTMYER, "Introduction to Modern Physics," p. 186; Physics
   Staff, University of Pittsburgh, "Atomic Physics," p. 51; "Radiation
   Terms," *R.S.I.*, **7**, 322 (1936).
3. F. K. RICHTMYER, "Introduction to Modern Physics," p. 187.
4. M. PLANCK, "Theory of Heat Radiation" (English translation by
   Masius).
5. *Sitzb. Akad. Wiss.*, Berlin. p. 55, Feb. 9, 1893.
6. *Ann. Physik*, **58**, 662 (1896).
7. *Phil. Mag.*, **49**, 537 (1900); **10**, 91 (1905).
8. *Verh. deut. phys. Ges.*, **2**, 237 (1900); also *Ann. Physik*, **4**, 553 (1901).
9. RUBENS and KURLBAUM, *Ann. Physik*, **4**, 664 (1901); Coblentz, *Bull.
   Bur. Standards*, **13**, 474 (1916–1917); Rubens and Michel, *Physik.
   Zeitschr.*, **22**, 573 (1921).
10. M. K. FREHAFER, and C. S. SNOW, *Misc. Pub. Bur. Standards*, No. 56,
    March, 1925.
11. *Jour. Optical Soc. Am.*, **17**, 329 (1928).
12. "*Photometria*," p. 324.
13. R. T. BIRGE, *Phys. Rev., Supplement*, **1**, 1–73, (1929); *Nature*, **137**, 187,
    1936.
14. F. K. RICHTMYER, "Introduction to Modern Physics," p. 180.
15. C. G. ABBOT, "The Earth and the Stars," p. 105.
16. COBLENTZ and STAIR, *Bur. Standards Jour. Research*, **11**, 79 (1933).
17. M. PLANCK, "Theory of Heat Radiation," p. 16 (English translation
    by Masius).
18. E. AUDING, trans. Lambert's 1860 Augsburg "Dissertation on Photom-
    etry," etc.
19. BUNSEN and ROSCOE, *Ann. Physik*, **101**, 237 (1857).
20. *Ann. Physik*, **86**, 78 (1852).
21. DRUDE, "Lehrbuch der Optik," 2d ed., p. 349.
22. E. P. HYDE, "Pyrometry," A.I.M.M.E., p. 289, 1920.
23. HYDE, CADY, and FORSYTHE, *Phys. Rev.*, N. S., **10**, 397 (1917).

* After this book was in type the Illuminating Engineering Society and
Standards Committee adopted some different radiation terms.

CHAPTER II

SOURCES OF RADIANT ENERGY

A. G. Worthing*

A very important item in radiation measurements is the source. Certain general characteristics may be noted that need to be considered in the selection of the source for a particular problem.

1. Does it supply energy at such a rate or in such an amount as to make measurements possible?
2. Does it yield an irradiation that is generally constant or that may be varied with time as desired?
3. Is it reproducible?
4. Does it yield irradiations of the desired magnitudes over areas of the desired extent?
5. Has it the desired spectral distribution?
6. Has it the necessary operating life?
7. Has it sufficient ruggedness for the proposed problem?
8. Is it sufficiently easy to obtain and replace, or is its purchase price or its construction cost reasonable?

Affirmative answers to all the listed questions are not always possible. One may find it necessary, for instance, when there is a need for a very intense irradiation or a very special radiation distribution, to sacrifice constancy of operation.

To illustrate, if an image is to be focused on the slit of a spectrometer, the source should be of such size that the image will cover the slit without the necessity of using so large a magnification that there is difficulty in filling the entrance angle of the spectrometer. Also, it is desirable that the image be of uniform brightness over the slit. Further, if one is studying the effect of radiation of a particular character such as, for instance, ultraviolet radiation, obviously the radiation must contain a sufficient amount of energy in that particular region. Some sources are affected by the surrounding conditions. Special precautions must be taken to overcome this difficulty. For some work it

* *Professor of Physics, University of Pittsburgh.*

25

TABLE 5. SOURCES OF RADIATION; THEIR CHARACTERISTICS AND USES

Source	Characteristics	Use
A. Continuous Spectra		
Blackbody	Depends upon construction	As standards
Incandescent lamp	See Table 6	Long ultraviolet to infrared limit of glass transmission
Carbon arc	See Table 7	Short ultraviolet to long infrared
Enclosed metallic arcs	30–500 watts concentrated sources of high brightness	Long ultraviolet to short infrared
Thorium lamp		Ultraviolet
Nernst glower	100–200 watts. Requires no container	Visible and infrared
Welsbach mantle	Requires no container	Visible and infrared
Globar	Requires no container	Infrared
Powder films	See Table 8	Infrared
Underwater spark	Very intense, high color temperature	Visible and ultraviolet
Concentrated discharges	Very high brightness	Ultraviolet
Wire explosion	Very high brightness and high color temperature	Ultraviolet and visible
Flame source	Low brightness	Standards of color
Photoflash	Continuous with certain lines and bands	High luminous intensity and short duration
B. Discontinuous Spectra		
Cadmium arc		Standard of wavelength
Iron arc		Standard of wavelength
Bunsen flame		Wavelength and brightness depending upon salt used
Flame arc	See Table 7	
Mercury lamp	Mercury spectrum; various types	Source of intensity, visible and ultraviolet
Tungsten mercury arc	Mercury spectrum and continuous, of heated tungsten	Source of intensity for visible and ultraviolet
Spark	Spectrum of material used as electrode. Some very intense	See text
Glow discharge tubes	Spectrum of substance used in tube. Many types	See text
Stroboscopic lamp	Various types. Using mercury, neon, and other gases to give a source of very short duration	Time indicator
Sodium-vapor lamp*	Intense. Sodium spectrum easy to operate.	Source of intensity
Fluorescence and phosphorescence lamp. Many such sources have been constructed	Depends upon material	Very little used as source

* Lamps of the same type, using other vapors such as cadmium, zinc, and thallium have been constructed.

is necessary to know very precisely the spectral characteristics of the energy used. In this chapter information enabling one to answer many of the above questions, as well as many others concerning the devising and operating of sources for different purposes, are discussed.

SOURCES WITH SPECTRA THAT ARE GENERALLY CONTINUOUS

The sources of this group are generally incandescent. Their spectral-energy distributions are generally similar to those of blackbody sources and generally vary similarly with temperature. To these, therefore, definite color temperatures may be

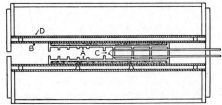

Fig. 7.—A standard blackbody as designed by Forsythe. Tubes *A*, *B*, and *D* are of alundum or porcelain. Tube *A* is wound uniformly with platinum ribbon 2 cm wide and 0.01 mm thick. Tube *B* is wound with the same kind of ribbon but with a space between windings uniformly increasing on going from the ends toward the center. *C* is the blackbody. To heat this blackbody to the palladium point a current of about 8 to 10 amp. at 115 volts is required in the winding of tube *A* and 5 to 10 amp. in the winding of tube *B*. The space around tube *D* is packed with some good heat insulator.

ascribed, except, perhaps, the underwater spark and Anderson's concentrated discharge in a low-pressure tube, since for these sources the temperature is probably not the controlling factor, although their spectra under certain conditions may be continuous and free from lines. Some of the sources listed are certainly not wholly incandescent. The flame carbon arc and the thorium lamp, for instance, have spectra which show lines superposed on continuous backgrounds. The boundary between this general group and the following group of sources with spectra that are generally discontinuous, is not sharp.

I. Blackbodies. The radiation from a blackbody is completely determined by its temperature. It therefore serves primarily as a radiation standard and as a standard of comparison for other sources.

It can be shown[1] that a cavity with uniformly heated opaque walls (with finite emissivities at all wavelengths) contains blackbody radiation which may be studied through a hole in the side wall, provided the dimensions of this opening are small in comparison with those of the cavity. The lower the emissivities of the walls, the smaller this hole must be.

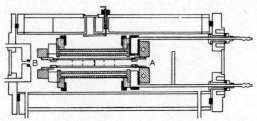

Fig. 8.—Specifications for a carbon-tube furnace capable of operating at temperatures up to 3000°K.

The primary consideration in constructing a blackbody of the cavity type is to provide means for maintaining the walls uniformly at a desired temperature. Several methods have been used to accomplish this, such as: winding special tubes with some conductor[2] to serve as a heater (Fig. 7); using the tube itself as a conductor,

PLATINUM

UNFUSED
THORIA

POWDERED
FUSED
THORIA

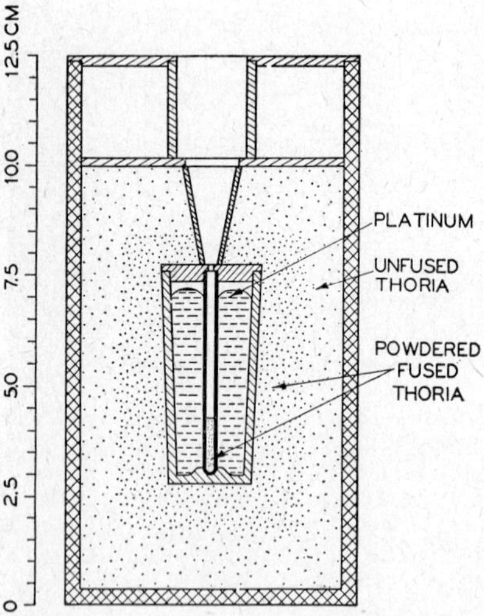

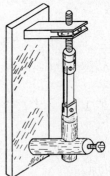

Fig. 9A.—Blackbody heated by immersing in molten metal. This blackbody was used in setting up the Waidner and Burgess standard of light intensity.

Fig. 9B.—Mendenhall's open-wedge blackbody.

as in a carbon-tube furnace[3] (Fig. 8); immersing refractory tubes in molten metal[4] (Fig. 9A); folding thin strips of metal into a sharp V and heating them electrically,[5] the inside of the

V being the blackbody cavity (Fig. 9*B*); providing electrically heated tubes with walls that are either solid or made of thin strips of metal with small radial holes[6] for observation purposes (Fig. 10*A* and *B*).

The primary standard of temperature for the study of incandescence is the melting point of gold, the "gold point," 1336°K.

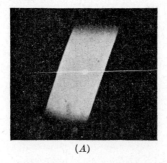

(*A*)

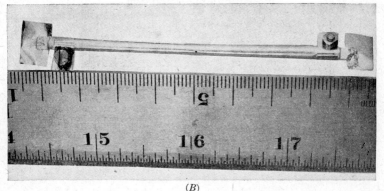

(*B*)

Fig. 10.—Miniature blackbodies consisting (*A*) of a tubular metallic filament with a small hole in its side wall, and (*B*) of a tube formed from a metallic ribbon.

Another temperature which serves as a secondary standard is the palladium point, 1828°K. A third is the platinum point, 2047°K. A standard blackbody should be operable at one or more of these temperatures; and, while it is not essential that conditions be such that the portion of such a blackbody on which measurements are to be made is directly visible without glass or other material in the line of sight, it is preferable that such be the case.

II. Incandescent Lamps. *Regular Types.* The regular types of incandescent lamps are highly reproducible as to characteristics. For instance, a 100-watt, 115-volt incandescent lamp of the single-coil gas-filled type with a rated life of 750 hr. and an efficiency ε of 15.4 lumens per watt, may be expected, while still reasonably new, to have a spectral distribution in the visible closely corresponding to that for a blackbody at a temperature T of 2870°K, the color temperature of the lamp, to within something of the order of 5 or 10°K. If the efficiency of the lamp is other than 15.4 lumens per watt, its color temperature, T_2, can be calculated from its efficiency, ε_2, and the above values of temperature and efficiency by use of the formula

$$\frac{\varepsilon}{\varepsilon_2} = \left(\frac{T}{T_2}\right)^{7.1} \tag{29}$$

TABLE 6.   TYPES OF TUNGSTEN INCANDESCENT LAMPS SHOWING RANGE IN VOLTS, WATTS, AND COLOR TEMPERATURE

Lamp	Volts	Watts	Color temperature, °K	Filament shape*
General lighting	110–120	10– 2000	2400–3000	Ring or draped
Street series	10– 60	65– 1200	2860–3000	Single and multiple segments
CX lamp†	110–120	60– 500	2840–3025	Ring or draped
Flood and spot lighting	110–120	500– 2000	2940–3145	Multiple segments
Projection	30–115	50– 1000	3200–3365	Monoplane and biplane
Photocell exciter and recorder.	5– 10	30– 100	3160–3300	Single and double segments
Studio and airport lighting.	30–115	500–10000	2950–3320	Draped and segments in monoplane
Auto lamp	6– 12	3– 25	2800–3000	Concentrated
Flashlight lamp	2¼– 6	.8– 12	2550–2700	Concentrated
Ribbon filament lamp.	4– 8	80– 250	2400–2800	5 cm long, 2–3 mm wide, 0.06 mm thick

* All these lamps have coiled filaments unless noted. The coils are mounted in various shapes as noted.

† The bulbs of these lamps have high transmission in the ultraviolet.

In Table 6, certain characteristics for a number of regular types of incandescent lamps are given, including the range of wattage, color temperature, and shape of filament mount. Although lamps may be operated at voltages higher or lower than rated, it should be understood that higher voltage means a disproportionately decreased operating life.   The relation between life (L) and voltage (V) is approximately exponential, with an exponent −13. Thus

$$\frac{L_1}{L_2} = \left(\frac{V_1}{V_2}\right)^{-13} \qquad (30)$$

Data[7] have been published on the spectral-energy distributions of a number of types of incandescent lamps which make satisfactory sources for the long ultraviolet, the visible, and the short infrared parts of the spectrum.

To meet the need for sources of larger area and more nearly uniform brightness than is provided by coiled-filament lamps, ribbon filament lamps are available with or without plane windows of glass or of fused quartz.   These are low-voltage lamps and require currents from about 15 to 40 amp., depending upon the width and thickness of the filament and the temperature of operation.

Specifications for Laboratory-made Lamps.   For those who may wish to make their own lamps to meet special requirements, the following suggestions and directions are given.   Consider the case of a long-filament lamp, *i.e.*, one in which the effects of the cooling leads and supports are negligible.   Assume further that the filament is uncoiled or at least very openly coiled.   For a vacuum lamp having such characteristics, the basic equations for design are

$$W = 2\pi r\eta L \qquad (31)$$

$$R = \frac{\rho L}{\pi r^2} \qquad (32)$$

$$V = \frac{\rho I}{\pi r^2}L \qquad (33)$$

where W, R, I, and V have their usual electrical significances and η, ρ, r, L refer respectively to radiancy (watts/cm²), resistivity, filament radius, and filament length at the temperature of operation desired.   It is to be noted that there are two independent equations among four independent variables, thus allowing two to be selected to determine the size of the lamp.

The values of these constants and further descriptions of methods of constructing lamps can be found in various published papers.[8]   After the filament has been prepared, it must be mounted on suitable leads and these must be mounted in a glass bulb or some other container.   The combination is then connected to a vacuum pump.   The bulb must be evacuated rather well before the heat is applied by an oven, so that the filament may not be discolored.   If no leaks show up, the bulb may then be exhausted and raised to a temperature between 350 and 500°C, depending upon the type of glass used in the bulb.   How well the bulb should be evacuated depends, of course, upon the use to which the lamp is to be put.

Any straight- or coiled-filament tungsten lamp, vacuum or gas-filled, whose temperature and resistance are known for one condition, can be operated at any other desired temperatures by the simple device of noting that for tungsten the very simple relation,[9]

$$\frac{R}{R_0} = \left(\frac{T}{T_0} \right)^{1.20} \tag{34}$$

holds with high precision for uniformly heated filaments.   To make allowances for the cooling effects of the leads and the supports of the filament, published works[10] on end losses should be consulted.   Sometimes it is desired to obtain radiation having a specified spectral distribution, especially within the visible spectrum.   Such special spectral distributions may usually be obtained from regular sources by the use of filters.[11]

III. Arcs.   There are two major types of arc sources, the incandescent and the flame arc.   Classification depends on whether the radiation emitted is largely due to incandescence or to luminescence, *i.e.*, whether or not the temperature of the source determines the spectral character of the radiation.   Of the former or incandescent type, (a) the plain carbon arc, (b) the high-intensity carbon arc, and (c) the enclosed metallic arc will be considered.

Plain Carbon Arc.   The incandescent terminals are the main source of radiation of the plain carbon arc.   In the direct-current arc, this radiation comes very largely from the relatively large crater which forms in the positive terminal, and to a much smaller extent from the smaller crater of the negative terminal. In the alternating-current arc, the combined radiation from the two terminals is less than that from the positive crater of the direct-current arc of the same wattage. When the source of radiation is to be an arc terminal, a direct-current arc is always to be preferred.

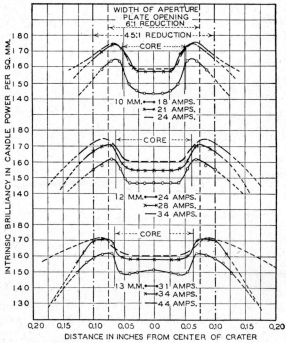

FIG. 11.—Variations in brightness across the craters of 10-mm, 12-mm, and 13-mm positive carbons of direct-current plain arcs operated at different currents in the regions of recommended operation.

Whether on alternating current or direct current, the arc is unstable and a ballast resistance or other current control must be used.

The carbons for the plain arc may be either solid or cored. Those that are cored contain salts which aid in the arc conduction and give increased steadiness to the arc stream without adding anything essential to the luminosity of the arc proper or of the terminals. These cored carbons give, however, somewhat deeper craters for a given arc current.

TABLE 7.　CHARACTERISTICS OF SOME CARBON ARCS*

1. Low-intensity and high-intensity projection and searchlight carbon arcs—direct current

	Carbon size, mm	Amperes	Volts	Horizontal candle-power‡	Crater light, lumens	Total light, lumens
Low intensity............................	10	20	55	5,400	16,500	16,500
	12	30	55	8,500	25,900	25,900
	13	40	55	11,900	35,800	35,800
High intensity (Suprex)............	6	40	32	8,150	29,500	43,400
(Suprex)†............	7	50	34	11,600 (30°)	41,000	60,500
(Suprex)............	8	65	35	17,100 (30°)	56,200	82,600
Rotating positive....................	9	75	56	15,900	53,300	81,500
Rotating positive....................	11	85	58	19,000	65,000	100,000
Rotating positive....................	13.6	130	76	46,000	169,000	260,000
Rotating positive....................	16	150	76	62,000	215,000	330,000
Superhigh intensity						
Rotating positive....................	13.6	180	75	68,000	249,000	383,000
Rotating positive....................	16	195	90	88,400 (20°)	294,000	555,000

2. Visible light from white-flame arcs—direct current

Type of carbons		Power	Amperes	Volts	Mean spherical lumens	Lumens per arc watt
Upper	Lower					
½ × 12 W.F. photo.	½ × 12 W.F. photo.	A.C.	30	55	87,800	53.2 ⎫ These efficiencies can
⅝ × 12 W.F. photo.	½ × 12 W.F. photo.	A.C.	45	55	123,100	49.8 ⎬ be realized by opera-
⅝ × 12 C.C. W.F. photo.	⅝ × 12 C.C. W.F. photo.	A.C.	60	55	169,700	51.3 ⎭ tion on transformers

Type of carbons		Power	Amperes	Volts	Mean spherical lumens	Lumens per arc watt	Two arcs at 45 volts each	
Upper Negative	Lower Positive						Mean spherical lumens	Lumens per line watt (115 volts)
½ × 12 W.F. photo.	½ × 12 W.F. photo.	D.C.	30	55	94,800	57.4	155,100	44.9
½ × 12 2 F neutral core	½ × 12 W.F. photo.	D.C.	30	55	87,800	53.2		
⅝ × 12 W.F. photo.	½ × 12 W.F. photo.	D.C.	45	55	148,800	60.0	234,500	45.3
⅝ × 12 proj. (neutral)	½ × 12 W.F. photo.	D.C.	45	55	109,500	44.2		
⅝ × 12 C.C. W.F. photo.	⅝ × 12 C.C. W.F. photo.	D.C.	60	55	200,600	60.8	328,300	47.6
⅝ × 12 C.C. proj. (neutral)	⅝ × 12 C.C. W.F. photo.	D.C.	60	55	143,400	43.4		

TABLE 7. (Continued)

Type of carbons		Power	Amperes	Volts	Mean spherical lumens	Lumens per arc watt	Two arcs at 45 volts each	
Upper Positive	Lower Negative						Mean spherical lumens	Lumens per line watt (115 volts)
½ × 12 W.F. photo..........	½ × 12 W.F. photo.	D.C.	30	55	127,100	77.0	207,900	60.3
⅝ × 12 W.F. photo..........	½ × 12 W.F. photo.	D.C.	45	55	170,000	68.7	278,200	53.8
⅝ × 12 C.C. W.F. photo.....	⅝ × 12 C.C. W.F. photo.	D.C.	60	55	265,700	80.5	434,700	63.0

3. Arcs for ultraviolet radiations or therapeutic purposes—alternating current

Carbon	Amperes	Voltage	Microwatts per cm² at 1 m from arc					
			2,300–3,100A	3,100–7,000A	7,000–14,000A	14,000–42,000A	14,000–120,000A	Total
Sunshine............	30	50	36	3,054	1,400	2,205	3,085	7,575§
Therapeutic C......	30	50	189	1,491	860	3,100	4,385	6,925§
Therapeutic E......	30	50	21	2,089	1,330	2,580	3,670	7,110§
					Direct current			
Low intensity........ Plain-carbon arc.....	30	55	60	4,710	8,280	11,930	14,650	27,700‖

* This table furnished by Research Laboratory of National Carbon Co., Inc., through the courtesy of A. C. Downes.

† The positive carbons in these high intensity arcs are stationary and do not rotate.

‡ Horizontal candlepower determined directly in front of the crater on the axis of the positive carbon, except where an angle is indicated, in which cases the candlepower was measured at this angle with the positive carbon axis. Candlepower of crater light only, except for Suprex arcs where values are total candlepower.

§ Practically all the radiant energy from these arcs is emitted by the arc stream between the electrodes and very little is emitted by the electrodes themselves.

‖ Practically all the radiant energy from this arc is emitted by the crater on the positive carbon and very little by the arc stream.

Some interesting radiation characteristics for plain arcs with neutral cored positive carbons are shown in Fig. 11. This shows, for recommended conditions of operation, that (a) with the higher currents the change in crater brightness with change in current is inappreciable; (b) the maximum brightness of the crater floor in each instance is quite uniform; (c) the edges of the craters are brighter than the crater floors; and (d) the maximum brightness, that which occurs just previous to the hissing stage, is the same for the three sizes of carbons; *e.g.*, 165 candles/mm². By varying somewhat the conditions of operation and the characteristics of

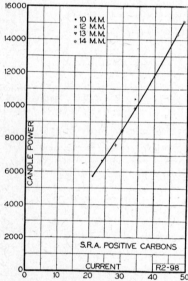

the carbons used, very high intensity outputs may be obtained, as in searchlight carbon arcs, for example.

Chaney[12] and his coworkers have shown that by using specially prepared carbons operated in a specified manner, a very constant and reproducible brightness may be obtained. As operated, the brightness temperature* ($\lambda = 0.665\mu$) of these arcs was 3815°K. By using these carbons, one can, without control measurement, be assured of an extended source having a high, uniform, and definite energy output for a wide spectral range; and one can obtain high image brightnesses and image illuminations, the values of which may be readily computed. The general considerations deduced for the visible radiations emitted by the positive crater undoubtedly hold equally well for the ultraviolet and the infrared radiations.

Fig. 12.—The candlepowers of the craters of various sized neutral cored positive carbons of direct-current plain arcs operated at various currents.

A surprising conclusion drawn from Fig. 12 is that the candlepower of an arc terminal is dependent on the current but not on the size of the carbon.

* See p. 23.

High-intensity Carbon Arc. Spectral-energy curves of high intensity as determined by Greider are shown in Fig. 13*A* and

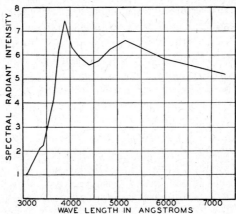

Fig. 13*A*.—Spectral-energy distribution curve for high-intensity motion picture projector. Positive crater radiation only. A 13.6-mm high-intensity white flame positive; $7/16$ in. Orotip negative; 125 amp.; 63 volts direct current.

13*B*. The maximum brightness (800 candles/mm²) of the crater is equal to that of a blackbody at about 4850°K. Benford[13]

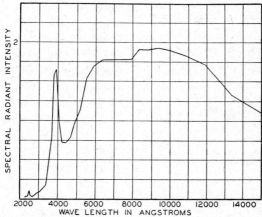

Fig. 13*B*.—The spectral-energy distribution curve for the 12-mm right-angle mirror arc; 30 amp., 55 volts, direct current.

found 5400°K as a color temperature for the radiation from another high-intensity arc.

Enclosed Metallic Arc with Incandescent Electrodes. An arc lamp of this type, known as the Pointolite (Fig. 14), is furnished with candlepower ratings of 30, 100, and 500 for the direct-current arcs and 150 for the alternating-current arc. The positive terminal is a tungsten ball which, in starting the arc, is held close to a tungsten coil. With the striking of the arc, the ball electrode

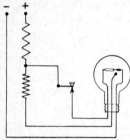

is automatically shifted by a bimetallic strip opposite a more rugged portion of the cathode. In operation, the ball electrode serves as a steady concentrated source of high brightness which depends upon the arc current.

FIG. 14.—The Pointolite enclosed-metallic-arc lamp.

Like the carbon arc, this arc in a gas at constant pressure has a negative potential-current characteristic, and a ballast resistance is similarly required. The potential-current curve determined by operation of the arc at a succession of steady states, owing to the consequent changes in gas pressure, may not, however, actually show the negative characteristic throughout. This fact should not be construed to mean that the ballast resistance is not necessary, for it is the effects of the sudden change, rather than the slow change, against which protection is needed.

The temperature of the ball of the 100-candlepower lamp is about 2920°K, corresponding to a brightness of about 10 candles/mm², a value low in comparison with the 800 candles/mm² of the high-intensity carbon arc, but still very high as ordinary sources go. On page 60 another tungsten arc is described that has some advantages.

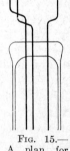

A design for a tungsten arc which may appeal to some is shown in Fig. 15. The cathode consists of a few turns of closely coiled heavy tungsten wire, the anode of a small block of tungsten separated from the coil by three or four millimeters. In the process of manufacture, it is necessary (a) to evacuate the

FIG. 15.—A plan for the mounting of a bulb-enclosed metal arc, designed to start at low voltages.

bulb containing the anode-cathode assembly rather well without heating the bulb, (b) to continue the evacuation for a period of about 30 min. while it is being baked in an oven at about 350 or 400°C, (c) to fill it with *dry* argon or some other atmosphere which will not react with the tungsten, and (d) to seal off the lamp.

Commercial argon (86 per cent argon, 14 per cent nitrogen) may be obtained from burned-out regular gas-filled lamps.

Another design of arc especially suitable for the study of radiation from the material of the electrodes in the neighborhood of the melting point of the substance is shown in Fig. 16. Initially the material which is to form the electrodes in this instance may be the two arms of a V-shaped filament of a gas-filled lamp. In manufacture it is well to have reduced the cross section at the apex of the V slightly (perhaps 5 per cent) in order that there shall be certainty as to the position of maximum temperature when the filament is heated. Thus mounted, the material may be studied while in filament form and then, when ready, raised gradually in temperature until it melts at the apex of the V. If, just as melting occurs, the current is lowered somewhat, there will be seen two ball terminals between which an arc is passing. If one desires, the arc current may be slowly raised until one may see a demarcation line between liquid and solid appear and spread over the ball. If the arc current is raised too high, and too much of a ball becomes liquid, it will recede somewhat down the solid stem. A ball terminal may be thus raised to the melting point many times in succession if desired.

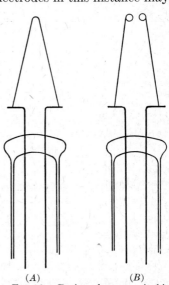

(A)   (B)

Fig. 16.—Design of an arc suitable for studying the radiation from the materials of the electrodes at temperatures near their melting point. A, as made; B, after melting at tip.

In case the arc is broken, it may be restarted with the aid of a transformer. Figure 17 shows two convenient arrangements. Starting is easier by the method A, but this method is not so desirable if one is not sure of insulation or grounds, or whether other workers are, or are not, using the same direct-current source. In either case, the experimenter should proceed with caution lest he pass too much current through his lamp. In case of no danger resulting from the connection of the direct-current and the alternating-current circuits, the special switch of Fig. 17B may be replaced by a common, double-pole, double-throw switch so modified as to make it quick-acting.

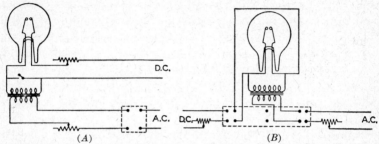

(A)　　　　　　　　　(B)

Fig. 17.—A. Arrangement for an easy (but not always safe) method for starting an arc between cold terminals in an enclosed bulb. B. Arrangement for a safe convenient method of starting an arc between cold terminals in an enclosed bulb.

IV. Special Incandescent Luminous Sources. *Thorium Lamp.*

This is a relatively recent source developed largely by W. M. Cohn.[14] It consists of a glass bulb (Fig. 18) (with or without a quartz window) evacuated to a pressure of from 0.5 to

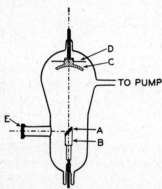

Fig. 18.—Diagram showing the construction of the thorium lamp. *A*, thorium disk; *B*, copper support; *C*, aluminum cathode; *D*, mica disk; *E*, quartz glass window.

5×10^{-3} mm Hg in which a 1-ma. stream of electrons under the application of potential differences of the order of 25 kv. impinge on a massive block of thorium. Its spectrum is continuous and extends with measurable intensities at least from 2200 to 6000A, being particularly strong in the ultraviolet (Fig. 19). The irregularities due to the line and band spectra of the residual gases in the bulb may be eliminated by further evacuation. Its spectrum is less bright than the continuous h y d r o g e n spectrum but is free, or nearly free, from lines and bands. It is also less bright than that from incandescent tungsten, but its particular value is that it is nearly free from red and infrared radiation.

Other sources in this group, the Welsbach mantle, the Nernst glower, and the incandescent flame (see Table 5) are considered

more fully below under infrared sources in which field their use is
believed to be most common.

V. Infrared Sources.　For the near infrared, ordinary incandescent lamps and arcs serve very satisfactorily, but as sources
for radiation in the far infrared, they suffer through being glass-
enclosed and from having a normal low spectral emissivity in the
case of the incandescent lamp and from a preponderance of
extraneous radiation in the near infrared and the visible for both.

Sources[15] of infrared radiations used in investigations in the far
infrared are the Nernst glower, the globar, and the Welsbach
mantle.

Nernst Glower.　The Nernst glower is composed principally of
rare earth oxides, such as zirconia, yttria, and thoria.　For

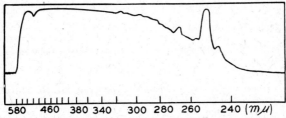

Fig. 19.—A microphotometer curve of a spectrum of the thorium lamp.

115-volt service, it is shaped into short rods about 2 cm long and
1 mm in diameter.　It is nonconducting at room temperatures
and must be heated by external means to bring it into a conducting state.　Like all semiconductors, it has a negative temperature
coefficient, and must be operated in series with a ballast resistance
when in a constant voltage circuit.　The emissivity of this source
is low in the far infrared, although it has been used to wavelengths of 25μ.

Welsbach Mantle.　The Welsbach mantle has a high emissivity
in the visible, a low emissivity in the near infrared and, again, a
high emissivity beyond 8μ.　It is thus a source of selective radiation for the far infrared.　Because of its porous structure, the
mantle does not emit so strongly as a blackbody, although its
emissivity, when account is taken of the actual projected area,
may be high.　Temperature control is difficult.　Pfund has
recently shown a source consisting of a piece of Welsbach mantle
heated by gaseous-discharge bombardment.　For some work this

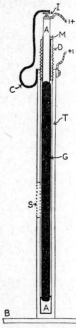

F I G .   20.—
Mounting for glo-
bar source. G,
Globar heater ($\frac{3}{8}$
in. by 9 in.); T,
tube of brass ($\frac{1}{2}$
in. i.d., $\frac{3}{4}$ in. o.d.)
—water-cooled by
copper pipes sol-
dered to tube on
both sides; S, ver-
tical slot in the
tube for emission
of radiation; B,
base; A, aluminum
electrodes to con-
nect to globar;
M, mica insulating
sleeve for upper
electrode; D, guide
for upper e l e c -
trode; C, spring,
of phosphor bronze
soldered to T to
put compression
on the electrodes;
I, asbestos disk
insulator.

is better than the gas-heated mantle and also makes a good substitute for the Nernst glower.

Globar.   As an extended open source of high infrared radiancy, the globar rod, common as an electric heater in the home, is very convenient and very valuable. The commercial 115-volt, 5-amp. units may be operated at voltages much above normal to yield radiancies as high as 60 watts/cm^2 and brightness temperatures of about 1800°K. When thus operated, it is desirable to have rather large, tightly fitting iron lugs at each end of a rod, to reduce the temperatures of the terminals and to prevent incipient arcing at those places.

For spectrometric measurements beyond 20μ, the globar, having high emissivity in the far infrared, makes a good source, especially in conjunction with a paraffin filter to make its effective total emissivity small. Figure 20 shows a convenient mounting for this source of radiation. The water-cooled brass container may be gold-plated inside to decrease heat transfer from the globar and thus decrease power consumption. The opening in this water-cooled container may be a simple round hole for Rest-strahlen experiments or a slot for use with a spectrograph.

Hot Glass.   Often with infrared sources, particularly where the far-infrared effects are being considered, it is necessary to suppress rela-tively the overwhelming radiation of the visible and the near infrared, without diminishing the de-sired effects of a high temperature for the source.

For the far infrared, hot glass is recommended by Cartwright[16]. Two parallel glass-covered platinum wires heated electrically will result in a more or less uniform temperature for the glass. Presumably Pyrex-covered tungsten wire (owing to the higher temperatures possible) will work even better.

Powder Films. For special regions, sources of a type recently described by Pfund[17] may be found satisfactory. It is based on the fact that crystals, whose particle size is comparable with the wavelength of selective absorption, absorb strongly in this region while diffusely reflecting shorter wavelengths and transmitting freely longer wavelengths.

The preparation of one such radiator consisting of powdered quartz is described by Pfund. Powdered crystalline quartz was shaken with water. The coarser particles were allowed to settle for 15 min. The milky fluid was then poured off into a flat dish and the water evaporated. The residue was found to have an

TABLE 8. EXPECTED CENTERS OF EMISSION BANDS OF SOURCES PREPARED
IN ACCORD WITH PFUND'S METHOD

Wavelengths are in microns. Data taken from paper by Pfund and *Handbuch der Physik* (Geiger-Scheel), **18**, 631.

K_2CO_3	7.05		11.50					
Quartz	8.50	9.02		20.75				
$BaSO_4$		9.35						
Mica	8.32	9.38	18.40	21.25				
Fluorspar					24.0	31.6		
Calc-spar	6.69		11.41		29.4			
Gypsum	8.69				30–40			
Alum		9.05			30–40			
Rock salt							51.2	
NaBr							50–55	
Sylvite								61.1
KBr								60–70

average particle diameter of about 1.35μ. For the support of the film a plate of polished rock salt was used. The powder was first placed on a sheet of ground glass and then thoroughly dispersed in butyl alcohol with a glass muller. Some of the resulting paste was then applied to the rock salt plate and was spread back and forth with a glass rod about 4 mm in diameter. By timing the last stroke properly a film of remarkable uniformity was obtained. It was not difficult to produce films consisting of but a single layer of particles. The device for heating the powder film (Fig. 21), owing to the low reflectivity and high transparency of the powder and the rock salt for all but the selectively absorbed radiation, is such as to insure that the radiation which finally reaches the slit of the receiving instrument is almost completely limited to that which is emitted by the powder. The same prin-

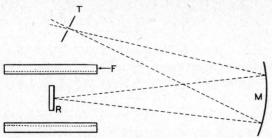

Fig. 21.—Pfund's device for obtaining selective infrared radiations from small particles. *F*, nichrome-wound open-tube furnace; *R*, a ground and polished plate of rock salt coated with a powder film; *M*, concave mirror; *T*, spectrometer slit.

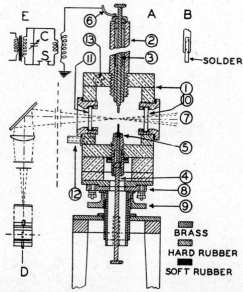

Fig. 22.—Underwater spark giving continuous spectrum for use in ultraviolet spectrophotometry. *A*, vertical median section through center of spark terminals and beams to photometer. (1) Hard-rubber box, inside dimensions 75 by 75 by 90 mm; built up from sheet stock 2 cm in thickness; plates held together by cement and metal screws. (2) Hard-rubber rod 3 cm in diameter. (3), (4) Brass rods carrying hard-metal terminals of spark gap and adjustable in vertical direction. (5) Packing box to prevent leakage of water. (6) Electrical connection to upper terminal; lower terminal and metal parts of base are grounded. (7) Beams of radiant energy to photometer. (8) Provision for horizontal adjustment of spark box, in direction perpendicular to beams. (9) Vertical adjustment of spark box. (10) Crystalline quartz window. (11) Glass window. (12) Inlet for distilled water. (13) Overflow tube. *B*, showing method for the support of tungsten or other hard metal terminals in brass rods (3) and (4). *D*, Lens and mirror arrangement by spark terminals are imaged on ground-glass screen; *E*, electrical circuits for operation of spark; *S*, primary spark gap; *C*, variable condenser (set of Leyden jars).

ciple may well be employed in connection with other substances for the obtaining of emission bands (Table 8), in the neighborhood of their residual rays (Reststrahlen).

VI. Electrical Discharges Yielding Essentially Continuous Spectra. *Underwater Spark.* Figure 22 gives details of construction of a source of this type used at the National Bureau of Standards.[18] Many other types have been used. The spectral-energy curve, according to Wyneken[19] and Wrede,[20] of a weak spark yields a color temperature of about 7500°K, while

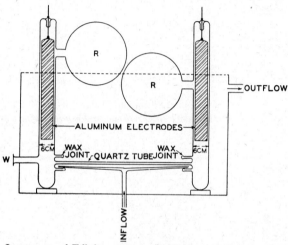

Fig. 23.—Lawrence and Edlefsen water-cooled hydrogen discharge tube of great current-carrying capacity.

that for a strong spark may yield about 10,000°K. Wilson,[21] from band absorption measurements, obtained about 5400°K.

Concentrated Discharges in Low-pressure Tubes. A possible defect of the underwater spark for certain types of work results from the fact that the spark path is constantly shifting. This feature seems to have been overcome in certain high-intensity ultraviolet sources developed by Lawrence and Edlefsen,[22] Kistiakowsky,[23] and Anderson,[24] all of whom, in addition to making use of a concentrated discharge, make use also of the increased brightness, first described by R. W. Wood, obtained by viewing a discharge lengthwise rather than laterally.

Lawrence and Edlefsen (Fig. 23) used hydrogen at a pressure of 1 to 2 mm Hg. After a clean-up of impurities by a continuous discharge for a day, a discharge of several amperes at 3,000 volts was said to have yielded a uniform continuous spectrum in the region 2000 to 3000A and to have a brightness viewed through the window lengthwise the discharge about equal, at 2536A, to that of a Cooper-Hewitt quartz mercury arc at ordinary currents.

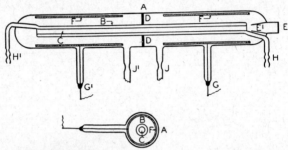

FIG. 24.—Kistiakowsky's high-power source of continuous ultraviolet spectrum. The discharge is produced between two large electrodes (*F*) placed inside the outer tubing (*A*) and is forced to pass through the central water-cooled tubing (*C*) because the quartz disk (*D*) which is sealed to the water-jacket tube (*B*) and to the outer tubing prevents a direct discharge between the electrodes. The radiation is obtained through the window (*E*), sealed to the end of a conical tubing (*E'*) which protects it from being obscured by spattered metal from the electrodes.

Kistiakowsky's apparatus is shown in Fig. 24. The device, as a result of certain novel features of construction, is quite compact. As gas for the carrying of the discharge, hydrogen at a pressure of 10 mm Hg was used. As used with a current of 0.7 to 0.8 amp. at 4,500 volts, it showed an unchanging voltage-current characteristic. The device was thought to be good for a load of

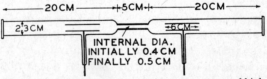

FIG. 25.—Anderson's tube for obtaining continuous spectrum of high brightness. Entire tube made of fused silica.

5 to 10 kw. No precise measurement of spectral character or of spectral brightness was made.

Anderson's method for obtaining a continuous spectral distribution is quite different. He used simple tubes of a more or less standard type which, however, were designed so that the discharge could be observed end on (Fig. 25) as well as transversely. They were made of fused quartz since Pyrex tubes lasted but a short

time. The discharge current was that obtained by shorting
through the tube a battery of condensers charged to a high
potential. The discharge itself was oscillating in character and
rather highly damped; usually not more than seven flashes could
be photographed. With current densities of the order of 30,000
amp./cm^2 through a 1-cm tube (2 μf, 35,000 volts, 60,000 cycles
per second, 25,000 amp.), the brightness of the tube, at least for
the first flash of the discharge, was as great viewed laterally as

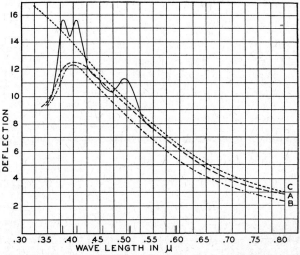

Fig. 26.—Spectral-energy curves from Anderson's special discharge tube shown
in Fig. 25. For curve A, 7 flashes, E = 30,000 volts; curve B for first two flashes,
E = 30,000 volts; curve C, blackbody at 10,000°K.

when viewed end on, showing that a 1-cm depth of discharge
served to yield complete opacity. With tubes having smaller
bores, higher current densities were required. For a 1-mm bore,
it was concluded that a current density of 100,000 amp./cm^2
would be needed.

Spectral-energy curves for the discharge show certain very
interesting facts. Curve A, Fig. 26, is the integrated spectral-
energy curve for the seven flashes accompanying a discharge with
the initial potential difference of 30,000 volts. Curve B is a
similar curve obtained by subtracting from the ordinates of
curve A, the ordinates of a corresponding curve with the initial
potential difference 14,000 volts, and is thought to show the
spectral-energy curve for the first two flashes only for the

30,000-volt case.   It is interesting that, through the visible region and only through this region roughly, the curve should be so nearly like that for a blackbody.   While an actual match with a blackbody is rather far from possible, the closest approximation occurs at from 12,000 to 13,000°K.   The author states that its brightness is about fourteen times that of a blackbody at 10,000°K.   This means an actual brightness about equal to that of a blackbody at 40,000°K.

Wire Explosion.   Still another method of obtaining high ultraviolet brightnesses, antedating the above, is the explosion method of Anderson[25] and of Sawyer and Becker.[26]   Anderson's plan

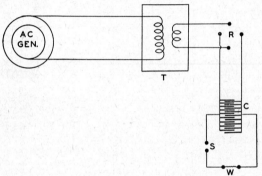

Fig. 27.—Anderson's arrangement of apparatus for exploding wires.

(Fig. 27) was simple.   It consisted of shorting a highly charged condenser through a fine metallic wire with as little inductance in the circuit as possible.   It was found desirable to place the wire in a wide groove in a block of wood.   The discharge was very noisy, and need was experienced for protecting the ears.   At pressures in excess of 20 cm Hg, the spectrum was found perfectly continuous between 2250 and 5700A with absorption lines due to the particular metal exploded.   Estimated temperatures of the order of 20,000°K were reached.

Sawyer and Becker modified Anderson's method by substituting a fine fiber of asbestos saturated with a solution of a soluble salt of the metal.   The fibers were not destroyed by the explosion and could be used in succeeding discharges.   Their apparatus was slightly different from Anderson's.   The capacitance of their condenser was about 0.3 μf; their charging voltage 50,000.

VII. Flame Sources. *Luminous Carbon Flames.* The most common of this group of sources are the candle, the kerosene flame, the luminous Bunsen flame, and the acetylene flame. The continuous spectrum in all or at least nearly all is due to the highly heated particles of carbon which are set free during combustion. In agreement with this fact, it is found that these flames very closely match blackbodies at appropriate temperatures and that their color temperatures are very close to their true temperatures. The brightness of such a flame for a given thickness depends on the temperature of the flame and the concentration of heated carbon particles.

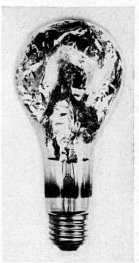

FIG. 28.—The photoflash lamp.

The temperature depends chiefly on the heat of combustion of the fuel but to some extent also on the concentration of carbon particles in the flame, since the loss of energy by radiation from the elementary particle sources tends to cool the source. Obviously, if the fuel is burned in an atmosphere of oxygen, higher brightness will result and in other atmospheres other values.

Common Noncarbon Flames. Of these the most common is the flashlight of photography and the photoflash lamp. For certain flames of this type Eder[27] gives the following interesting data regarding actinicity and temperature for 1 mg of three fuels.

TABLE 9.   CHARACTERISTICS OF SOME FLASH SOURCES

Source	Output of 1 mg of fuel	Color temperature
Flashlight powder in air........	200–300 candles × sec.	3000–3100°K.
Magnesium in air..............	413 candles × sec.	3700°K.
Magnesium in oxygen..........	770 candles × sec.	4000°K.

These flames have been used for flashlight photography and as such have often been not only a source of light but as well a source of discomfort and danger to those in the near neighborhood.

Both of these unsatisfactory features seem happily remedied in the photoflash lamp.

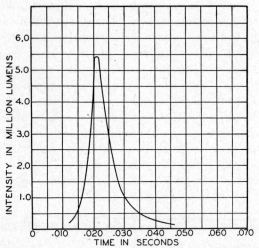

FIG. 29.—Time intensity relation for the average photoflash lamp.

The Photoflash Lamp. As a recently developed and widely used source similar to the common noncarbon flames just dis-

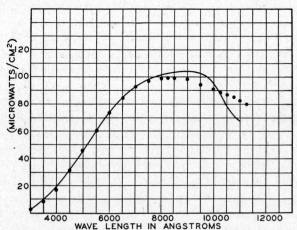

FIG. 30.—Spectral distribution of radiation from the No. 20 photoflash lamp. Points are for a blackbody at 3500°K.

cussed, we have the photoflash lamp. The lamp itself (Fig. 28) consists essentially of a crumpled thin (0.00004 cm) sheet of aluminum (65 mg) enclosed with an excess of oxygen in a glass bulb, with two current leads connected by a short filament for the electrical starting of combustion. A potential difference between 3 and 115 volts suffices to start the action. The flash is of the order of 0.03 to 0.06 sec. in duration, its probable temperature between 5000 and 9500°K, its maximum intensity about 360,000 candles.[28] This luminous intensity is somewhat more than twice that of the 50-kw. tungsten lamp whose luminous intensity is about 166,000 candles perpendicular to the plane of its filament. For the time distribution of the luminous-flux output, that shown in Fig. 29 has been found. The spectrum of this source, as is shown in Fig. 30 is made up largely of a continuous spectrum with certain lines and bands superposed. Though designed for photographic work, the photoflash lamp may well be of value for other purposes.

SOURCES WITH SPECTRA THAT ARE GENERALLY DISCONTINUOUS

These sources are generally luminescent rather than incandescent in character, *i.e.*, their radiating characteristics are primarily dependent not on their temperatures, but rather on electrical or other conditions. Usually they are of a gaseous nature, and their spectra are generally composed of spectral lines, sometimes broadened, and bands.

VIII. Sources Yielding Wavelength Standards. *Cadmium Arc.* The fundamental standard in terms of which wavelengths are measured is the red cadmium line. Michelson[29] was the first to make a precise determination of this wavelength in terms of the standard meter. Later Benoit, Fabry, and Perot[30] made certain slight corrections to the value which Michelson had obtained, and repeated the measurement. In consequence of the work thus done, it has been internationally agreed that 6438.4696A shall be taken as the wavelength of this particular radiation. The specifications for the standard source given in the International Critical Tables, Vol. V, page 274, are "the primary (cadmium) standard of wavelength shall be produced by high-voltage electric current in a vacuum tube having internal electrodes and the form described by Michelson. The tube shall be maintained at a temperature not higher than 320°C, and shall have a volume not less than 25 cm³. The effective value of the

exciting current shall not exceed 0.05 amp.   At room temperature
the tube shall be nonluminous when connected to the usual high-
voltage circuit." Strictly speaking this source is not an arc.

Iron Arc. For secondary and tertiary standards of wavelength, the iron arc (Fig. 31), as described by Pfund,[31] has been
internationally agreed upon as the source.   The iron lines whose
wavelengths have been carefully determined in terms of the

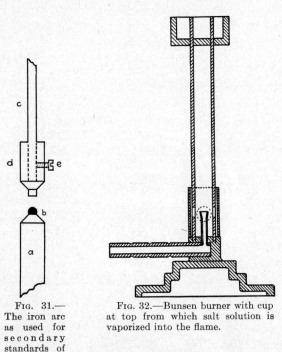

Fig. 31.—
The iron arc
as used for
secondary
standards of
wavelength.

Fig. 32.—Bunsen burner with cup
at top from which salt solution is
vaporized into the flame.

primary cadmium lines number about 200.   They may be found
listed in various places, in physical tables, together with about an
equal number of tertiary standards of wavelength whose values
have been obtained by interpolation from those of the secondary
standards.

IX. The Bunsen Flame. The simplest type of source for line
spectra is the Bunsen flame into which an appropriate salt has
been introduced, as by forming a bead of the salt on a platinum
wire, and holding it in the flame.   Chlorides, particularly of the

alkalis and the alkaline earths, because of their volatility, are generally satisfactory.

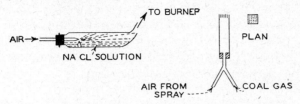

Fig. 33.—Spray for sodium chloride solution.

A fairly satisfactory method of introducing salt into a flame for such work consists in soaking a very open web of asbestos cord in

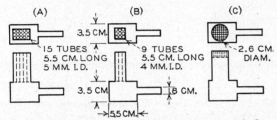

Fig. 34.—Gas burners for use in producing opaque salt flames.

a concentrated solution of the salt and then supporting it in the flame. Another convenient source of sodium lines of this type consists of a rod of Pyrex glass or, preferably, a web of fine tubes

Fig. 35.—King's graphite-tube furnace, open with jacketing material removed.

of Pyrex glass shrunk onto tungsten wire which is held in position in the flame by a clamp. Figure 32 illustrates another good method for getting the salt into a flame.

Sources for Flame-temperature Measurements. The precise measurement of flame temperatures by means of the line-reversal method requires a high flame opacity with a uniform steady coloration by a salt. The most satisfactory method for accomplishing this introduces the salt in the air stream which feeds the flame either as a dry pulverized dust or as a fog sprayed from a salt solution.

A procedure for the dry method was described by Jones, Lewis, Friauf, and Perrott.[32] The wet- or salt-solution spray method was early used by Gouy.[33] More recent designs (Fig. 33) are described by Griffiths and Awbery.[34] Other arrangements found satisfactory which may be varied to give any desired depth of flame are shown in Fig. 34. Chlorides or carbonates of sodium or lithium are thought to be especially suitable for purposes of temperature measurement.

X. Graphite-tube Furnace. King developed a graphite-tube furnace for heating various materials to high temperatures in order to study their spectra. The furnace (Fig. 35) consists essentially of a graphite tube, capable of being electrically heated, which was mounted in a heat-insulated chamber which might be either evacuated or subjected to high pressure. Residual gases and enclosed atmospheres were necessarily limited to neutral gases. This furnace was heated by a current through the graphite tube to temperatures ranging from about 2000 to 3300°K.

XI. Open-flame Arcs. *Luminous Arcs.* How the common luminous flame arc differs from the plain carbon arc or the high-intensity direct-current arc is well shown in Fig. 36.

Commercial flame arcs are divided, largely on the basis of electrode construction, between two types, *viz.*, the flame carbon and the magnetite. The electrodes of the flame-carbon arc are cored carbons with cores containing, in particular, salts of calcium, cobalt, strontium, and sodium. In operation these substances, in the arc stream and the flames which stretch upward from it, are chiefly responsible for the light which is produced.

The magnetite arc has an upper electrode of solid copper. In operation this electrode is negative, and at a relatively low temperature. The lower electrode is positive and consists chiefly of the oxides of iron (magnetite), titanium, and chromium, and certain alkali salts packed in an iron sleeve. In this case, the light-giving salts are vaporized chiefly from the positive terminal.

(A)

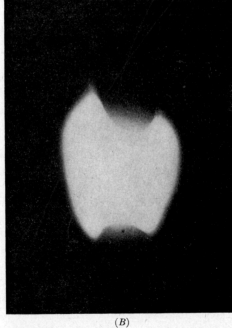

(B)

FIG. 36.—Photographs of a high-intensity arc A and of a flame arc B.

The Arc as a Spectroscopic Source. Arcs are found quite satisfactory for spectroscopic analyses of compounds and alloys. When the sample under examination is a metal or an alloy, the arc electrodes are very often made entirely of the material itself. In other cases, known amounts of the sample, usually a few milligrams, are volatilized into the arc from a hollow pure silver, copper, or graphite electrode.

The pure-carbon or graphite arc is the one most generally used in industrial analysis. Graphite rods of about $5/16$ in. diameter are cut into lengths of about 2 in.; one portion is pointed at one end and used as the upper or negative electrode; the other is bored out to a depth of about $1/4$ in., loaded with the sample to be examined, and made the lower or the positive electrode. The carbon arc is operated from a 220-volt direct-current supply at a current of about 6 amp. or higher depending upon the ease with which the sample volatilizes. Metallic arcs are usually run at 3 or 4 amp. and higher. The length of exposure given the arc on a photographic plate varies from several seconds to several minutes, it, too, depending upon the relative ease with which the sample volatilizes as well as the time necessary to break down all of the chosen amount.

The purity of the electrodes is extremely important. Impurities like uranium and titanium that have a many-line spectrum, mask some lines of the weaker elements, and in some cases their presence acts as a kind of flux on other elements, causing them to appear disproportionately stronger on the photographic plate than their amounts justify. One of the purest and most satisfactory carbons produced at the present time is the "spectrographic grade" of pure graphite of the National Carbon Company.

High-current Density Arcs. Another interesting arc is the high-current arc of King[36] in which the terminals are held horizontally in water-cooled clamps connected by water-cooled tubing to a 500-kw, 150-volt generator. In his study of the iron spectrum the terminals were iron rods 4 mm in diameter projecting 5 cm from 19-mm graphite rods. Other elements studied were titanium, magnesium, calcium, copper, and aluminum. The titanium as a powder was packed in a small tube of copper which was inserted into the graphite in much the same way as had been done with the iron.

This arc gives, for the most part, the spectrum (Fig. 37) of the neutral atom and is characterized by distinctive features in which it supplements the spectroscopic sources regularly used. These are an intensification of the high-temperature lines, an absence of the band spectrum of the metal or compound, except as it may appear in absorption if a favorable background is present, and the development of any peculiarities of widening, especially dissymmetry toward red or violet, to which the individual lines are subject.

Gerdien and Lotz'[37] improvement upon King's device has the advantage of continuity of operation over a considerable period at much reduced currents.

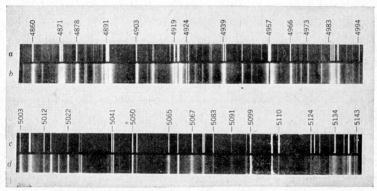

Fig. 37.—A portion of the spectrum of a high-current iron arc showing unsymmetrical broadening and reversals of iron lines.

XII. Enclosed Metallic Arcs. *Mercury Lamps.* Mercury lamps are usually classified according to the pressure at which they are normally operated because the voltage gradient and the brightness of the discharge both are markedly dependent on the vapor pressure. Some lamps are designed to operate at a rather low pressure (0.05 to 0.5 mm Hg). The Cooper-Hewitt tube,[38] which runs at about 0.25 mm Hg pressure, is a lamp of this type. It has a voltage gradient of only 0.5 volt per centimeter; hence a tube about 130 cm long is required for efficient operation on a 110-volt line. Since the discharge fills the entire cross section and the input per unit length is small, the brightness is relatively low. This, together with the fact that a shorter tube is ordinarily more convenient to use, limits the usefulness of this lamp as a source in a radiation laboratory.

Another low-pressure type is the mercury "glow" lamp (Fig. 38). This lamp has oxide-coated externally heated electrodes about 1 cm apart. It is a compact low-intensity source of mercury radiation. Operated at a very low pressure, and with a thin, ultraviolet-transmitting "bubble" window, it is a convenient-source of the resonance line at 2537A.

High-pressure mercury-arc lamps with mercury-pool cathodes[38] and with fused quartz tubes transmit ultraviolet with relatively little absorption to 2200A or less. There are a number of strong lines in the infrared, visible, and ultraviolet portions of the spectrum.

Lamps of this type are made either with a single anode for direct-current operation or with two anodes for alternating-current.

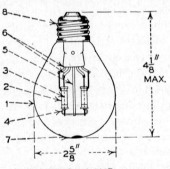

TYPE G-1 LAMP

Fig. 38.—The structure of an ultraviolet low-pressure mercury-arc, G-1 lamp.

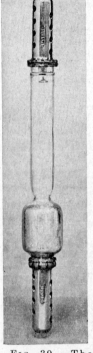

Fig. 39.—The vertical direct-current type of Uviarc.

The vertical direct-current type (see Fig. 39) is more constant than any of the others. Such a lamp has an extremely long life if properly used. On the other hand, it is ruined by a few seconds' operation with polarity reversed, by attempting to restart it immediately after operation while the anode and the quartz opposite it are still hot, or by using insufficient ballast. The recommendations of the manufacturer as to operation should be read carefully and followed closely.

A high-pressure quartz mercury-arc lamp with ballast for operation on a 115-volt line has an arc length of the order of 10 cm. The luminous discharge is only a few millimeters in diameter and has a high brightness. Used with a monochromator, it is a suitable source for many purposes, such as measuring glass transmissions and photocell sensitivities and obtaining wavelength calibrations of spectrometers. With a suitable ballast (reactor and resistance in series using at least 40 per cent of line voltage) a direct-current arc with controlled ventilation gives line intensities constant to within 1 per cent (except for 2537A) over many hours. However, it is quite necessary to control the ventilation so that the vapor pressure (indicated by the voltage-current relation) remains constant.

High-pressure mercury lamps for lighting purposes[39] are made with oxide-coated or impregnated electrodes and a small measured quantity of mercury. Since this mercury is all vaporized before the final operating temperature of the tube is reached, these lamps are little affected by changes in ventilation. This, combined with easy starting and a quick warm-up, makes them desirable sources. Although designed for alternating current, some of them will operate on direct current. This gives greater steadiness but is apt to spoil the oxide coating of the electrode used as anode. Certain of these lamps are made in ultraviolet transmitting glass,[40] but most of them give only lines of wavelengths greater than 3000A. Since the conditions of operation (pressure and current) are roughly the same as normally used for high-pressure quartz-mercury arcs, the intensities of the visible and infrared lines are of the same order.

Another type is an ultra high-pressure mercury lamp[41] in a quartz capillary tube 1 to 2 cm long. This lamp may be operated at a vapor pressure of 40 atm. when in open air or of several hundred atmospheres when water-cooled. Its spectrum is similar to that of an arc at atmospheric pressure, but the lines are much broader and the continuous spectrum in the red is more intense. The brightness of the discharge is of the same order of magnitude as that of the tungsten in an ordinary incandescent lamp. Since most of the light is radiated in the yellow and the green lines, these lines are very intense, far exceeding the spectral intensities given by most sources. However, the broadness of the lines limits the usefulness of this source in a radiation laboratory. Furthermore, the fact that it is operated on alternating current is apt to be a handicap, because the usual line-voltage fluctuations of 1 to 2 per cent would probably make the output vary 5 to 10 per cent.

Tungsten-mercury Arcs. The tungsten-mercury-arc lamps used in various sunlamps (Fig. 40) are essentially high-pressure mercury arcs with incandescent tungsten electrodes. As in many

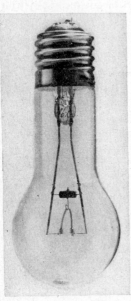

mercury lamps, a rare gas filling at a pressure of a few millimeters Hg carries the discharge when the lamp is turned on, but in the steady state the mercury vapor is practically the only active constituent in the arc. The mercury lines predominate in the ultraviolet portion of the spectrum, but the tungsten radiation furnishes most of the light and infrared radiation from the lamp.[42] The line intensities and continuous spectrum intensities are both quite high, but the former are not sufficiently constant for general use in a radiation laboratory. If a sufficiently constant alternating-current supply were available and if the ventilation were controlled, constancy to within 5 per cent during 10 hr. of operation might be attained. This lamp is also constructed with one ring electrode and mounted in a clear bulb. This allows the other solid electrode to be observed

Fig. 40.—The tungsten mercury arc.

through the ring and thus to be used as a high-temperature source.

Laboratory-made Mercury Arcs. Many designs of mercury arcs for use in the laboratory have appeared from time to time in journals, and most of them, without doubt, have certain advantages over other types. One type which has been found very satisfactory for laboratory use is shown in Fig. 41. This arc is started by tilting the lamp in the ordinary way to yield a streak of mercury between the anode and the cathode. Then, with the shorting switch closed, the lamp is brought into its normal operating position. After a minute or so, the shorting switch is released and a resistance thrown in series without interrupting the current.   A second laboratory form of convenient construction is that due to Pfund[43] (Fig. 42).

One of the difficulties experienced with metallic vapor arcs in conjunction with spectroscopic studies is the line reversal produced by the outer cooler layers of the arc.   Wood[44] has shown how to overcome this to a considerable extent.   In his lamp a quartz tube is inserted until the end of the tube is in or near the

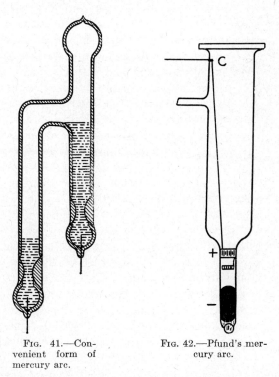

FIG. 41.—Convenient form of mercury arc.

FIG. 42.—Pfund's mercury arc.

central part of the discharge current.   Owing to the fact that the quartz can stand a high temperature and is protected considerably from cooling in that immediate neighborhood, the radiation from the central heated portion of the arc does not pass through vapor which is appreciably cooled and, therefore, there is in this instance no indication of a reversal of lines, in particular, of line 2537A.   Houtermans[45] has developed a lamp giving a narrow, unreversed resonance line with a constant intensity (within 2 per cent in a 2-hr. run).

A capillary mercury arc of considerable interest because of the high brightness and the long life claimed for it is that due to Crist.[46]

Other Metallic-vapor Arcs. Arcs of this class include particularly arcs in vapors of sodium, potassium, and cadmium.

Hoffman and Daniels[47] constructed an arc quite similar to the mercury arc described by Daniels and Heidt[48] and used it in arc studies of bismuth, cadmium, lead, mercury, thallium, and zinc. All these substances except mercury are normally solid and tend to break their quartz containers on cooling down after use either on account of expansion on freezing or from the effects of surface adhesive forces due to differential contractions. Hoffman and Daniels believed it desirable to make a lamp so simple and cheap that it can be discarded at the end of an experiment. The lamp (Fig. 43) which they developed is made by fusing a 12-mm section of quartz capillary, 1 mm inside diameter and 2 mm outside diameter, between two thin-walled quartz tubes 2 mm in outside diameter and 5 cm long. Thin bulbs are blown out at these joints to localize the arc. The end pieces may be used over and over again. The upper electrode is formed by stopping the lower end of the capillary with a pointed iron rod and gently melting down small pieces of the metal being studied to fill the whole capillary and the upper tube. Any bubbles are floated out of the molten metal. The lower electrode is cast or scraped down from a larger rod so as to fit snugly into the lower quartz tube. It is pointed and set so as to leave a short gap between the two electrodes. The metal at both ends of the lamp is then melted and short iron wires connected to flexible leads are inserted. Connections are insulated and rendered gastight with deKhotinsky cement. The air space in the lower bulb serves as a spark gap, for starting the lamp, and as a reservoir into which the molten metal runs down from the capillary when the arc is struck.

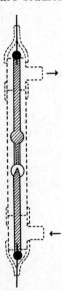

Fig. 43.— Quartz capillary-arc lamp for easily fusible metals.

Many lamps operated for 10 hr. or more, but trouble was experienced from oxygen in certain cases. In such cases, it was possible to evacuate the air space in which the arc was formed through a tiny hole in one electrode and to fill with an inert gas at any desired pressure. The arrangement of the apparatus for the starting of these arcs which required from 80 to 400 volts is shown in Fig. 44.

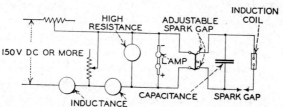

FIG. 44.—Hoffman and Daniels' apparatus for the starting and operating of the quartz capillary arc. The adjustable spark gap consists of a double-pole switch with a long insulating handle.

Another method for overcoming breakage of arc containers in the case of cadmium has been proposed by Bates and Taylor.[49] They formed alloys of tin and cadmium melting at temperatures between 176 and 200°C. which apparently, because they did not wet the quartz, could be used like mercury in Cooper-Hewitt lamps without danger of breaking the containers.

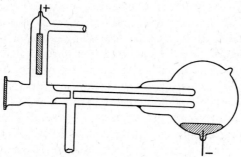

FIG. 45.—Arc by Cario and Lochte-Holtgreven yielding an intense source of sodium *D* lines free from self-reversal.

The third arc in this group is that due to Cario and Lochte-Holtgreven[50] (Fig. 45). This lamp, made of Pyrex glass with electrodes of iron and of sodium, was originally evacuated, then sealed off with an atmosphere of argon at a pressure of from 5 to 20 mm of Hg. In operation, a diffusion pump keeps the argon in circulation, the direction being such as to prevent the sodium vapor from passing down the tube to the window. The source is one of high brightness; and, since there is nothing but a column of transparent argon between the portion of the flame where the temperature is highest and the observing window, it is free from self-reversal in the direction of observation.   This lamp was found of considerable value in the study of the excitation of fluorescence of the sodium D lines by means of sodium light.

XIII. The Spark.   Though closely related to the arc, the spark differs in that the electrons needed for the carrying of the current result mainly from the high electrical field at the cathode, whereas in the arc the supply results from thermionic emission.   Further in the case of the spark, cathode material is commonly made available to be carried into the path of discharge by ion bombardment, while in the case of the arc electrode, material is ordinarily brought into the path of the discharge by vaporization.   In both instances the radiation is characteristic of the bombarded or vaporized electrode as well as of the gas initially present. The spectra are generally quite different, however.   The lines of the arc generally characterize the neutral atoms, while those of the spark characterize the singly and the multiple ionized atom.   For the production of a spark there is needed some source of high potential which may vary from a few hundred volts or so on upward. Occasionally generators or batteries, but usually transformers of high or low frequency, induction coils, or influence machines are necessary.   The disruptive feature of the discharge generally demands a spark gap with a condenser in parallel.

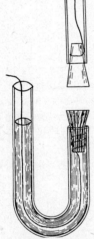

Fig. 46.—Hartley's arrangement for a spark discharge showing lines of materials present in liquid form.

Where the spark spectra of solids are desired, those materials may be used as the electrodes of the spark gap.   Where the material is in gaseous form, it is conveniently held in some glass or quartz container between electrodes of some material such as tungsten which does not easily vaporize or disintegrate.   Where the material is in a liquid form, special devices are needed. Of these, only two will be mentioned.

In Hartley's[51] device (Fig. 46) the upper or positive electrode consists of a chisel-shaped piece of graphite with the blunt end encased in a piece of glass tubing. The negative terminal consists of a similarly shaped piece of graphite, which is held sharp edge up in a U-shaped glass tube with the blunt end projecting downward into a solution of the material whose spark spectrum is desired. For the convenient and rapid bringing of the liquid to the spark by capillary action, sharp grooves are cut lengthwise in the graphite, as shown. The sharp edges of the chisel-shaped terminals serve to maintain the spark in a definite plane, a condition much to be desired when the spark is used with a spectroscope.

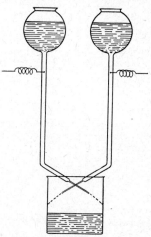

FIG. 47.—Krulla's device for obtaining a spark spectrum of material in solution.

A second device is that due to Krulla[52] (Fig. 47). Two jets of the solution flowing at right angles pass within a short distance of one another. Their points of closest approach serve as the terminals of a spark discharge. These sparks are said to be brilliant and perfectly steady.

The Vacuum Spark. Work in this field has been done by many. The present discussion will, however, be confined to the source

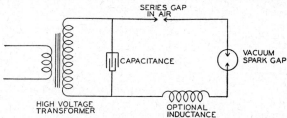

FIG. 48.—Arrangement of apparatus for the vacuum spark of Millikan and his coworkers. The length of the series gap, depending on the vacuum obtained and the potential used, ranged from 1 to 3 cm, the capacitances from 0.01 to 0.02 μf, the potentials from 40 to 50 kv. To obtain 8- to 10-fold ionized atoms, capacitances ranging from 0.3 to 0.5 μf and direct-current potentials from an induction-coil source ranging from 70 to 80 kv. were used.

devised by Millikan, Sawyer, and others[53] (Fig. 48). In most of this work the sparks were formed in front of a slit, in a very high vacuum, between metallic electrodes with separations ranging from a small fraction of a millimeter to a few millimeters.   On applying the potential, a little greenish glow was observed around the electrodes.   There was no general glow, however, and most of the discharge passed between the electrodes in the form of a brilliant spark, bluish white in color in the case of zinc.   This discharge so heated the electrodes, conductors, and insulation that a considerable quantity of gas was thrown out.   After the passage of a series of sparks, it was necessary to pump out this gas. Eventually the discharges were very brilliant sparks.

Miss Carter[54] described similar apparatus in which a large induction coil with an electrolytic interrupter fed with 15 to 20 amp. was used.   The condenser consisted of copper plates separated by 5-mm glass plates.

Wire Explosion in Vacuum.   Reference has been made to the continuous spectra obtained by Anderson and by Sawyer and Becker in connection with the explosion of fine wires.   When this same procedure is applied to filaments in high vacuums, or as by Sawyer and Becker, to asbestos fiber soaked in salt solution, line-spectra characteristics of the spark are obtained.

XIV. Glow-discharge Tubes.   Glow-discharge tubes are generally distinguished from arcs and sparks by the fact that in their operation there is little vaporization of material from the electrodes and no destructive concentrated discharge.   It is still necessary to maintain an emission of electrons from the cathode.

Owing to low vapor pressure, difficulty is sometimes experienced in exciting spectra of substances.   In such cases an admixture of one of the gases of the helium group may facilitate the production of the spectrum of the vapor in which interest is centered without the spectrum of the inert gas showing.   In the case of argon and the band spectrum of nitrogen, there is a decided effect upon the distribution of the radiation from the nitrogen, probably due to collisions of the second kind.   In the particular case of the nitrogen afterglow, the effect is marked and such as to give a spectrum changing with the time after excitation.   In the case of water vapor mixed with hydrogen or of water vapor alone, one can easily obtain the Balmer series characteristic of hydrogen, whereas difficulty is experienced when the water vapor is absent.

Geissler Tube.   These tubes are given various shapes and dimensions and many substances in gaseous or vapor form are used in them.   A high difference of potential of the order of a few thousand volts, such as may be obtained from induction coils or transformers, is generally required. However, with certain materials for electrodes and certain residual gases this minimum may be considerably reduced. Among the substances that may be used for terminals is nickel which has been treated with barium or a barium compound.

Hollow-cathode Tube. It has been found advantageous sometimes to use a type of cathode first described by Paschen[55] (Fig. 49), consisting of a hollow cylindrical shell with one end closed. With a residual atmosphere of an inert gas at sufficiently low pressures, the radiation, largely confined to the interior of the cathode leaving the outer space dark, consists largely of the

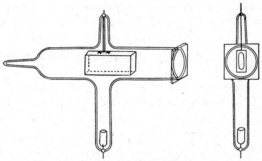

FIG. 49.—Paschen's hollow-cathode tube.

cathode glow which is here relatively very intense and shows favorably the spark spectra of the metal composing the cathode. Materials that vaporize easily may be encased behind a fine sieve at the bottom of such a cathode tube. In such cases, their vapors may predominate inside the cathode and the spark spectra may be characteristic of them. Sometimes the anode is made to surround the cathode, but this does not seem essential. Schüler[56] found it desirable to have as the anode a wire located in the axis of the cylindrical cathode and to view the discharge through a small opening in the end.

Cathodoluminescence Device. This method first described by Hertz[57] has been more thoroughly developed by King and Miss Carter.[58] The apparatus in its final form is shown in Fig. 50. The container was highly evacuated and current furnished by a transformer passed between the cathode C and the anode A.

The cathode rays more or less focused on the metal at M not only vaporized the metal but excited that vapor to emit its spectrum. Several metals were studied.

The Electrodeless Tube. For the electrodeless ring discharge, the tube containing the gas or vapor is usually of the simplest kind, without electrodes, and of sufficient size to fill snugly the

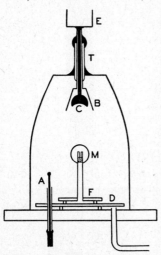

coil which surrounds it and carries the current which produces the discharge. Figure 51 shows Dunoyer's[59] arrangement of apparatus for the production of electrodeless ring discharges for a gas where it is necessary to operate the tube in a furnace. The discharge in this case is necessarily of high frequency, and the greatest electrical field strengths will be found in the tube next to the turns of the coil. The field falls off toward the center of the coil. Accordingly various spectral lines will extend various distances toward the axis, a fact which is important in this classification.

Fig. 50.—Diagram of apparatus used by King and Miss Carter in the production of spectra of vapors by cathode-ray bombardment. The main housing is an inverted crucible of silica which rests with a ground fit on a piece of plate glass. T is a silica tube, B a silica shield, C an iron terminal supported by a copper rod with an ice chamber E at the top. A is a silica-enclosed anode, D an aluminum plate, F a silica plate, M the metal being studied in a slotted silica-tube container.

Low-voltage Neon Lamp. The low-voltage neon lamp made to operate on 115-volt or 230-volt circuits has electrodes of nickel treated with barium and an atmosphere of neon or neon and helium at low pressure. For operation on direct current the cathode is commonly a sheet of the material shaped as desired; and the anode a wire which reaches to some point to within 2 or 3 mm of the cathode. In tubes meant for alternating circuits the two electrodes are similar in design, one form consisting of two wires which are helically wound. Although the luminous area may be of the order of 10 cm^2, the luminous intensity of a lamp as a source is only about $\frac{1}{10}$ candle. As a light producer it is very inefficient. It has, however, great value as an indicator cf positions of objects of one kind or another in the dark.   It also is of value as a simple stroboscopic indicator.

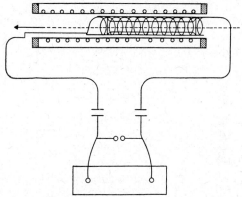

FIG. 51.—Dunoyer's arrangement of apparatus for the production of the electrodeless ring discharge.

Hot-cathode Neon Lamp.   The electron supply for the maintaining of the discharge in this lamp is obtained from the cathode which is heated by a separate current.   The main voltage supply is thus available for the carrying of the current to the anode. As shown in Fig. 52, the greatest dimension of this lamp is about 26 in.   The accessory arrangements (Fig. 53) are such that, when the control switch is closed, a 6-volt 9-amp. current heats the cathode and that, following a 60-sec. delay when the desired temperature for the cathode is obtained, a second switch is automatically closed. Current can flow through the tube in one direction only.   In alternating-current circuits it operates as a rectifier.   The 500-watt alternating-current lamp,

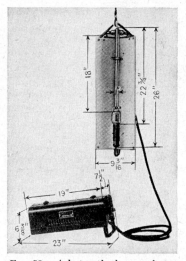

FIG. 52.—A hot-cathode neon lamp.

with 200 watts used in the rectifying resistance ballast, has a total yield of about 5,000 lumens with an overall efficiency of about 10 lumens/watt.   Its color is reddish orange and it is of particular value in architectural relief lighting, flood lighting, beacons, etc.

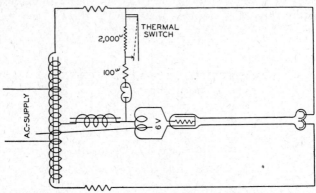

FIG. 53.—Circuit diagram for hot-cathode neon lamp.

The Stroboscopic Lamp. Common sources of this type are the grid glow[60] and the thyratron[61] tube. (Fig. 54). They are very much alike. Each is a three-element device with cathode, grid, and anode, and an atmosphere of neon or of mercury vapor at low pressure. The cathode is coated with oxides of barium or thorium and may be operated hot or cold. The grid except for small openings separates the electrodes, and, while extremely sensitive to the threshold control of electron flow from the cathode to the anode, it is without appreciable effect once the flow is started. In use with a potential difference between cathode and anode sufficient to produce a discharge in case the grid is not operating, the grid is kept negative with respect to the cathode thus preventing a discharge until the instant that light is wanted. Then by means of a contactor the grid is momentarily made positive and a flash of light occurs as a condenser discharges through the neon atmosphere. Because of a slow charging rate for the con-

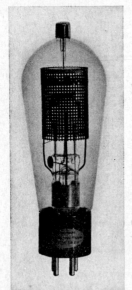

FIG. 54.—The thyratron.

denser, the tube at once returns to its dark condition when
the grid is again made sufficiently negative. The circuit
connections found suitable for this in the stroboglow[62] are
shown in Fig. 55. In this instrument, though the flash is

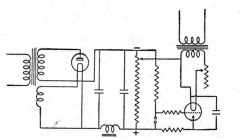

Fig. 55.—Circuit connections for the stroboglow.

said to last but 3×10^{-7} sec., the upper frequency for the range
for which accuracy is claimed is but 10,000 cycles/sec. Other
arrangements are described for the case where mechanical operation of the contactor is not feasible.

Edgerton[63] and his colleagues have applied this principle to the
taking of high speed (slow-motion) pictures. For their sources of

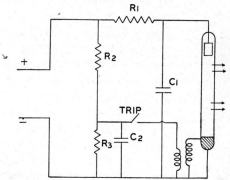

Fig. 56.—Edgerton and Germeshausen's grid-controlled mercury-arc stroboscope
tube.

light, specially constructed mercury-arc tubes were used. Various arrangements of accessory apparatus were made. In Fig. 56
one plan is shown. With this setup, rapid flashes of high
intensity are produced. Closing the trip switch discharges
the condenser C_2 through the step-up transformer. Normally
during the dark period, the grid about the anode is main-

tained negative and no discharge takes place from or to it; but with a sudden operation of the transformer the potential barrier due to the grid collapses and a flash due to the charge on C_1 occurs in the tube.   In consequence of the slow charging of C_1 through the high resistance R_1, time is given for the transformer current to die out, the deionization of the space in the side tube to take place, and the potential barrier due to the grid to be reestablished. For the most delicate work a thyratron-controlled tube is proposed. For the type of tubes considered, an upper limiting frequency of pulses is set for something between 1,000 and 4,000 cycles/sec. The time for deionization is considered the most important factor.

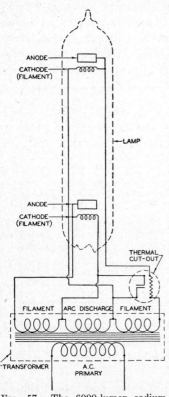

FIG. 57.—The 6000-lumen sodium-vapor lamp and its circuit diagram.

High-voltage Tube. Two types of tubes were used by Moore,[64] the nitrogen-filled tube which yielded a yellow-orange tint, and the carbon dioxide-filled tube which gave a white light. The pressure of the gas in each case was of the order of $\frac{1}{10}$ mm Hg. Claude[65] has developed tubes of this type containing either neon or mercury vapor which are in common use for advertising purposes.

Sodium-vapor Lamp. The lamp together with its circuit diagram is shown in Fig. 57. It has a double-walled tube with the intervening space highly evacuated. The inner tube itself contains a small amount of sodium vapor, and neon (or argon) at a pressure of about 1.5 mm Hg for easy starting. The melting point of sodium is 97°C. The temperature of operation is about 200°C., as Fonda and Young[66] have shown (Fig. 58) that the luminous output of such a sodium lamp, whatever the current of operation, is greater at this temperature than at other tempera-

tures. The radiation output of this lamp consists essentially
of the sodium *D* lines and the lines 8183A, 11,382A, and 11,404A
in the near infrared. Some time is required for the lamp to come
to its full brightness, after which the neon does not contribute
significantly to the spectrum. The discharge voltages for two
of the tentatively standardized sizes[67] are 20 and 25 volts, respectively, the corresponding currents 5.0 and 6.6 amp., respectively.

Other Metallic-vapor Lamps. Lamps similar in construction
to the sodium lamp have been made[68] for other metallic vapors,

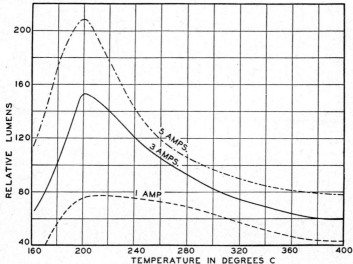

FIG. 58.—The effect of temperature on the light output of a sodium-vapor lamp
with different currents of operation.

such as cadmium, zinc, mercury, and thalium, and thus variously
colored sources obtained. Filters are described that enable
about 15 monochromatic sources ranging from $\lambda = 2537$ to
6438A to be obtained from these lamps.

The Ultraviolet Lamp. This lamp is generally used for producing fluorescent and phosphorescent effects. Because of the
generally low brightnesses obtained for these effects, the bulbs
of these lamps are sometimes made of a dense purple glass so
that the light from the discharge in the mercury vapor within
is reduced to nearly zero. The two electrodes, heated internally
by currents through tungsten coils, are oxide-coated. The radiation, that due to an electric discharge between the electrodes,

fills the bulb completely. It has the characteristics of all mercury-arc sources. With the dense purple glass bulb, the radiation
which is obtained is chiefly that of the near ultraviolet. This
lamp may be regularly obtained in 50- and 100-watt (for lamp
and accessory as supplied) sizes. The mean arc voltages are
17 and 15 volts, the currents 2 and 5 amp. A reactance or resistance ballast is necessary.

FLUORESCENCE AND PHOSPHORESCENCE*

Sources of low-temperature luminescence may exist in the form
of solids, liquids, or gases. Solid luminescent materials, in
general, contain a small amount of some impurity, but the
uranyl salts which have been extensively studied by Nichols and
Howes[69] and others[70] and the double cyanides of platinum are
striking exceptions. Synthetic luminescent solids may be prepared by adding to a nonluminescent compound, called the
diluent, small traces of a second material called the activator.
The two must be intimately mixed and heated to redness, the time
and temperature of heating making a great difference in the
intensity and sometimes in the color of the luminescence. The
brightness of the product varies also with the relative amounts
of the two ingredients. As the amount of activator varies from
a very small percentage of the diluent upward, the intensity of
luminescence quickly increases to a maximum, then steadily
diminishes. In order to excite luminescence the luminescent
substance must be exposed to some source of excitation, some
substances responding better to one source and some to another.
Materials may be prepared which respond to light, visible and
ultraviolet, to cathode rays, to the hydrogen flame, to xrays,
and to radium. Some materials become thermoluminescent upon
exposure to some source of excitation. especially to cathode
rays,[71] to xrays,[72] or to radium.[73]

Striking examples of materials which are strongly luminescent
under photoexcitation are the Lenard and Klatt sulfides.[74]
These are alkaline-earth sulfides activated by different metals
and also containing some easily fusible salt. A comparison of

* The sources in this field are extremely numerous and it has seemed
advisable to include here mainly a brief statement with bibliography which
has been kindly prepared by Miss Frances Wick of Vassar College.

ultraviolet sources for exciting fluorescence has recently been made by Barrett.[75]

Excitation by ultraviolet radiation has been the basis of a recent development of some interesting light sources. Using as the source of excitation a low-pressure mercury arc which gives principally radiation in the neighborhood of 2537 and 3650A, and coating the inside of the bulb with various salts or mixtures of salts give light sources of very high efficiency and of a brightness beyond what was ordinarily thought possible for fluorescent sources.

Among materials strongly excited by cathode rays may be mentioned compounds in which rare earths are used as activators. These materials were extensively used by Urbain[76] and others.[77] Many materials in the form of solid solutions activated by cathode rays are described by Nichols and his collaborators.[78]

Materials strongly luminescent under hydrogen flame include certain oxides and sulfides,[79] a few phosphorescent preparations, and certain crystals and inorganic salts. These incandescent solids show, under the flame, luminescence bands which are greatly in excess of the temperature radiation. Nichols and Boardman[80] introduced different "activators" into the oxides and sulfides, which greatly increased the intensity of luminescence.

THE SUN AS A SOURCE OF CONTINUOUS RADIATION

C. G. Abbot*

Nature and Modifications of Solar Emission. It is now generally admitted that the sun (except possibly a central core which may be liquid[81]) is completely gaseous. The continuity of its spectrum depends in part on its immensity (diameter 865,000 miles[82]), in part on its high-pressure conditions (mean density 1.41[82]), but is principally due to the opacity of ionized gases at high temperatures.[83] Nevertheless, an absorption spectrum of many chemical elements in various states of excitation is superposed on this continuous spectrum, which, especially in the violet and ultraviolet, greatly modifies its spectral-energy distribution. As received at the earth's surface, the solar spectrum is also profoundly modified (a) by the scattering produced by the molecules of the earth's atmosphere,[84] (b) by the scattering pro-

* *Secretary, Smithsonian Institution.*

duced by dust, (c) by the absorption produced by atmospheric gases and vapors, notably by water vapor, ozone, oxygen, and carbon dioxide. The scattering by dust and the absorption by water vapor and ozone vary widely from day to day and from place to place. All types of atmospheric losses increase as the sun approaches the horizon, and thus the mass of air traversed by the solar-beam increases. Important changes in the spectral quality, as well as in the total intensity of the solar rays, are

TABLE 10. DISTRIBUTION OF RADIANCY OVER THE SUN'S DISK

Wavelength, μ	Fraction of radius								
	0.00	0.40	0.55	0.65	0.75	0.825	0.875	0.92	0.95
0.323	144	129	120	112	99	86	76	64	49
0.386	338	312	289	267	240	214	188	163	141
0.433	456	423	395	368	333	296	266	233	205
0.456	515	486	455	428	390	351	317	277	242
0.481	511	483	456	430	394	358	324	290	255
0.501	489	463	437	414	380	347	323	286	254
0.534	463	440	417	396	366	337	312	281	254
0.604	399	382	365	348	326	304	284	259	237
0.670	333	320	308	295	281	262	247	227	210
0.699	307	295	284	273	258	243	229	212	195
0.866	174	169	163	159	152	145	138	130	122
1.031	111	108	105.5	103	99	94.5	90.5	86	81
1.225	77.6	75.7	73.8	72.2	69.8	67.1	64.7	61.6	58.7
1.655	39.5	38.9	38.2	37.6	36.7	35.7	34.7	33.6	32.3
2.097	14.0	13.8	13.6	13.4	13.1	12.8	12.5	12.2	11.7
Wavelength of max., μ	0.458	0.467	0.471	0.474	0.478	0.483	0.489	0.496	0.505

produced by these changing atmospheric conditions.[85] Therefore loose references to "sunlight" as if to a standard source of radiation should be avoided.

The Solar Constant. As it would be found by an observer at the earth's mean solar distance, outside our atmosphere, the intensity of the sun's radiation, usually called the "solar constant," may be taken as 1.94 cal./(cm² min.).[86]

Distribution of Radiant Intensity over Solar Disk. The radiation of the sun, being altered as noted above by terrestrial hindrances, is also profoundly modified by solar conditions. The rays emitted by the center of the visible solar disk arise, on the whole, from considerably hotter layers than do those emitted by the edges of the disk, where sufficient length of path for complete extinguishment is found in the nearly tangential course through superficial layers.[87]   These facts are shown in Table 10.

TABLE 11.   DISTRIBUTION OF SOLAR INTENSITY IN WAVELENGTH

Wave-length, μ	Assumed solar intensity; units arbitrary	Transmission coefficients Altitude		Energy curves at earth's surface					
		5,500 ft.	Sea level	Air mass 1.0 Zenith distance 0°		Air mass 2.0 Zenith distance 60°		Air mass 2.5 Zenith distance 66° 30′	
		a	b	a	b	a	b	a	b
0.295	33	0.20	0.00	7	0	1	0	0	0
0.305	90	0.36	0.03	32	3	12	0	8	0
0.315	143	0.45	0.07	64	10	29	0	20	0
0.325	155	0.51	0.13	79	20	40	3	26	2
0.336	164	0.56	0.20	92	33	51	7	39	3
0.346	168	0.60	0.26	101	44	60	12	47	5
0.355	171	0.64	0.31	109	53	70	17	56	10
0.366	178	0.67	0.37	119	66	80	25	66	16
0.378	175	0.71	0.42	124	74	88	32	74	19
0.391	168	0.74	0.48	124	81	92	39	81	27
0.405	209	0.77	0.52	161	109	123	56	109	40
0.450	272	0.84	0.62	228	169	193	103	171	82
0.500	276	0.89	0.71	246	196	218	138	204	116
0.600	240	0.93	0.77	223	185	206	142	199	125
0.700	195	0.96	0.85	187	165	178	140	175	128
0.800	144	0.96	0.90	138	130	132	117	130	104
0.900	111	0.97	0.92	108	102	104	94	103	90
1.000	93	0.97	0.93	90	87	88	81	87	78
1.20	66	0.97	0.94	64	62	62	58	61	57
1.40	45	0.97	0.95	44	43	42	40	42	40
1.60	34	0.98	0.96	33	33	33	31	32	31
1.80	26	0.98	0.95	25	25	25	23	25	23
2.00	18	0.96	0.94	17	17	17	16	16	15
2.20	10	0.96	0.93	10	9	9	9	9	8
2.40	6	0.95	0.94	6	6	5	5	5	5

a: Corresponds to clear weather at 5,500 ft. altitude.
b: Corresponds to average cloudless weather at sea level, as observed at Washington.

Inasmuch as the sources of different wavelengths are thus effectively at different temperatures, and inasmuch as the absorption spectra of superficial solar gases are much stronger on the whole in the short-wave rays, it is obvious that the energy spectrum of the sun rays as a whole must depart greatly from that of the blackbody at whatever temperature.

Distribution of Solar Radiant Intensity in Wavelength. Serious difficulties interfere with the determination of wavelength distribution of solar rays outside our atmosphere. The continual change of the length of atmospheric path of the rays as the sun traverses the heavens from east to west, the continual change of extinctive properties of the atmosphere as its humidity and dustiness alter during the day, and the large and variable losses suffered by different wavelengths in traversing optical apparatus, all raise great obstacles. Despite numerous attempts made at several stations and during many years, it cannot be claimed that the wavelength distribution of the total solar emission is yet satisfactorily determined. More particularly is this true for the ultraviolet spectrum where the difficulties multiply, and where, indeed, it is impossible to observe beyond 2900A on account of complete extinction by high-level atmospheric ozone.

The energy-distribution curves in Table 11 are computed from data on the distribution of energy in the solar spectrum outside the atmosphere, using atmospheric transmission coefficients found at Washington and other stations. No allowance is made for the powerful absorption of oxygen and water vapor. The values given, in other words, are for the smooth curve, not considering atmospheric absorption bands.[88] Solar lines are allowed for.

SUMMARY

As has been noted, the source is very important in radiation measurements; in particular the source should be suitable for the wavelength interval and the purpose. For transmission measurements in the very short ultraviolet some form of underwater spark, wire explosion, or a hydrogen discharge under heavy current and viewed end on makes a satisfactory source. For the near ultraviolet from about 2000A some form of mercury arc is very satisfactory for such purposes as measuring reflection and transmission. For a continuous source the high-pressure

TABLE 12. SOURCES FOR WAVELENGTH CALIBRATION OF SPECTROMETERS (See also Table of Persistent Lines and Raies Ultimes of the Chemical Elements, W. F. Meggers, I.C.T., vol. V, p. 322)

~ signifies blend of two or more lines

			Discharge tubes or arcs					
Hydrogen	λ^{-1} cm^{-1}	λ A	Helium	λ^{-1} cm^{-1}	λ A	Mercury	λ^{-1} cm^{-1}	λ A
				4859	20582.		6538	15295.
				9234	10830.			
Hα	15236	6562.8		13734	7281.4		9862	10140.
Hβ	20570	4861.3		14154	7065.2		14477	6907.5
Hγ	23039	4340.5		14974	6678.2		17269	5790.7
Hδ	24374	4101.7	D_3	17020	5875.6		17332	5769.6
Hϵ	25188	3970.1		19937	5015.7		18313	5460.7
Hζ	25713	3889.1		20317	4921.9		22945	4358.3
Hη	26073	3835.4		21217	4713.1		27412	4046.6
Hθ	26330	3797.9		22364	4471.5		27301	3662.9
				24837	4026.2		27361	3654.8
				25716	3888.6		27396	3650.2
							39424	2536.5
							54066	1849.6

Alkali metals in Bunsen flame*			Fraunhofer lines			Residual rays		
	λ^{-1}	λ		λ^{-1}	λ		λ^{-1}	λ
Li	14908	6707.9	A	13169	7593.8~	Quartz	1130.	8.85μ
	16384	6103.5	B	14556	6870.0		482.	20.75
Na	16961	5895.9				LiF	575.	17.4
	16978	5890.0	C	15237	6562.8	CaF$_2$	417.	24.0
			D_1	16961	5895.9		316.	31.6
K	12989	7699.0				NaF	315.	31.7
	13046	7664.9	D_2	16978	5890.0	ZnS	312.	32.0
			E	18977	5269.6~	NH$_4$Cl	194.2	51.5
	24708	4047.2				NaCl	192.3	52.0
	24727	4044.2				NH$_4$Br	168.6	59.3
			F	20571	4861.3	AgCl	122.7	81.5
			G_1	23039	4340.5	KBr	121.1	82.6
Rb	12820	7800.3				TlCl	109.2	91.6
	15877	6298.3	G	23214	4307.8~	KI	106.3	94.1
			h	24380	4101.7	calcite	101.3	98.7
			H	25198	3968.5	Hg$_2$Cl$_2$	101.2	98.8
Cs	12120	8251.1	K	25421	3933.7	Ag Br	88.7	112.7
						TlBr	85.5	117.0
	16096	6212.9	L	26175	3820.4	TlI	65.9	151.8
	21771	4593.2	M	26827	3727.6			
	21952	4555.4	N	27924	3581.2			

* Any sufficiently volatile salt of these metals may be used.

hydrogen discharge may be used for the shorter wavelengths, and a tungsten filament or other incandescent source for the longer wavelengths. Where high intensity is more important than steadiness, some form of carbon or metallic arcs is very satisfactory.

For the visible spectrum any number of sources may be used, including the mercury arc or other discharge tubes, even the carbon arc where a very intense source is required, but where it is important to keep the source very constant in output some form of filament, coil or ribbon, in gas or in vacuum, in a bulb with or without plane windows, may be necessary. In general, there is no difficulty in getting sufficient intensity in this part of the spectrum.

For the infrared spectrum the tungsten filament may be used out to 2 or 3μ, and beyond this, the Welsbach mantle, the globar, and the Nernst glower have been used.

In Table 12 are given a number of common sources with the wavelengths generally used for obtaining a wavelength calibration of the different types of spectrometer.

References

1. RICHTMYER, "Modern Physics," p. 183. University of Pittsburgh Physics Staff, "Atomic Physics," p. 49.
2. E. P. HYDE and W. E. FORSYTHE, Astrophys. Jour., 51, 244 (1920).
3. HYDE, CADY, and FORSYTHE, Phys. Rev., 10, 395 (1917).
4. WENSEL et al., Bur. Standards Jour., 6, 1103 (1931).
5. C. E. MENDENHALL, Astrophys. Jour., 33, 91 (1911).
6. WORTHING, Phys. Rev., 25, 588 (1925).
7. FORSYTHE and BARNES, Jour. Optical Soc. Am., 26, 313 (1936).
8. FORSYTHE and WORTHING, Astrophys. Jour., 61, 146 (1925).
   JONES and LANGMUIR, Gen. Elec. Rev., p. 310 (1927).
9. FORSYTHE and WORTHING, Astrophys. Jour., 61, 146 (1925).
10. I. LANGMUIR, S. McLANE and K. B. BLODGETT, Phys. Rev., 35, 478 (1930).
    WORTHING, Jour. Franklin Inst., 194, 597 (1922).
11. K. S. GIBSON, E. P. T. TYNDALL, and H. J. McNICHOLAS, Bur. Standards Tech. Paper No. 148, 1920.
    K. S. GIBSON, Jour. Optical Soc. Am., 13, 267 (1926). (Bibliography.)
    EASTMAN KODAK CO., "Wratten Light Filters." Mees, "Light Filters," "Dictionary of Applied Physics," 4, 176 (1923). Corning Glass Works, "Glass Color Filters."
12. N. K. CHANEY, V. C. HAMISTER, and S. W. GLASS, Trans. Electrochem. Soc., 67, 107 (1935).
13. F. A. BENFORD, Gen. Elec. Rev., 25, 555–559 (1922).

14. W. M. Cohn, *Physik. Zeitschr.*, **32**, 559 (1931).

15. J. Strong, *Rev. Sci. Inst.*, **3**, 816 (1932).

16. C. H. Cartwright, *Phys. Rev.*, **35**, 415 (1930).

17. A. H. Pfund, *Jour. Optical Soc. Am.*, **23**, 270 (1933).

18. H. J. McNicholas, *Bur. Standards Jour.*, **1**, 939 (1928).

19. I. Wyneken, *Ann. Physik*, **86**, 1071–1088 (1928).

20. B. Wrede, *Ann. Physik*, 823–839 (1929).

21. Wilson, *Jour. Optical Soc. Am. and Rev. Sci. Inst.*, **17**, 37 (1928).

22. E. O. Lawrence and N. E. Edlefsen, *Rev. Sci. Inst.*, **1**, 45 (1930).

23. Kistiakowsky, *Rev. Sci. Inst.*, **2**, 549 (1931).

24. J. A. Anderson, *Astrophys. Jour.*, **75**, 394 (1932).

* 25. J. A. Anderson, *Astrophys. Jour.*, **51**, 37 (1920).

26. R. A. Sawyer and A. L. Becker, *Astrophys. Jour.*, **57**, 98 (1923).

27. J. M. Eder, *Zeitschr. wiss. Phot.*, **27**, 337 (1930).

28. Forsythe and Easley, *Jour. Optical Soc. Am.*, **21**, 685 (1931).

29. Trav. et Mém. Bur. Int. Poids et Mesures, **11** (1895).

30. R. Benoit, C. Fabry, and A. Perot, *Compt. rend.*, **144**, 1082 (1907).

31. A. H. Pfund, *Astrophys. Jour.*, **27**, 298 (1908).
    International Critical Tables, V, 275.

32. G. W. Jones, B. Lewis, J. B. Friauf and G. St. J. Perrott, *Jour. Am. Chem. Soc.*, **53**, 869 (1931).

33. *Ann. chim. phys.*, **18**, 5 (1879).
    Baly, "Spectroscopy," p. 57.

34. E. Griffiths and J. H. Awbery, *Proc. Roy. Soc. A.*, **123**, 401 (1929).

35. *Astrophys. Jour.*, **28**, 300 (1908).

36. *Astrophys. Jour.*, **62**, 238 (1925).

37. H. Gerdien and A. Lotz, *Zeitschr. tech. Physik*, **4**, 157 (1923); **5**, 515 (1924).

38. L. J. Buttolph, *Rev. Sci. Inst.*, **1**, 487 (1930).

39. H. Krefft and E. Summerer, *Das Licht*, **4**, 23 (1934).

40. W. Ende, *Zeitschr. tech. Physik*, **15**, 313 (1934).

41. B. T. Barnes and W. E. Forsythe, *Jour. Optical Soc. Am.*, **27**, 83–86 (1937). *Das Licht*, **5**, 84 (1935).

42. W. E. Forsythe, B. T. Barnes, and M. A. Easley, *Jour. Optical Soc. Am.*, **21**, 30 (1931).

43. A. H. Pfund, *Astrophys. Jour.*, **27**, 299 (1908).

44. R. W. Wood, *Phil. Mag.*, **50**, 761 (1925).

45. F. G. Houtermans, *Zeitschr. Physik*, **76**, 474 (1932).

46. R. H. Crist, *Jour. Optical Soc. Am.*, **21**, 690 (1931). See also F. Daniels and L. J. Heidt, *Jour. Am. Chem. Soc.*, **54**, 2381 (1932).

47. R. M. Hoffman and F. Daniels, *Jour. Am. Chem. Soc.*, **54**, 4226 (1932).

48. F. Daniels and L. J. Heidt, *Jour. Am. Chem. Soc.*, **54**, 2381 (1932).

49. J. R. Bates and H. S. Taylor, *Jour. Am. Chem. Soc.*, **50**, 771 (1928).

50. Cario and Lochte-Holtgreven, *Zeitschr. Physik*, **42**, 22 (1927).

51. W. N. Hartley, *Phil. Trans.*, **175**, 49 (1884).
    Baly, "Spectroscopy," vol. II, p. 120.

52. Krulla, *Zeitschr. physik. Chem.*, **66**, 78 (1909).
    Baly, "Spectroscopy," vol. II, p. 122.

53. R. A. Millikan, *Astrophys. Jour.*, **52**, 47 (1920).

R. A. Sawyer, *Astrophys. Jour.*, **52**, 286 (1920).

54. Miss E. Carter, *Astrophys. Jour.*, **55**, 162 (1922).
55. F. Paschen, *Ann. Physik*, **50**, 901 (1916).
56. H. Schüler, *Physik. Zeitschr.*, **22**, 264 (1921).
57. Hertz, *Wied. Ann.*, **19**, 809 (1883).
58. A. S. King and E. Carter, *Astrophys. Jour.*, **44**, 303 (1916).
    E. Carter and A. S. King, *Astrophys. Jour.*, **49**, 224 (1919).
59. M. L. Dunoyer, *Jour. phys.*, **3**, 261 (1922). See also R. Wachsmuth and B. Winawer, *Ann. Physik*, **42**, 585 (1913); A. Hagenbach and W. Frey, *Physik. Zeitschr.*, **18**, 544 (1917).
60. Knowles, *Elec. Jour.*, **26**, 176 (1928); **27**, 116 (1930).
61. A. W. Hull, *Trans. A.I.E.E.*, **47**, 753 (1928).
    A. W. Hull, *Gen. Elec. Rev.*, **32**, 213 (1929).
62. Bahls and Knowles, *Elec. Jour.*, **28**, 250 (1931).
    L. R. Quarles, *Rev. Sci. Inst.*, **3**, 85 (1932).
63. H. E. Edgerton, *Elec. Eng.*, **50**, 327 (1931).
    H. E. Edgerton and K. J. Germeshausen, *Rev. Sci. Inst.*, **3**, 535 (1932).
64. D. F. Moore, *A.I.E.E.*, Sept. 20, 1893.
65. M. G. Claude, *Compt. rend.*, **151**, 1122 (1910).
66. G. R. Fonda and A. H. Young, *Jour. Optical Soc. Am.*, **24**, 31 (1934).
67. L. J. Buttolph, *Trans. I.E.S.*, **30**, 147 (1935).
68. H. Alterthum and M. Reger, *Das Licht*, **3**, 69 (1933).
69. Nichols and Howes, Carnegie Publication No. 298.
70. Baly, "Spectroscopy," vol. II, pp. 256–283.
71. F. G. Wick and E. Carter, *Jour. Optical Soc. Am.*, **18**, 383 (1929).
72. F. G. Wick and M. K. Slattery, *Jour. Optical Soc. Am.*, **14**, 125 (1927); **16**, 398 (1928).
73. F. G. Wick, *Jour. Optical Soc. Am.*, **21**, 223 (1931).
74. Klatt and P. Lenard, *Ann. Physik*, **38**, 90 (1889); Nichols, Howes, and Wilber, Carnegie Publication No. 384, p. 235; Baly, "Spectroscopy," vol. II, p. 293.
75. Barrett, *Am. Mineralogist*, **18**, 578 (1934).
76. M. G. Urbain, *Ann. chim. phys.* (8), **18**, 289–386 (1909).
77. F. G. Wick and C. G. Throop, *Jour. Optical Soc. Am.*, **25**, 57 (1935).
78. Nichols, Howes, and Wilber, *Carnegie Publication* 384, pp. 35–88.
79. Nichols, Howes, and Wilber, *Carnegie Publication* 384, p. 225.
80. E. L. Nichols and L. J. Boardman, *Jour. Optical Soc. Am.*, **20**, 115 (1930).
81. Sir J. Jeans, *Mon. Not. Roy. Astr. Soc.*, **87**, 400 and 720 (1927).
82. C. G. Abbot, "The Sun," 2d ed., p. 3.
83. Russell, Dugan, and Stewart, *Astronomy*, **2**, 581.
84. Lord Rayleigh, *London, Edinburgh and Dublin Phil. Mag.*, **41**, 107 (1871).
85. C. G. Abbot, "The Sun," 2d ed., pp. 287, 288.
86. *Ann. Smithsonian Astroph. Obs.*, **3**, 134 (1913); **4**, 192 (1922).
87. C. G. Abbot, "The Sun," 2d ed., pp. 105–108 and 241–246,
88. See *Ann. Smithsonian Astrophys. Obs.*, **1**, Plates 20 and 30; also **5**, Plates 10 and 11.

CHAPTER III

ANALYSIS OF RADIATION

ELLIOT Q. ADAMS*

Given a source, the making of spectral-radiation measurement necessitates some means of analyzing the total radiation. There are a number of methods that may be used and the one selected is finally determined by the accuracy desired and the use for which the measurements are made. These methods must be based on some property of matter or form which varies with the frequency of the radiation, *e.g.*, on differential reflection, transmission, refraction, diffraction, or optical rotation. The methods depending on reflection, transmission, and optical rotation give in general relatively wide bands of radiation, hence are used only where economy of radiation is important and gross separation adequate.

QUANTITATIVE ANALYSIS OF RADIATION

When the problem requires the isolation of a narrow frequency band, an instrument based on refraction or diffraction is almost invariably employed. Such an instrument comprises entrance and exit slits, means (lenses or mirrors) for focusing the radiation onto the exit slit, dispersing means (prism or grating), and the necessary mechanical means for support and adjustment. When a plane grating or prism is employed, the focusing means are customarily divided so that a parallel beam of radiation is incident on the grating or prism. The focusing and dispersing means may be combined, as in a Féry prism[1] or a concave grating.[2] The choice between lenses and mirrors as focusing means will be determined by secondary considerations: the lack of materials of uniformly high transmission in the extreme infrared, or of uniformly high reflection in the ultraviolet; the circumstance that mirrors are achromatic, while the achromatization of

* *Physical Chemist, Incandescent Lamp Department, General Electric Company, Cleveland, Ohio.*

lenses is impossible in some regions of the spectrum, and in any case imperfect. In default of achromatization, means for moving the lenses may be provided, or the photographic plates in a spectrograph may be both tilted and curved to follow the focal surface of the instrument.

Unfortunately no general term (*e.g.*, spectrophore) is in use to include the various types of prism and grating dispersing instruments, and at the risk of ambiguity "spectrometer" is often used both in a general and in a specific sense. It may be well at this point to define the specific instrument names (even if these distinctions are not always observed in the literature). An instrument for visual observation of spectra is a *spectroscope*, even when provided with a wavelength scale and comparison prism. An instrument for recording spectra is a *spectrograph*. An instrument with means for varying the brightness of one or both of two fields (of the same spectral range) visually compared is a *spectrophotometer*. An instrument in which wavelengths are determined by angular (*i.e.*, goniometric) measurements is a *spectrometer*. An instrument in which a physical receiver measures a beam of "monochromatic" radiation is a *spectroradiometer*, while an instrument used with a source of radiation as a means for furnishing monochromatic radiation for use in other apparatus is a *monochromator*.

It is inconvenient to have to provide means for varying the angle between the collimator and telescope tubes of a prism or grating spectrometer both on account of the necessity of providing elaborate angle-measuring devices, and because of the resultant necessity of moving the source or the receiver of the radiation. This may be avoided by using one of the many types of constant-deviation spectrometer, which may be classified according to the angle of deviation maintained, as follows:

Zero Degree. By using two or more prisms of different materials, or a prism and grating, spectroscopes may be built in which a selected ray suffers no deviation.[3] Most hand spectroscopes are so constructed. A number of direct-vision constant-deviation prisms depending on internal reflection have been described,[4] and Fuchs[5] devised a mounting, later improved by Wadsworth, in which external reflection was used.

Sixty Degrees. Uhler[6] has shown that the use of a "half prism" (30-deg. right triangular prism) as a 60-deg. constant-deviation prism gives certain advantages over the Pellin and Broca 90-deg. form.

Ninety Degrees.   Pellin and Broca[7] devised a prism which may be regarded as the combination of two half prisms with an isosceles right triangular total-reflection prism—a convenient arrangement now in very general use.

Wadsworth generalized the Fuchs[5] mounting to give a constant deviation of almost any desired angle.

One Hundred and Eighty Degrees.   The same lens and slit can be used for collimator and telescope (autocollimating) if the axial ray after passing through, *e.g.*, a 30-deg. prism, is returned by a mirror or isosceles right prism (roof prism).   This is the well-known Littrow[8] mounting which is even more economical of space than of materials.   It has the disadvantage of astigmatism, since the entering and emerging rays cannot pass symmetrically through the lenses.

Spectrometers fall into two groups according as the dispersion is secured by means of prisms or gratings.   With a grating the dispersion is a simple geometrical function of the wavelength and may be increased by diminishing the interval between the rulings, or by using a spectrum of a higher order.   The grating puts only a fraction of the incident radiation into any particular order of spectrum,* and means must always be provided to avoid errors due to overlapping of orders.   It is not always realized that a similar hazard exists with the prism spectrometer:[9] all prism materials in use have at least one absorption band in the infrared and at least one in the ultraviolet.   These bands are regions of anomalous dispersion, and any setting of a prism spectrometer in general will pass radiation of three frequencies, one lower than the infrared resonance frequency, one in or near the visible which is the one almost invariably used, and one higher than the ultraviolet resonance frequency.   Only the shape of the frequency distribution of radiation and the absorption of air and window materials permit a prism to put practically all the energy of any one frequency in a single narrow band and prevent this anomalous dispersion from being a frequent source of error.

With a prism spectrometer and a given prism material, greater angular dispersion can be secured only by a (real or virtual) increase in the total prism angle.   Thus some spectrometers

* See p. 143.

with as many as six 60-deg. prisms have been used in astronomic observatories. With so many air surfaces the loss of light by reflection may exceed 50 per cent.

The most common method of stating the dispersing power of a prism material is to give the ratio of the difference of the index of refraction at two (visible) wavelengths to the index at one wavelength or to a mean value. This gives no certain indication of the dispersion in other regions of the spectrum. The rate of change of index with wavelength, $dn/d\lambda$, gives a very misleading

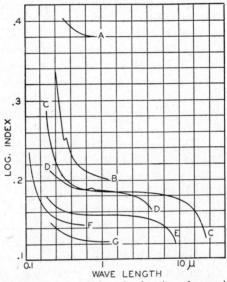

Fig. 59.—Logarithmic plot of index of refraction of several materials as a function of wavelength. The slope of the lines is a "figure of merit" for the respective material (see Table 13). *A*, diamond; *B*, carbon bisulfide; *C*, rock salt; *D*, quartz (ordinary ray); *E*, fluorite; *F*, lithium fluoride; *G*, water.

impression, both because it discriminates in favor of materials of high index of refraction, and because 1 A is a tremendous change in the xray region, and a negligible one in the long infrared. The best simple "figure of merit" is the logarithmic derivative, $\dfrac{d \log n}{d \log \lambda}$. This is proportional to the slope of the lines in Fig. 59.

Prism Materials

For an ideal prism material the specifications are easy to write, but it is equally easy to demonstrate that no one substance possesses, or could be expected to possess, all these properties.

The ideal prism material has a high degree of transparency (*i.e.*, a low extinction coefficient) and a high dispersion for the radiations to be studied. Its index of refraction is low, to minimize reflection losses. It is cheap. It is uniform and unirefringent, *i.e.*, on the one hand free from flaws, strains and inclusions, on the other, free from double refraction and optical rotatory power. It is easily polished, but resistant to air and water. The material used in any actual case represents a suitable compromise among these requirements.

Unirefringence requires either that the material be liquid or vitreous, or that it crystallize in the cubic system with holohedral or with tetrahedral or pentagonal hemihedral symmetry. Most molecularly complicated substances crystallize in systems of lower symmetry. The cubic holohedral class contains diamond; halides of the types MX and MX_2, *e.g.*, rock salt, NaCl; sylvite (sylvine), KCl; fluorite, CaF_2; and the spinels, $M''M'''_2O_4$, *e.g.*, $MgAl_2O_4$. The hemihedral classes include a number of oxides and sulfides, *e.g.*, sphalerite (blende), ZnS. Some highly hydrated salts, *e.g.*, alums, crystallize cubic, but effloresce (lose water) too readily to use as prism material.

A birefringent (uniaxial) crystal must be so cut that the (acute) bisectrix of the angle between the prism faces is perpendicular to the unique axis of the (tetragonal or hexagonal) crystal. In this way, when the prism is in the position of minimum deviation (for the particular radiation in which one is interested), the deviation will be the same whether the radiation be polarized parallel or perpendicular to the prism edge.

If, as in the case of quartz, the crystal also possesses optical rotation, it is necessary to build up the prism out of half prisms of respectively dextro- and levorotatory material, to avoid a separation of circularly polarized components.

In a trirefringent (biaxial) crystal there are two optic axes, one of which should be set perpendicular to the bisectrix of the prism angle. Since the location of the optic axes in these (rhombic, monoclinic, or triclinic) crystals varies with the wavelength of radiation used,[10] they are not suitable prism materials for general use. In special cases in which all measurements are to be made at a single wavelength the use of such a crystal might be justified.

Specific Prism Materials

Materials for which data are given in Fig. 59 and Table 13, are indicated by a star[*]. For precise work the original references should be consulted.

A. Liquids. The use of a liquid prism material requires a suitable container. The requirements for the material of the container are in general like those for a prism material except that

Table 13. Index of Refraction for Several Materials at Even Wavelengths

(Read from curve; for design purposes only.   For more accurate values see references)

Wave-length, μ	Water	Lithium fluoride	Fluorite	Quartz	Rock salt	Carbon bisulfide	Dia-mond
0.12	.....	1.618					
0.15	.....	1.500					
0.20	1.413	1.441	1.496	1.641	1.820		
0.25	1.381	1.419	1.466	1.603	1.668	2.24	
0.30	1.362	1.409	1.452	1.581	1.611	1.863	2.55
0.40	1.343	1.398	1.441	1.556	1.567	1.710	2.46
0.50	1.335	1.393	1.436	1.545	1.552	1.648	2.43
0.60	1.331	1.388	1.432	1.545	1.542	1.630	2.41
0.80	1.327	.....	1.432	1.544	1.535	1.607	2.40
1.	1.325	.....	1.431	1.535	1.531	1.596	
1.5	1.325	.....	1.429	1.528	1.528		
2.	.....	.....	1.429	1.522	1.528		
3.	.....	.....	1.422	1.500	1.524		
4.	.....	.....	1.416	1.469	1.521		
5.	.....	.....	1.403	.....	1.521		
8.	.....	.....	1.352	.....	1.507		
10.	.....	.....	.....	.....	1.493		
20.	.....	.....	.....	.....	1.387		

the dispersion is unimportant, and the index ought not to exceed that of the liquid.   There is the additional requirement of resistance to attack by the prism liquid.   Prisms built up of plane-parallel plates of glass or vitreous silica are suitable for either aqueous solutions or organic liquids (within the transmission range of the solids), but the cementing material must be suitably chosen.   Glue is resistant to most organic liquids but attacked by water; the reverse is true with most waxes.   Bakelite cement gives a joint resistant to both.   Constructing the prism by fusing together the edges of the plates would be ideal if it could be accomplished without destroying the planeness of the optical surfaces.

1.* *Water*[11] is abundant and easily purified.   It is transparent in the visible and in the ultraviolet to 0.25μ, but opaque to the infrared beyond 1μ.   As a prism material in the longer ultraviolet it deserves more attention that it has received.

2.* *Carbon bisulfide*[12] has a high dispersion, and a reasonably high transmission to 3μ.   According to Coblentz,[13] "in the region of 0.5 to 2μ, [it] is especially adapted for certain fields of spectroradiometry."

3. *Aliphatic hydrocarbons,*[14] *e.g.*, hexane, and *aliphatic alcohols, e.g.* ethyl alcohol, have transmission limits, refractive indices and dispersions much like those of water.   *Glycerol*[15] (glycerin) has a higher index and is less transparent in the ultraviolet.

4. *Aromatic hydrocarbons, e.g.*, benzene,[11] toluene,[14] xylene[11] (in German benzol, etc.) have greater indices of refraction and higher dispersion than water or the aliphatic hydrocarbons or alcohols, and similar infrared limits of transmission.   They are less transparent in the ultraviolet.

5. *Halogen-substituted hydrocarbons,*[14] *e.g.*, α-chloronaphthalene, α-bromonaphthalene, carbon tetrachloride, methylene iodide. The introduction of halogens, except fluorine, raises the refractive index and dispersion.   Substances of this class are well known as index liquids in mineralogy, and α-bromonaphthalene has been recommended[16] for use in liquid prisms.

6. *Esters*, specifically the aromatic esters, methyl salicylate and ethyl cinnamate, were used by Wernicke[17] as the central component of a three-element prism.

7. *Solutions* have been used to get high indices of refraction[18] or to match the mean index of the solid component in a direct-vision prism.[19]

B. Vitreous Materials.   1. *Vitreous silica*†[20] has a lower index of refraction and a narrower transmission region than the crystalline material.   Its low coefficient of thermal expansion makes its optical properties less sensitive to temperature changes and reduces the danger from thermal shock.   The absence of

† The usual term *fused quartz* is doubly a misnomer.   The material as used is no longer fused, and no longer quartz.

double refraction and optical rotation simplify the construction of the prism.   In principle, it should be possible to make prisms of any desired size, but up to the present it has not been possible to get the material optically homogeneous enough for use in fine work.

2. *Glass*[21] is the most generally useful prism material.   The term covers materials with a wide range of index of refraction, dispersion, and transmission limits.   The range of properties is so great that information about any specific prism must be obtained from the maker or by experiment.

3. *Paraffin* is, properly speaking, not vitreous but microcrystalline.   In the longer infrared, where the wavelength exceeds the crystal size, it has been used for lenses,[22] but probably has too low a dispersion for use as a prism.

C. Unirefringent Crystals. 1.* *Halite* (rock salt, sodium chloride, NaCl)[12] occurs native in large amounts.   It has a wide range of transmission.   It is easily scratched and soluble in water. While it is not hygroscopic in the ordinary range of relative humidities, fluctuations in temperature may result in the deposition of moisture on the prism faces.

A simple 60-deg. prism is ordinarily used and great skill and care must be used in fabricating it.   The finished prism may be dipped in a very dilute solution of asphaltum dissolved in water-free xylene.   This affords excellent protection and does not detract materially from its transmission properties.   Whenever it is possible, the prism should be mounted in an enclosed chamber in which a quantity of calcium chloride or other water absorbent may be kept.

2. *Sylvite* (sylvine, potassium chloride, KCl)[12] has a lower dispersion than halite.   Its region of transparence extends farther into the infrared, so that at 15 to 20μ it is the most promising prism material.   Like halite, it is soluble in water.

3. *Potassium bromide*[11] (KBr) has a lower dispersion than KCl but is transparent to about 24μ.

4. *Potassium iodide*[11] (KI) is very hygroscopic and is difficult to polish.   The data on prisms of this material are meager, and their long-wave limit of transparency has not been determined precisely.

Single crystals of all three potassium halides have been grown from the molten salt: a tedious process, developed nearly simultaneously at a number of universities[23] (cf. lithium fluoride).

5.* *Fluorite* (fluorspar, calcium fluoride, CaF_2)[12] is most useful in the infrared from 2 to 9μ.   It is difficult to obtain, but artificial fluorite crystals have been made of a size which holds promise.[24] The transmission in the ultraviolet is variable, but the best specimens are very useful in this region.[25]

6. *Periclase* (β-magnesia, magnesium oxide, MgO) can be obtained[26] in artificial crystals measuring 3.7 by 3.7 by 1 cm.   It is gradually attacked by carbon dioxide in moist air, polish being lost in two to six months but can be kept indefinitely in a desiccator or in vacuum.   It has a relatively high index of refraction, $n_D = 1.738$, a dispersion approximately twice that of quartz or three times that of fluorite, and is transparent from 0.22 to 5μ.

7.* *Lithium fluoride* (LiF) has been prepared by Stockbarger[27] in crystals 7.6 cm in diameter.   It has a low index of refraction, $n_D = 1.39$, and is presumably transparent to the long infrared, since its Reststrahlen have the shortest wavelength (ca. 17.5μ) of any of the alkali halides.   Its ultraviolet transparency has been found by Schneider[28] to vary markedly from specimen to specimen, the most transparent transmitting several per cent at 1100A. Schneider gives also a plot of the index of refraction from 1100 to 2700A.

8.* *Diamond*[12] (carbon) has a high index and dispersion.   Were the cost not prohibitive, it would be a very promising prism material.[29]

D. Birefringent Crystals.[30]   1.* *Quartz*,[20,31] in spite of the difficulties in construction caused by double refraction and optical rotatory power, is second only to glass as a prism material. In the middle ultraviolet (0.2 to 0.3μ) and short infrared ($<4\mu$), it is nearly always used.   Beyond 50μ quartz becomes sufficiently transparent for use in thin lenses or prisms but gives little resolution.

2. *Ice*[30,32] can be used only at temperatures below 0°C.   Since in freezing the unique axes of the crystals usually are oriented perpendicular to the free surface (in artificial ice, perpendicular to the wall of the container), even polycrystalline ice behaves as an optically homogeneous material.   Subject to the restriction as to temperature, it should have a real field of usefulness.

Choice of Prism Materials.   Liquid prisms have been little used for precise work.   They are useful for demonstration apparatus, particularly with carbon bisulfide and visible radiation.

For very short ultraviolet (0.12 to 0.20μ) fluorite has been found most useful.   Quartz is the material of choice just beyond the limits of transmission of optical glass, *i.e.*, 0.2 to 0.3μ and 2 to 4μ, but is inferior to glass where all measurements are to be made in the visible.   Rock salt is to be preferred from 4 to 15μ, sylvite from 15 to 20μ, and potassium bromide (and iodide) from 20 to 24μ.   Paraffin from 24 to 50μ, and quartz beyond 50μ, are reasonably transparent, but of too low dispersion for satisfactory prism materials.   The place of the newer prism materials, β-magnesia and lithium fluoride, must be determined by experience.

QUALITATIVE ANALYSIS OF RADIATION

The high resolving power of prism and grating spectrometers is purchased at the price of a low overall utilization of the available energy—low for three reasons, the smallness of the spectral region passed at any one time, the limited angular aperture of the mirrors or lenses used, and the losses by reflection or absorption.   In many radiation problems a much coarser resolution is adequate and a greater overall transmission imperative, either because the spectral intensity of the source cannot be increased, or because a high receiver sensitivity is not attainable.

In such a case several methods, used singly or in combination, are available for what may be termed a "qualitative analysis" of the radiation; three of these will be considered in detail in following sections: analysis by reflection (residual rays), selective absorption (light filters), and scattering (Christiansen filters). The dispersion of optical rotatory power offers another method of analysis.   If a plate of a material capable of rotating the plane of polarization of radiant energy is placed between Nicol prisms, the transmitted beam will be wanting in those frequencies for which the prisms are effectively crossed, the frequency interval between the bands transmitted being smaller, the greater the thickness or the higher the rotatory dispersion of the material of the plate.   Priest[33] has used this effect for the production of artificial daylight, but it is capable of a much greater selectivity, *e.g.*, separating the *D* lines of sodium, or removing the exciting frequency in a study of the Raman effect.

Another method depends, like prism radiometry, on the refractive dispersion.   Many materials on the low-frequency side of their characteristic infrared absorption have a higher index

and a lower dispersion than in or near the visible.   Rubens and
Wood,[34] using lenses of quartz whose index is from 1.55 to 1.43 on
the high-frequency side of the absorption region and 2.14 on the
low-frequency side, and screens of black paper which, while
opaque to the visible and short infrared, is fairly transparent at
100μ, were able to demonstrate that the radiation from the
Welsbach mantle extends to 150μ, and probably to 200μ, and to
measure the transmission and reflection characteristics of a
number of materials in this region of the spectrum.

Selectivity of the receiver may be used in either of two ways:
by using a receiver tuned to the frequency characteristic of the
source[35] or of the filter used, the danger of error from stray
radiation may be minimized, or by combining receiver selectivity
with a different selectivity of the filter, an effective transmission
band narrower than either alone could have given may be
secured.   As illustrations, the combination of a human eye
practically insensitive beyond 0.76μ with a red glass whose transmission for wavelengths shorter than 0.6μ is negligible, gives an
effective transmission little sensitive to the temperature of the
source; and the combination of a phototube of long-wave limit
0.30μ with a glass cutting off at 0.28μ gives a receiver well
adapted to assay radiation to be used for its antirachitic effect.

The proof of the adequacy and reliability of any method of
qualitative spectral analysis, particularly in measuring radiation
in absolute value, is obtained by comparison with the measurements made with a spectroradiometer—the deluxe method of
obtaining such data.

Analysis by Selective Reflection (Residual Rays).   The
deepening of the color of gold or copper by multiple reflection
inside a reentrant object made of, or plated with, one of these
metals is a matter of common observation.   Copper and gold,
unlike most other metallic elements, have reflecting properties
markedly selective in favor of lower frequencies (longer wavelengths) in the visible region of the spectrum.

Many crystalline substances, transparent in the visible, show
an analogous selectivity of reflection in the infrared, differing
from that of metals both in its more sudden onset and in its disappearance when a frequency of resonant response has been
passed.   A few substances are known which behave similarly in
the visible, the most familiar being methyl and crystal violets—

used in indelible pencils—which are violet by transmitted and green by reflected light.

E. F. Nichols,[36] in 1896, noted that the reflection of quartz, which at $\lambda = 7.4\mu$ is probably less than that of any known material in the visible, at $\lambda = 8.4\mu$ rivals that of burnished silver for violet light. This suggested to Rubens and Nichols[37] a method by which, without prisms or gratings, homogenous radiation in the long infrared could be obtained in quantities sufficient for determination of its wavelength* and intensity, and also for studying the properties of various materials for these wavelengths,† *viz.*, by multiple reflection, preferably of radiation from a source selective in favor of the same region of the spectrum.

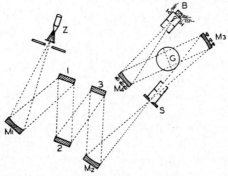

Fig. 60.—Arrangement of apparatus used by Rubens and Nichols in study of residual rays.

With the apparatus shown in Fig. 60, they located the regions of metallic reflection of quartz, mica, and fluorite, and detected the residual rays (German Reststrahlen) of rock salt, sylvite, crown glass, flint glass, sulfur, potash alum, shellac, and calcite. In the figure, Z is the zircon plate of a Linnemann burner, M_1, M_2, M_3, and M_4 concave mirrors, 1, 2, and 3 plane surfaces of the material under investigation, S a slit and G a grating of wires whose diameter was equal to the space between them, and 0.3716 mm apart (on centers). As is well known, such a grating gives only spectra of odd orders. The receiving instrument is the bolometer B.

Table 14 gives the wavelengths of maximum energy in the grating spectrum of a number of residual-ray bands. Measure-

* See Table 14.
† See Table 15.

ments by Rubens and von Wartenberg[38] are indicated by §. Most of the unmarked wavelengths have been redetermined a number of times by Rubens and his coworkers.[39] The values marked with a † were obtained by E. F. Nichols and E. Q. Adams,[40] using the apparatus shown diagrammatically in Fig. 61. The source of radiation is a Welsbach mantle A, surrounded by a water jacket J. A slit S defines the beam which, after reflection from the crystal surfaces 1. 2. 3. 4. and the concave

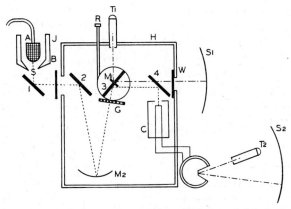

FIG. 61.—Arrangement of apparatus used by Nichols and Adams in study of residual rays.

mirror, M_2, and dispersion by the wire grating G falls on a Coblentz thermopile, C. The third reflecting crystal, 3, is mounted on a turntable which is rotated by the tangent screw R. The beam of infrared radiation may be cut off by the cardboard shutter B.

If the Ketteler-Helmholtz dispersion formula be written in the form

$$n^2 = 1 + \sum_{p=1}^{p=\omega} \frac{k_p}{1 - \dfrac{v^2}{v_p{}^2}} \tag{35}$$

n is the index of refraction at frequency v, and k_p is the contribution of the pth resonance frequency v_p to the dielectric constant ($n_0{}^2$, the square of the index of refraction for infinitely long waves), and n^2 be plotted against log v, the point of inflection between the pth and $(p + 1)^{th}$ resonance frequency will correspond to a value of

$$n_{\sim}^2 = 1 + \sum_{p+1}^{\omega} k_p \qquad (36)$$

with an accuracy which is greater, the greater the ratio of the successive resonance frequencies.

Much work has been done on selective reflection in the infrared shorter than 15μ, but as this is a region in which adequate

TABLE 14. WAVELENGTHS IN MICRONS OF RESIDUAL RAYS FROM VARIOUS SUBSTANCES*

	F	Cl	Br	I	CN	CO₃''
Li.............	17.4†					
Na.............	31.7‡	52.0				
K..............	......	63.4	82.6	94.1		
NH₄...........	......	51.5§	59.3§			
Ag............	......	81.5	112.7	......	(93)‡	
Tl.............	......	91.6§	117.0§	151.8§		
Ca''..........	{24.0 }31.6	......	......	......	......	98.7‡
Hg''..........	......	(95)‡				
Hg₂''.........	......	98.8‡				
B'''N''''......	20.9†	Zn''S''	32.0†	Si''''O₂''	8.85,	20.75‡

Elements and radicles are univalent unless otherwise indicated ('', ''', or '''').
* *E.g.*, lithium fluoride, sodium fluoride, sodium chloride, potassium chloride.
Substances crystallize in the regular (cubic) system unless marked ‡.
† Measurements of E. F. Nichols and E. Q. Adams presented before the American Physical Society (but published only in abstract).[40]
§ Measurements of H. Rubens and H. von Wartenberg.[38]

intensity and greater purity can be obtained by the use of prisms and gratings, selective reflection is here not a particularly useful method of analysis.

Martens,[41] in 1901, computed the wavelengths of metallic reflection (resonance) of carbon bisulfide, α-bromonaphthalene, cassia oil, barium mercuric chloride in aqueous solution, benzene, alcohol, water, and xylene. Flatow,[42] in 1903, found ultraviolet residual rays of carbon bisulfide near 230 mμ. Hulburt[43] observed a reflection maximum of 9 per cent against quartz, computed 13 per cent against vacuum, and resonance at $\lambda = 240$ mμ; for α-bromonaphthalene, 9 per cent, 19½ per cent and 229 mμ, respectively; for cinnamic aldehyde, 4%, 9½%, 275 mμ. The ultraviolet optical properties of cassia oil were attributed to its content of cinnamic aldehyde. Barium mercuric iodide in aqueous solution, phenol, and bromine were found to give no appreciable selective reflection (less than 4 per cent against quartz).

TABLE 15. REFLECTION FACTOR OF VARIOUS MATERIAL FOR RESIDUAL RAYS

Material*	Dielectric constant	CaF₂ 23μ	CaF₂ 33μ	NaCl 52μ	KCl 63μ	KBr 83μ	KI 94μ	TlBr 117μ	TlI 152μ	Hg lamp 313μ	∞
Calcite	8.3	4.9	61.0	19.6	12.7	31.6	65.6	39.6	..	25.0	23.5
Marble	8.2	5.2	53.3	18.0	11.8	25.1	54.4	36.0	..	24.5	23.2
Gypsum	7.5	13.2	18.5	33.0	28.5	30.9	35.4	23.8	..	22.1	21.6
Fluorite	6.82	55.3	83.0	30.0	25.2	21.6	20.4	20.6	..	19.9	19.9
Rock salt	5.82	2.1	1.7	80.2	64.5	27.5	24.3	19.9	..	17.9	17.2
Sylvite	4.75	2.3	1.6	39.9	80.0	37.5	24.4	17.4	..	14.0	13.8
Potassium bromide	4.66	3.8	3.2	2.2	18.0	82.8	56.3	21.9	..	14.9	13.5
Potassium iodide	5.10	5.6	4.4	2.2	2.3	30.2	75.0	23.0	..	15.8	14.9
Ammonium chloride	6.85	3.8	3.1	79.5	54.7	32.3	26.3	23.4	..	19.8	20.0
Ammonium bromide	6.98	6.0	3.8	55.1	66.4	41.5	28.8	24.4	..	21.1	20.3
Silver chloride	10.9	9.4	6.9	19.9	38.8	48.9	49.3	39.1	..	31.4	28.5
Silver bromide	12.1	12.9	11.7	6.10	4.3	25.9	40.0	42.7	..	35.6	30.7
Silver cyanide	5.57	8.3	7.0	4.0	3.2	32.4	48.8	22.0	..	17.3	16.4
Mercuric chloride	6.52	....	....	....	....	....	....	22.6	..	19.3	19.1
Mercurous chloride	9.36	9.8	8.3	6.8	4.5	35.0	56.5	51.3	..	33.5	25.7
Thallous chloride	35	13.9	10.5	8.1	38.0	74.0	80.6	76.0	57	56.7	51
Thallous bromide	42	15.1	13.1	9.6	5.5	8.2	28.0	76.8	60	59.7	54
Thallous iodide	30	17.4	16.7	16.3	12.1	7.2	6.9	48.6	51	50.3	47
Lead chloride	42	10.2	6.9	23.3	43.2	61.8	71.4	58.9	52	51.8	54
Water	81	6.5	7.2	9.3	10.6	10.9	11.1	12.7	..	15.1	64
Sulfuric acid	.....	8.8	7.9	16.9	18.7	17.7	17.7	18.4	..	21.7	
2:1 mixture	.....	9.2	10.9	19.4	20.6	22.3	....	....	..	28.8	
1:2 mixture	.....	8.1	9.6	14.2	17.0	19.0	....	....	..	26.5	
Glycerol	56.2	5.8	5.5	5.2	6.3	7.5	....	8.5	..	9.4	58.1
Castor oil	4.78	4.0	4.0	4.1	4.5	4.4	....	4.3	..	4.8	13.9

* See section on prism materials.

Martens also found it necessary to postulate two ultraviolet resonance frequencies to explain the dispersion curves of halite and of sylvite. Haber in 1911 "discovered" that one of these was related to the infrared (Reststrahlen) frequency by the square root of the ratio of the molecular weight of the salt to that of the electron, the other being greater in the ratio $\sqrt{2}$. As the precision of the dispersion measurements is insufficient to locate at all precisely *two* resonance frequencies, the conclusion is inescapable that Martens had used the same ratios to locate his assumed resonance frequencies.

As an illustration of the utility of the method of analysis by selective reflection, Rubens and Michel[44] were able to extend their measurements on the spectral distribution of the blackbody to 22.4 and 51.8μ by the use of radiation filtered after multiple reflection from fluorite and rock salt, respectively. It may be seen from Table 15 that this method is capable of extension to at least 150μ (residual rays of thallous iodide).

FILTER RADIOMETRY

D. C. Stockbarger*

The advantage of using a filter to separate radiant energy into more or less definite spectral intervals is the simplicity of the operation. Using standard filters having known filter factors and wavelength limits for typical sources, the long tedious spectral-radiation measurements (and subsequent integrations in wide spectral bands), which require relatively high intensities and delicate spectroradiometric apparatus, are reduced to a few simple measurements with auxiliary equipment to be found in almost any physical laboratory. If the character of the results obtained is satisfactory for the purpose at hand, considerable time and effort are saved.

By means of filter radiometry it is possible to analyze the spectral radiation of inaccessible sources, whether mercury-arc-lamp installations under life tests[45] or the radiation from stars[46] and planets,[47] and obtain information that would be impossible by the more accurate methods.

A beam of radiant energy incident on a filter loses, in general practically nonselectively, by reflection an amount depending on the angle of incidence. This reflection represents a loss of about 8 per cent for normal incidence, which usually is unimportant unless it is allowed to reach the detector through one or more subsequent reflections. The remainder of the incident radiation is transmitted by the filter with an average efficiency ranging from zero to 100 per cent, that which is not transmitted being absorbed and converted into another form of energy. Care

* *Associate Professor of Physics, Massachusetts Institute of Technology.*

should be taken that the absorbed radiation does not reach the measuring instrument by reradiation and thus introduce an error. Some screens may be affected by the absorbed radiation and their transmission changed.   If this is due to an increase in temperature, the screen may be cooled by blowing a blast of air upon it.

It is an inherent characteristic of filters that the absorption coefficient varies continuously with the wavelength so that the transmission cutoff is never sharp.   For some purposes it would be ideal if filters possessed abrupt cutoffs, but, as will be indicated below, correction for the departure from rectangular spectral-transmission characteristics can be applied in many cases.

The simplest kind of spectral separation is the isolation of a line by a so-called monochromatic light filter.   In those rare cases in which a complete isolation is effected by either a single filter or else a combination of filters used simultaneously, evaluation of the line is straightforward.   The true intensity is obtained by dividing the observed value by the corresponding spectral transmission of the filter.   Usually, however, the isolation is only apparent and for its effectiveness depends on the selective response characteristics of the detector and to a large degree on the energy distribution of the source.   As an example may be cited the combination of didymium and orange glasses which is often employed to isolate the strong green line of mercury for visual work.   In this instance the transmission is relatively high in the red and well into the infrared region, but since the red lines are weak, the filter serves its intended purpose satisfactorily. The green line can be evaluated with the aid of such a filter by visual, photographic, or photoelectric photometry, appropriate selection of detector being made in the last two cases, but cannot be measured directly with a nonselective detector unless additional filters be provided to absorb the unwanted radiation. An indirect determination can be made by evaluating the transmitted infrared and red radiation and applying a correction to the observed total intensity, after which the corrected value must be divided by the green-line transmission of the filter. Accurate results are hard to obtain if the unwanted radiation is equal to, or greater than, the radiation studied.

If two lines are present in a completely isolated region, it is possible to evaluate each by making two intensity determinations with two filter combinations having different spectral-transmission characteristics and solving a pair of simultaneous equations. If I_1 and I_2 are the line intensities, A and B are the observed total intensities, τ_{a1} is the transmission of the first filter for the first line, etc., the equations are:

$$I_1\tau_{a1} + I_2\tau_{a2} = A \qquad (37)$$
$$I_1\tau_{b1} + I_2\tau_{b2} = B \qquad (38)$$

The accuracy with which the line intensities can be determined is dependent on the accuracies of the six separate measurements, *viz.*, A, B, τ_{a1}, etc.

In general, broad spectral regions are separated quite easily; thus for problems where, say, the fraction of the radiant energy in the infrared, the visible, and the ultraviolet spectrum or similar information is needed, filter radiometry may be quite satisfactory. Some bands can be isolated and others evaluated through subtraction. Here the sloping cutoffs are often troublesome, especially when a large fraction of the radiant energy lies in the regions of diminishing transmission, *i.e.*, near the ends of the bands. Filters possessing as nearly as possible hypothetically ideal spectral-transmission characteristics are chosen and suitable corrections are applied to the observed radiant powers.

In each case there is a factor, analogous to the spectral transmission for monochromatic radiation, by which the observed intensity must be divided to obtain the true value. Unfortunately, however, its magnitude depends not only on the filter characteristics but also on the quality of the radiation transmitted and the spectral sensitivity of the receiving instrument. This factor[48] is readily expressed mathematically as a ratio

$$F = \frac{\int_{\lambda_a}^{\lambda_n} J_\lambda \tau_\lambda S_\lambda d\lambda}{\int_{\lambda_a}^{\lambda_n} J_\lambda S_\lambda d\lambda} \qquad (39)$$

where F = filter factor.

J_λ = intensity of the incident radiation of wavelength λ (between the filter transmission limits λ_a and λ_n).

$J_\lambda \tau_\lambda$ = intensity of the same radiation after transmission.

S_λ = spectral sensitivity of the measuring instrument.

Whereas the numerator is the observed intensity through the filter, the denominator represents the weighted energy, *i.e.*, it represents the energy within the limits λ_a to λ_n as weighted by the receiving instrument.   If a nonselective measuring device is used, the factor S_λ may be omitted from both numerator and denominator.   If the radiation within the limits consists of a few lines, the integration could be a summation.

The determination of these corrections, *i.e.*, the filter factor, is the most difficult part of filter radiometry.

Sometimes a factor

$$F' = \frac{\int_{\lambda_a}^{\lambda_n} J_\lambda \tau_\lambda^2 S_\lambda d\lambda}{\int_{\lambda_a}^{\lambda_n} J_\lambda \tau_\lambda S_\lambda d\lambda} \tag{40}$$

is determined experimentally by measuring the fraction of the radiation transmitted by the filter when an additional identical

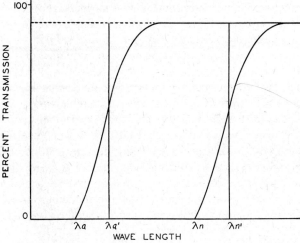

Fig. 62.—Schematic representation of calculated cutoffs for use with filter factor.

filter is held in the path to isolate the spectral region.   This transmission of the second filter is apt to be quite different from that of the first because the first filter alters the spectral-energy distribution.   This, however, is a good method for checking the accuracy of the method of calculation.

A close approach to an ideal filter is realized by utilizing the concept of effective cutoffs, as illustrated in Fig. 62, whereby a real filter or combination of filters is made to serve as an ideal one.   By shifting the spectral-transmission limits to $\lambda_{a'}$ and $\lambda_{n'}$

the energy discarded between these and the real limits compensates for the energy losses due to abnormal absorption in cutoff regions. The factor for these limits is therefore

$$F_e = \frac{\int_{\lambda_a}^{\lambda_n} J_\lambda \tau_\lambda S_\lambda d\lambda}{\int_{\lambda_{a'}}^{\lambda_{n'}} J_\lambda S_\lambda d\lambda} = \tau_{max} \tag{41}$$

Thus if the factors J_λ, τ_λ, and S_λ are known, the limits $\lambda_{n'}$ and $\lambda_{a'}$ can be found by some process of successive approximation. If a nonselective receiver is used as the measuring instrument, S_λ is constant and drops out. For a wide band and good screens (*i.e.*, sharp cutoff) these wavelength limits can often be readily approximated since the energy near the limits is but a small part of that transmitted by the filter. The measurements are in no way affected by the adoption of this concept and the energy distribution of the source needs to be known only in the cutoff regions if the filters have constant spectral transmission between the limiting regions.

The kind of filters to be used depends upon the problem under investigation. They may be designated "exclusion" or "transmission" filters depending upon whether the spectral range to be evaluated is obtained by excluding it from the measurement made without the filter, or by evaluating the part transmitted through the filter.

The complete spectrum may be evaluated in selected wavelength bands by a proper combination of the measurements (corrected for losses by reflection in the spectral range transmitted) resulting from the insertion of suitable filters, singly or in combination.

For example, in determining the spectral quality of the radiation from the planet Mars[47] which, owing to atmospheric absorption, is confined to wavelengths between 8 and 15μ, a thin piece of microscope cover glass[49] was used to exclude the radiation of wavelengths longer than 8μ; and a plate of fluorite was used to exclude incident radiation of wavelengths longer than 12.5μ. By comparison of the ratio of the intensities of the observed spectral components (8 to 12.5μ, and 12.5 to 15μ) with calculated blackbody values, assuming different temperatures, an estimate was obtained of the probable surface temperature of Mars.

This, of course, assumes that Mars radiates as a blackbody or a graybody in this region.

Another typical example in which use was made of filters was in an investigation of the carbon arc[50] in which, by means of filters of quartz,[51] of water, and of water combined with white crown (a new filter, Pyrex is better), Cruxite, Noviol C, (Noviol A is better) and with red glass, the spectrum was integrated in wide bands extending from 0.2 to 0.29μ; to 0.35μ; to 0.45μ; to 0.65 to 1.4μ; to 4.1μ; and 15μ. Figure 63 shows the transmission of these filters.

The discussion of effective wavelength of the monochromatic screens* for optical pyrometry is in fact a discussion of screens

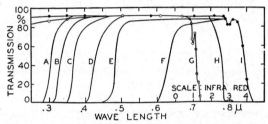

FIG. 63.—Spectral transmission of a number of filters: A, pyrex 2 mm; B, Ba—flint 3 mm; C, cruxite; D, noviol A; E, noviol C; F, red glass; G, water cell, 10 mm; H, pyrex, 12 mm.; I, quartz, 5 mm. Infrared scale refers to curves G, H, and I.

for selecting a band of radiant energy whose intensity can be measured and ascribed to a definite wavelength interval. Three screens can be selected,[52] a red, a green, and a blue, which, if properly used, will permit measurements to be made, with an optical pyrometer, of the relative intensity for the three parts of the spectrum and the results interpreted as the intensity for definite wavelengths. In this case each of the screens, in particular the red and the blue screens, is made much more nearly monochromatic by the selectivity of the receiver, *i.e.,* the eye.

Spectral bands of various widths may be selected by a set of screens with transmissions similar to those shown in Fig. 63. With such screens, using two together, the intensity may be measured within a band from λ_2 to λ_5 with two particular screens and using a third screen with one of these from λ_3 to λ_5 and then by difference obtain the intensity in the band λ_2 to λ_3, where the

* See p. 360.

wavelength limits λ_2, λ_3, λ_5 have been determined by Eq. (41). To do this, one must first know the spectral response of the receiver and the spectral transmission of the different screens and the spectral distribution of the energy of the source studied. The first two may be measured and in many cases the relative spectral distribution in the source studied can be approximated with sufficient accuracy to enable one to obtain quite accurate values for the amount of energy within certain spectral bands of various widths.

THE CHRISTIANSEN FILTER

C. G. ABBOT*

A filter that offers some promise was suggested by Christiansen[53] and has been described recently by McAlister.[54]

In their commonest form these filters are made up of a solid pack of optical-glass particles (0.5 to 2 mm in size) in a glass cell, with the spaces between filled with a liquid having an index of refraction that varies with the wavelength in a different manner from that of the glass and equal to that of the glass at some wavelength. For the wavelength where both liquid and glass have the same index of refraction, the filter acts as a solid plate, and the rays of this wavelength are transmitted without deviation or reflection loss within the filter. All other rays of shorter and longer wavelengths are deviated and reflected in an amount dependent upon the difference in the indices at the interfaces— glass to liquid and liquid to glass.

These filters cannot be used like the ordinary colored-glass filters since the "undesired" colors are not absorbed, but are scattered symmetrically in a halo about the center line through the filter. The angular position of a given undesired color about the axis of the filter depends upon two factors: (1) the difference in the indices of the liquid and glass for that wavelength; and (2) the number of interfaces through which the beam passes (*i.e.*, particle size and thickness of the filter). Also, since the interfaces are oriented in a random or probability manner, there exists only a "most probable" angle for a given undesired color and this color is in evidence in varying amounts at all angular positions about the axis of the filter. Some means of

* *Secretary, Smithsonian Institution.*

intercepting these undesired wavelengths is necessary. The simplest means is to use an optical system consisting of two lenses with the filter placed between them in parallel light. In this case the undesired wavelengths are cut out by a diaphragm placed at the image of the source of light.

Figure 64 shows the transmission of a set of five Christiansen filters at 20°C. They are all made of borosilicate-crown-glass

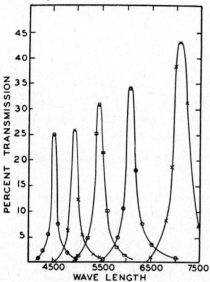

Fig. 64.—Transmission curves of a set of five Christiansen filters at 20°C.

particles (1 to 2 mm in size) immersed in mixtures of carbon bisulfide and benzene. McAlister points out methods of constructing and using these filters to obtain improved separation.

References

1. Ch. Féry, *Jour. Phys.*, **9**, 762 (1910); *Astrophys. Jour.*, **34**, 79 (1911).
   The use of a 60-deg. prism with convex faces does not appear to be recorded, but would seem promising for a low-dispersion instrument, since the reflection losses are reduced to a minimum.
2. H. A. Rowland, *Phil. Mag.*, **13**, 469 (1882).
3. J. B. Amici, *Museo fiorentino*, **1**, 1 (1860); *cf.* J. Janssen, *Compt. rend.*, **55**, 576 (1862); **56**, 189 (1863); R. Radan, *Ann. Physik*, **118**, 452 (1863); *Rep. Physik*, **2**, 241 (1867).
4. A. S. Herschel, *Am. Jour. Sci.*, **39**, 232 (1865); H. Ernsmann, *Ann. Physik*, **150**, 636 (1873); F. Kessler, *Ann. Physik*, **151**, 507 (1874); A. Ricco, *Mem. Soc. Spett. It.*, **8**, 21, 87 (1879); H. Goltzsch, *Rep. Physik*, **18**, 188 (1882).

5. F. L. O. Wadsworth, Phil. Mag., **38**, 337 (1894); Astrophys. Jour., **1**, 232 (1895).
Fr. Fuchs, Zeitschr. Instrumentenk., **1**, 349 (1881).
6. H. S. Uhler, Astrophys. Jour., **47**, 74 (1918).
7. Ph. Pellin, and A. Broca, Jour. Phys., **8**, 314 (1899).
8. O. Littrow, Sitzber. Akad. Wiss. Wien, **47**, 26 (1863); Am. Jour. Sci., **35**, 413 (1862).
F. L. O. Wadsworth, Phil. Mag., **38**, 137 (1894); Astrophys. Jour., **2**, 264 (1895).
9. F. Paschen, Ann. Physik, **53**, 812 (1894).
10. H. Rubens, Sitzber. preuss. Akad. Wiss. (Physik.-math. Klasse) **1919**, p. 976.
11. I.C.T., VII, p. 13.
12. I.C.T., VII, p. 14.
13. W. W. Coblentz, Bur. Standards Sci. Papers, **16**, 705 (1920).
14. I.C.T., VII, pp. 34–62.
15. I.C.T., VII, p. 12.
16. H. Th. Simon, Ann. Physik, **53**, 542 (1894); H. Kayser, "Handbuch der Spektr.," Leipzig, vol. I, 363 (1900).
17. W. Wernicke, Zeitschr. Instrumentenk., **1**, 353 (1881).
18. G. D. Liveing, Proc. Cambridge Phil. Soc., **4**, 257 (1879); W. Gibbs, Am. Jour. Sci., **50**, 50 (1870); Phil. Mag., **40**, 229 (1870); W. H. Hartley, Nature, **44**, 273 (1891).
19. Ch. V. Zenger (K. W. Zenger), Zeitschr. Instrumentenk., **1**, 263 (1881); Compt. rend., **96**, 521, 1039 (1883); Nature, **27**, 596 (1883); Am. Jour. Sci., **25**, 469 (1883). This is the essence of the mineralogical measurement of refractive index, cf. R. C. Emmons, Am. Mineral., **13**, 504 (1928); **14**, 414, 482 (1929); H. G. Fisk, Am. Mineral., **15**, 263 (1930;) V. F. Harrington and M. J. Buerger, Am. Mineral., **16**, 45 (1931); J. H. C. Martens, Am. Mineral., **17**, 198 (1932); R. D. Butler, Am. Mineral., **18**, 386 (1933); J. J. Glass, Am. Mineral., **19**, 459 (1933).
20. I.C.T., VI, p. 341.
21. I.C.T., II, p. 104.
22. E. F. Nichols and J. D. Tear, Phys. Rev., **21**, 589 (1923).
23. P. W. Bridgman, Proc. Am. Acad. Sci., **60**, 307 (1925), **64**, 19 (1929). F. Stöber, Zeitschr. Krist., **61**, 299 (1925); S. Kyropoulos, Zeitschr. anorg. allgem. Chem., **154**, 308 (1926); H. Ramsperger and E. H. Melvin, Jour. Optical Soc. Am., **15**, 359 (1927); J. Strong, Phys. Rev., **36**, 1663 (1930).
24. D. C. Stockbarger, Jour. Optical Soc. Am., **14**, 448 (1927).
25. T. Lyman, Astrophys. Jour., **25**, 45 (1907); E. G. Schneider, Phys. Rev., **45**, 152 (1934); W. M. Powell, Jr., Phys. Rev., **45**, 154 (1934).
26. J. Strong and R. T. Brice, Jour. Optical Soc. Am., **25**, 207 (1935).
27. D. C. Stockbarger, Phys. Rev., **49**, 200 (1936).
28. E. G. Schneider, Phys. Rev., **49**, 341 (1936).
29. H. Rubens and R. W. Wood, Phil. Mag., **21**, 256 (1911).
30. H. E. Merwin, I.C.T., VII, p. 16.

31. T. M. Lowry, *Phil. Trans. A.*, **212**, 261 (1913); T. M. Lowry and W. R. C. Coode-Adams, *Phil. Trans. A.*, **226**, 391 (1927); W. R. C. Coode-Adams, *Proc. Roy. Soc. A.*, **117**, 209 (1927), **121**, 476 (1928).

32. J. M. Adams and W. Lewis, *Rev. Sci. Inst.*, **5**, 400 (1934).

33. I. G. Priest, *Phys. Rev.*, **6**, 64 (1915); *Jour. Optical Soc. Am.*, **7**, 75, 1175 (1923).

34. H. Rubens and R. W. Wood, *Phil. Mag.*, **21**, 249 (1911).

35. F. Eckert, *Ber. deut. physik. Ges.*, **15**, 307 (1913); J. D. Tear, *Phys. Rev.*, **21**, 611 (1923).

36. E. F. Nichols, *Ann. Physik*, **60**, 401 (1897); *Phys. Rev.*, **4**, 297 (1897).

37. H. Rubens and E. F. Nichols, *Ann. Physik*, **60**, 418 (1897); *Phys. Rev.*, **4**, 314 (1897).

38. H. Rubens and H. von Wartenberg, *Sitzber. preuss. Akad. Wiss.*, **1914**, 169.

39. H. Rubens, *Ber. deut. physik. Ges.*, **17**, 315 (1915); *Sitzber. preuss. Akad. Wiss.*, **1915**, 4; **1919**, 976. Th. Liebisch and H. Rubens, *ibid.*, **1919**, 198, 876.

40. E. F. Nichols and E. Q. Adams, *Phys. Rev.*, **21**, 712 (1923).

41. F. F. Martens, *Ann. Physik*, **6**, 603 (1901).

42. E. Flatow, *Ann. Physik*, **12**, 85 (1903).

43. E. O. Hulburt, *Astrophys. Jour.*, **46**, 1 (1917).

44. H. Rubens and G. Michel, *Sitzber. preuss. Akad. Wiss.*, **1921**, 590. *Physik. Zeitschr.*, **22**, 569 (1921).

45. Coblentz, Long, and Kahler, *Bur. Standard Sci. Papers* (S.P. 330), **15**, 1 (1918).

46. Coblentz, *Bur. Standards Sci. Papers* (S.P. 438), **17**, 725 (1922).

47. Coblentz, *Bur. Standards Sci. Papers* (S.P. 512), **20**, 371 (1925).

48. Coblentz, Stair, and Hague, *Bur. Standards Jour. Res.* (R.P. 370), **6**, 951 (1931).
   Stockbarger and Burns, *Phys. Rev.*, **34**, 1263 (1929).

49. Coblentz, Investigation of Infrared Spectra, *Pub.* 65, p. 65. Carnegie Institution of Washington (1906).

50. Coblentz, Dorcas, and Hughes, *Bur. Standards Sci. Papers* (S.P. 539), **21**, 535 (1926).

51. Coblentz, Stair, and Hague, *Bur. Standards Jour. Research* (R.P. 370), **7**, 723 (1931).

52. Forsythe, *Jour. Optical Soc. Am.*, **5**, 85 (1921).

53. Christiansen, *Ann. Physik Chem.*, neue Folge, **23**, 298 (1884).

54. McAlister, *Smithsonian Misc. Coll.*, **93**, No. 7 (1935).
   Barnes and Bonner, *Phys. Rev.*, **49**, 732 (1936).

CHAPTER IV

SPECTROMETRIC INSTRUMENTS AND THEIR ADJUSTMENT

Henry F. Kurtz*

Several types of spectrometers, monochromators, and spectrographs have been developed for special purposes. While each of these instruments depends upon the same fundamental principle, they differ in construction and methods of adjustment. For the best results, the various parts of any such instrument must be in proper alignment, and when there are any moving parts, they must function properly.

If the prism or grating that has been selected for the particular problem is to function properly, it must be properly mounted, *i.e.*, the mechanical supports and parts as well as any additional optical equipment must be so chosen that the prism or grating may operate up to its own limiting precision. While it is necessary for the adjustments, scales, bearings, etc., to be made adequately delicate and of sufficient range, it is undesirable to make them excessive in either accuracy or range.

Manipulation of the adjustments should be possible without the assistance of special tools, and any manipulation of the instrument during the course of adjustment should require at the most no more than a screw driver or a pin wrench. Further, it is desirable to have all adjusting screws and nuts provided with means for locking them securely after the adjustment has been made and all exposed knobs and buttons should be provided with removable caps to prevent accidental disturbance or tampering. In keeping with these requirements, of course, is the further one that the entire ensemble be sufficiently strong and rugged to maintain such adjustments over a long period of time and to withstand the vicissitude of at least reasonable use, if not a moderate degree of abuse.

* *Physicist, Bausch & Lomb Optical Company.*

All bearings and moving parts should be so designed as to resist wear and, whenever possible, should be provided with means for taking up for such wear as occurs. Since spectrometers and spectrographs frequently stand idle for long periods and may be wanted for use within short notice, it is desirable to incorporate, insofar as possible, bearings and moving parts that do not require lubrication since the lubricant may become gummy and cause the mechanism to "stick." It is not always possible to provide moving parts that do not require lubrication, and where the use of such parts cannot be avoided, adequate and convenient means for cleaning and renewing lubrication should be provided.

Limb screws, tangent screws, fine adjustment screws, and eyepiece micrometer screws should be made of German silver or, better, of stainless steel. The bearings should be made of bronze, fine grain cast iron or some other material that will "work" well in contact with the material of which the screw is made, and which will have approximately the same coefficient of expansion as the screw.

In addition to the foregoing, every instrument should be designed with careful attention to the convenience of its use. All operating handles and mechanisms should be within easy reach of the operator, and should operate smoothly and unfailingly. This matter of convenience is important in that it permits the operator to work with a minimum of fatigue. The reduction of fatigue, of course, always promotes accuracy of results and increases the quantity of work that can be turned out in a given period of time.

Mounting of Optical Parts. Lenses should be mounted in cells that will hold them firmly but without undue pressure. Improper mounting will inevitably ruin the performance of good optical elements. Lens cells should be attached to the telescope and collimator, or to the support for the lens cells, by well-fitted threads, the axes of which are concentric with the optical axis of the lens. The cells, when screwed down, should rest on a shoulder which is accurately perpendicular to the axis of the thread. Any focusing mechanism should operate smoothly and should be of such a nature that it cannot be inadvertently disturbed. It should further move the lens in a path that is accurately parallel to the principal axis of the lens. All eyepieces should be adjustable for focus by means of a multiple thread or a helical slot with a feather pin.

Prisms or gratings should be held down firmly to the seat or table by means of a bridge clamp with pieces of cork under the clamp to provide a cushion. There should, however, be no cork between the prism or grating and its table. The prism or grating should be laterally located and retained upon its seat or table by means of snugly fitted cleats so that it may be removed for cleaning and replaced without the need to resort to a tedious method of trial and error for its correct relocation.

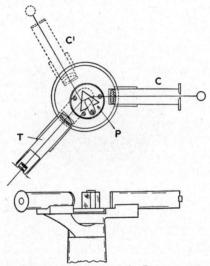

Fig. 65.—Schematic diagram of the Bunsen spectroscope.

The Spectrometer. Modern spectrometers are refined forms of the Bunsen spectroscope. This type of instrument is illustrated schematically in Fig. 65. C is a collimator with an achromatic objective. The prism is of the 60-deg. type and is made of glass of high dispersion. T is a telescope, also achromatic, with a crossline at its principal focus and an eyepiece which can be focused on the cross wire. The collimator, telescope, and prism are so located that radiation of wavelengths near the center of the visible spectrum will pass through it at minimum deviation. The arm carrying the telescope is usually pivoted about an axis which intersects the bisector of the refracting angle of the prism at an appropriate point and is parallel to the refracting edge of the prism.   Rotation of the telescope about this axis makes the crossline traverse the entire spectrum.

C' in Fig. 65 is an auxiliary collimator which is used to project a scale by reflection from the prism face into the plane of the spectrum in the telescope.   The scale consists of fine open lines in an otherwise opaque coating on a glass disk; it is calibrated either in wavelengths or in arbitrary units.   In present-day instruments, this auxiliary collimator is ordinarily omitted, and a graduated circle is supplied for indicating the position of the telescope.   In some cases provision is made for rotation of the

FIG. 66.—A laboratory spectroscope.   (*Courtesy Gaertner Scientific Corporation.*)

prism table, and a graduated circle is attached to it for indicating its position.   The most elaborate instruments have means for focusing both the collimator and the telescope to correct for residual chromatic aberration, leveling screws for the collimator, the telescope, and the prism table, fine motions and clamps for the necessary adjustments, means for determining the angular position of the telescope with great accuracy and a Gauss eyepiece, or its equivalent, for use in adjustment of the instrument by autocollimation.*   Figure 66 is a photograph of a precision instrument of this type.   The filar micrometer microscopes permit reading the graduated circle to one second of arc.   Instruments of this type find their greatest usefulness in the measurement of the refractive indices of glass and the angles of prisms.   They are not particularly suited for routine deter-

* See p. 116.

mination of the wavelengths of spectral lines, or for use as a dispersing device in measurements of spectral intensities. Other special types of instruments, described in the following sections, have been developed for these uses.

Constant-deviation Instruments. A constant-deviation prism due to Abbe, and a special case of this prism due to Pellin and Broca, are shown in Fig. 67. The Abbe prism has a constant angle of deviation of 60 deg., while the Pellin-Broca has one of 90 deg. As indicated by the dotted lines, the Pellin-Broca prism may be assumed to be composed of two 30-deg. refracting prisms, with a 90-deg. reflecting prism interposed between them. The ensemble, however, is invariably made of a single piece of glass. Since reflection in both of these prisms takes place within the critical angle (provided, of course, that the mean index of refraction of the glass is high enough), it is not necessary to coat the surface with a reflecting metal layer. Possibility of intensity errors due to selective absorption of the reflecting medium is thereby avoided.

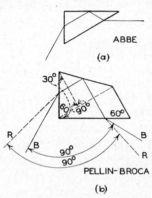

Fig. 67.—Constant-deviation prisms: (a) due to Abbe; (b) due to Pellin-Broca, which is a special case of the Abbe, giving a constant deviation of 90 deg. This angle may be varied within limits by choice of suitable angles between the refracting and reflecting surfaces.

Spectrometers equipped with constant-deviation-prism systems are particularly useful for spectrophotometric combinations of apparatus.

The usefulness of any spectrophotometer stands or falls, with respect to dependability of results, upon the proper location of the system of pupils, and upon the maintenance of this condition during traverse of the spectrum. Since the pupil system of the spectrometer becomes a part of the system of pupils of the spectrophotometric ensemble, it is essential to have the axis of rotation of the prism of the spectrometer so located that the constantly changing limiting aperture of the prism does not cut unsymmetrically into the beam of light passing through it. This condition must be maintained for all wavelengths. Uhler[1] has made a study of the location of the axis of rotation for prisms of the Abbe and Pellin-Broca types.

DeLaszlo[2] described a very clever mechanical arrangement for the automatic fulfillment of the necessary conditions. The method of incorporation of the Pellin-Broca prism into a constant-deviation spectrometer is shown in Fig. 68. The body of the instrument has three faces mutually perpendicular to each other like the corner of a cube. On two of these faces the telescope and collimator are held in bushings, while the lower face supports the bearing for the prism table. The latter has a lever arm attached to it, or integrally cast with it, and is rotated by a screw pressing on this arm. The wavelength drum is held to

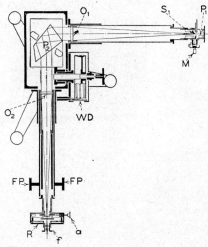

Fig. 68.—Diagram of a spectrometer of constant deviation of 90 deg.

this screw by friction in such a manner that it can be rotated independently of the screw to permit adjustment to one or more known wavelengths. The eyepiece end of the telescope tube is fitted with a removable adapter containing a crossline, sometimes adjustable laterally for wavelength adjustment. When the instrument is to be used as a monochromatic illuminator, this eyepiece adapter is exchanged for a slit. The degree of purity is, of course, dependent upon the narrowness of the entrance and exit slits, or upon the separation of the lines of a line spectrum. The telescope objective is provided with a rack-and-pinion focusing mechanism. A camera may be substituted for the telescope, making the instrument a useful spectrograph for work that is not too exacting.

The requirements that a constant-deviation spectrometer or monochromatic illuminator are ordinarily expected to meet are:

1. The prism angles must be accurate to about 1 min. of arc.
2. The optical dimensions of the prism must be accurate to about 0.1 mm.
3. Telescope axis, collimator axis, and axis of prism rotation must be mutually perpendicular to the order of about 3 min. of arc.
4. The wavelength drum must be accurately divided.
5. The wavelength drum should be provided with facilities for turning it independently of the screw for wavelength adjustment, or the eyepiece crossline should be provided with lateral adjustment for the same purpose.

These specifications, as given, are for instruments of the size most commonly built commercially, *viz.*, with objectives of about

Fig. 69.—A laboratory spectrometer of 90-deg. constant deviation using a Pellin-Broca type prism, with telescope.   (*Courtesy Bausch & Lomb.*)

30 mm free aperture and 250 to 300 mm in focal length.   Such an instrument should read wavelengths with an accuracy of 2 to 4A in the violet and 15 to 20A in the red.   If the instrument is used exclusively in the ultraviolet, these tolerances will be correspondingly smaller because of the greater dispersion in the ultraviolet, while if it is used exclusively in the infrared, the tolerances will be correspondingly larger owing to the decreased dispersion.

If the optical axes are not properly located, if the prism is not correctly made, or if the wavelength drum is not accurately divided, the wavelength readings will not be correct.   If any one of these three conditions of failure obtains, there remains nothing to do but to return the instrument to the maker for correction. Some rectification of error due to lack of perpendicularity of the optical axes of the collimator and telescope, or of error of a progressive nature in the wavelength calibration, may be accomplished by shifting the prism on its table with respect to the axis of rotation, but this can be done only at the expense of the maintenance of the important condition of central pupils in the instrument.   If a shift of the prism produces a noticeable asymmetry of pupils, the instrument should be returned to the maker. If the axis of rotation of the prism is not perpendicular to the plane containing the telescope and collimator axes, the spectrum will not move horizontally through the field upon rotation of the

FIG. 70.—Another laboratory spectrometer similar in characteristics to that shown in Fig. 69.   (*Courtesy Gaertner Scientific Corporation.*)

prism, but will move through an inclined path.   Rectification for this condition can also be carried out only by the maker.

To adjust the wavelength scale, light having spectral lines of known wavelengths is passed through the instrument and one of the known wavelengths (preferably in the green or blue, but sodium yellow will do in the absence of other sources) is brought to coincidence with the crossline by operating the wavelength screw and drum.   Now, by whatever means is provided, the wavelength screw is held fast and the drum is rotated independently until it reads the wavelength of the spectral line in coincidence with the crossline.   Having made this adjustment carefully, the entire drum may be checked for accuracy by using as many lines of known wavelength as the available source* provides.   As indicated above, the adjustment for wavelength

* See p. 79.

is not always accomplished by rotation of the drum independently of the screw, but sometimes by a lateral movement of the cross-line or the exit slit of the telescope.

Fig. 71.—The same instrument shown in Fig. 69, but with a spectrographic camera substituted for the telescope. (*Courtesy Bausch & Lomb.*)

Figures 69, 70, 71, and 72 are photographs of constant-deviation spectrometers, the first two with observation telescopes, and the second two with spectrographic cameras substituted for the telescopes.

Fig. 72.—The telescope of the instrument in Fig. 70 replaced by a spectrographic camera. (*Courtesy Gaertner Scientific Corporation.*)

Autocollimating Instruments. Autocollimating spectrum-producing instruments, *i.e.*, instruments that use the same lens for the collimator and telescope, possess two very distinct advantages. They are:

1. A high degree of compactness.

2. The requirement for much smaller pieces of optical material of which to make the prism system than for instruments of nonautocollimating characteristics of similar size.

Autocollimating instruments, however, suffer from some very distinct disadvantages. The source is near the receptor which often causes inconvenience and sometimes severe difficulties. Autocollimating apparatus is difficult to adjust, and presents considerable difficulty in the removal of parasitic images and stray radiation. However, a suitable set of diaphragms and screens often greatly reduces this trouble. While some small and medium sized spectrometers are built to operate by autocollimation, this method is not commonly used for the reasons indicated. Large spectrographs of high dispersion are almost invariably made of the Littrow type, which is autocollimating, because of the

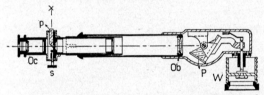

Fig. 73.—An autocollimating spectrometer, with wavelength drum.

advantages of compactness and because of the ease of securing pieces of optical material of adequate size. Spectrographs of small and medium size, however, are not commonly made autocollimating.

An autocollimating spectrometer with wavelength scale is shown in Fig. 73. The prism P has a refracting angle of 30 deg. with a reflecting medium (silver for visible light, mercury-tin amalgam or aluminum for ultraviolet) applied to the surface which is normal to the optical axis. The upper part of the single slit is covered by the small prism p in such a manner that the light originating in X passes through p through the upper part of the slit S to the objective Ob to the prism P, where it is dispersed, reflected and passed again over the same path to the lower part of the slit, then through the eyepiece Oc. It is seen that since the radiation traverses the 30-deg. prism twice, it suffers the dispersion of a 60-deg. prism, and the one combination of slit and objective serves both for collimator and telescope.

If an instrument of this type is large, say 10 in. or more in length, the telescope objective should be provided with a means for focusing. The prism is rotated by a screw fitted with a wavelength drum W.

Instruments with Quartz Optical Parts. Straubel[3] pointed out that, if the optics of an autocollimating instrument are made of quartz, the dispersing prism P having the crystal axis perpendicular to the reflecting surface, the system becomes an ultraviolet instrument with the radiation traveling through the prism at minimum deviation and along the optic axis of the quartz.

Fig. 74.—A monochromatic illuminator for the ultraviolet. Wadsworth prism system using a Cornu prism and aluminum-coated reflector. (*Courtesy Gaertner Scientific Corporation.*)

This arrangement results in the elimination of the doubling of the spectral lines due to the rotating dispersion of the quartz. The lenses should be cut from the quartz in such a way that the optic axis of the crystal is coincident with the telescope axis, and an attempt should be made to have half of the optical path through the lenses pass through right quartz and half through left quartz. The small prism p may be cut with the optic axis in any direction, or preferably may be made from good fused quartz. This instrument, like its visible-light counterpart, is much more interesting than useful and for the same reasons.

Since quartz lenses cannot be achromatized except by the use of fluorite in combination with it, and since adequately large pieces of fluorite are not at present practically available, most of the lens systems of ultraviolet apparatus are not achromatized. This means that the lenses for monochromatic illuminating apparatus must be provided with means for focusing, and the focusing mechanism must further be provided with a scale.

A quartz monochromatic illuminator or spectrometer for use in the ultraviolet is shown in Fig. 74. In this instrument, the collimator and telescope are at a fixed angle of 90 deg. to each other, and the prism system is one based on the Wadsworth* system, shown in Fig. 75. The prism is a Cornu prism, and the reflector is a first surface mirror coated with evaporated aluminum. The instrument shown in Figs. 76 and 77 was designed particularly to serve as a source of monochromatic ultra-

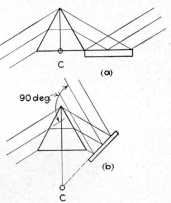

FIG. 75.—The Wadsworth prism-reflector system for maintenance of constant deviation and minimum deviation automatically. (*a*) arranged for a constant deviation of 180 deg. (*b*) arranged for a constant deviation of 90 deg.

violet radiation.   In such an instrument, the primary requirement is that the intensity of the transmitted radiation be great.   The

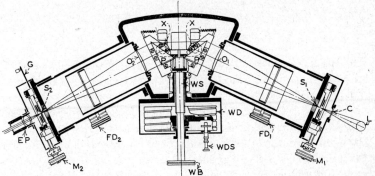

FIG. 76.—Diagram of quartz monochromatic illuminator for the ultraviolet.

slit S_1 is of the bilateral type and is operated by a micrometer screw with an adjustable drum M_1. A quartz window C protects the jaws from dust and corrosion. The collimator O_1 and tele-

* See p. 135.

scope O_2 lenses are of single pieces of quartz with aspheric surfaces and are of 150-mm focal length for sodium light. The use of aspheric surfaces allows the aperture ratio to be carried as high as $f:4$ for wavelength 2000A and $f:4.9$ for 8000A with excellent definition throughout the spectrum. The lenses have a free aperture of 30 mm. Both the telescope and collimator lenses are focused by rack and pinion and are provided with wavelength drums *FD* which permit the setting of the lenses for any desired wavelength. The prism system P_1 and P_2 is a modified Young

Fig. 77.—A photograph of the monochromatic illuminator of which Fig. 76 is a diagram. (*Courtesy Bausch & Lomb.*)

or Thollon[4] type, consisting of two 30-deg. quartz prisms, one of right- and the other left-rotating material. The arrangement of the prism is shown in Fig. 76. The system is arranged to transmit radiation of wavelength 2000A when the longer cathetal faces of the prisms are normal to the telescope and collimator, so that reflection losses will be at a minimum for this wavelength. The optic axes of the quartz pieces are so located that radiation travels parallel to these axes when the prisms are at the center position of their motion. The result is that there is zero doubling at the center of the spectrum and a very slight equal but opposite doubling at the two ends. The amount at the extreme positions is 1 min. 10 sec. of arc; too small to be of any consequence. The prisms are rotated in opposite directions, the center of rotation being about vertical axes XX passing through the centers of the hypothenuse faces.   The screw *WS* by which the motion is secured carries a wavelength drum *WD* graduated in millimicrons.   This drum is adjustable for wavelength and is equipped with stops to prevent accidental displacement of the adjustment.

The bilateral slit S_2 is a duplicate of the entrance slit but, for purposes of adjustment, is fitted with a fluorescent screen and an eyepiece *EP*.   The slit jaws are curved to match the curvature introduced by the prismatic magnification.   The screen is carried on a slide *G* so arranged that it may be introduced into the

Fig. 78.—A monochromatic illuminator for the ultraviolet.   Note how completely the principle of complete enclosure has been carried out.   (*Courtesy Gaertner Scientific Corporation.*)

path of the radiation.   It carries a reference mark for adjustment of the wavelength scale.   When the screen and eyepiece are in position, the instrument serves fairly well as a visible spectrometer in the ultraviolet because of the fluorescent image of the spectrum. When they are removed, the instrument becomes a monochromatic illuminator.   All operating parts are completely enclosed and, therefore, protected against dust and corrosion.

An instrument suited for use as a monochromatic illuminator or spectrograph of constant deviation of 90 deg. is shown in Fig. 78.

Direct-vision Spectroscopes.   The direct-vision instrument is perhaps the simplest of all the spectroscopes.   The prism known as an Amici* prism after its inventor is a combination of one

* See p. 84.

flint and two crown prisms cemented together with Canada balsam and disposed with the bases of the crowns opposite to the base of the flint, and with refracting angles so disposed as to

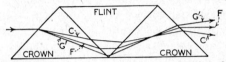

Fig. 79.—The Amici prism. The F line (or any other for which the prism is computed) enters and leaves the prism parallel to the base, *i.e.*, without deviation; hence it is also frequently called direct-vision prism and is used in so-called direct-vision spectroscopes.

cause no deviation of the wavelength at the center of the spectrum. Figure 79 shows such a prism. It will be noted that the F line is parallel to the entrant ray and to the base of the assembled prism. Figure 80 shows such a prism assembled into a

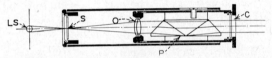

Fig. 80.—A direct-vision hand or pocket spectroscope. The slit of this small simple model is made by cutting it in a metallic coating on glass. Such a slit has the advantages of extreme thinness, sharp edges, absolutely constant width, and automatic protection against dust. It is easily cleaned.

simple hand spectroscope. The slit is in the focus of an achromatic objective which passes a pencil of parallel light through the prism, thence through an aperture to the eye. In the particular model shown, the slit is cut in silver on glass and the eye aperture is covered with a cover glass, making the whole assembly dust-

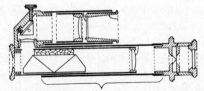

Fig. 81.—A direct-vision spectroscope with wavelength scale.

proof. Since there are no means for measuring, this instrument is truly a spectroscope. It is intended for pocket use.

The pocket instrument illustrated in Fig. 81 is a direct-vision spectroscope with wavelength scale, but which is, strictly speaking, a small, compact and crude, but useful, hand or pocket spectrometer.   The slit is adjustable in width, is covered by a glass, and is operated by a knurled annulus.   A projection system designed to image a wavelength scale coincident with the spectrum is mounted on the main tube.   The image of the scale is reflected from the last surface of the Amici prism, after being directed on to it by an adjustable 90-deg. prism which may be rotated about an axis perpendicular to the page, to displace the scale to the right and left in order to adjust to a known wavelength.   The scale, imaged just above the spectrum, appears as bright lines on a dark background, and no extraneous light is permitted to be superimposed upon the spectrum.   The slit in an instrument of this type should be accurately perpendicular to the plane of refraction of the prism.   To set for focus, it is quite satisfactory to direct the instrument to the sky and focus for the principal Fraunhofer lines which should be easily visible.   To adjust the wavelength scale, the use of a sodium flame is most satisfactory and the method is simply to rotate the screw operating the 90-deg. prism until the sodium D-line image is coincident with the 589 division on the scale.

Spectrographs.   The spectrograph is, as its name implies, an instrument used for making a record of a spectrum on a photographic plate, or otherwise, providing means for the leisurely quantitative or qualitative study of the spectrum.   It differs from the spectrometer essentially only in that the photographic plate (or other recording device) is used as a receptor.   The simplest of the spectrographs therefore consists of means for replacing the observing telescope of a spectrometer or a spectroscope with a suitable camera.   The more modern of these cameras are made almost wholly of metal, to avoid the difficulties incident to the warping and checking of wood.   Two of these cameras, shown in Figs. 71 and 72, are fitted with means for adjusting the objective, a simple shutter for making exposures, means for tilting the plate to secure best focus, and means for moving the plate vertically to permit making multiple exposures on a single plate.

Spectrometers are designed particularly for the direct observation and measurement of the spectrum without the assistance of the photographic plate.   This means, of course, that spectrometers are fitted with many parts not useful for spectrography, such as rotating-prism systems, and wavelength drums, etc., and further, spectrometers lack the optical characteristics required to make the ensemble the most efficient and desirable spectrographic equipment. The optical arrangement most suitable for visual observation is naturally not most suitable for photographic work. The addition of a camera to a spectrometer is useful only when the spectrographic work is to be limited to the few cases where an incidental photographic record may be desirable. If serious spectrographic work is to be done, an instrument designed for this kind of work is indispensable. It is to be expected that if an instrument primarily designed for visual spectrometric work is used, only results of a caliber to be expected from an inappropriate apparatus can be achieved.

Because of the facts that the eye is not responsive to the ultraviolet and the photographic plate is a very sensitive receptor of ultraviolet, many spectrographs are made with quartz optics so designed as to give optimum service throughout the ultraviolet and the shorter visible range. This means that a slit must be provided which will permit adjustment to the narrow openings dictated by the laws of optimum width set forth in Chap. V. The lens system must be designed to exhaust, in so far as possible, the resolving power inherent in the prism system, and to image the spectrum throughout its length with a minimum of disturbance due to coma and to render a field as flat as possible. The prism and lens system, in combination, must be so designed as to reduce curvature of field to the least possible amount.

There are two types of optical system used: (1) that consisting of slit, collimator lens, Cornu prism, and imaging lens; and (2) that consisting of slit, autocollimating lens and prism of the Littrow type. A variant of the latter case, not commonly used, is the system consisting of the slit and a Féry prism. A Féry[5] prism is one in which the lens surfaces are ground directly upon the prism surfaces.

A well-designed spectrograph should meet practically all of the requirements set forth for the spectrometer with particular emphasis placed upon those for ruggedness, facility, and permanence of adjustment, protection of optical and mechanical parts against tampering and corrosion, and convenient disposition of operating mechanisms. It is highly essential, if collimator and camera tubes are used in a spectrograph, that they be generously supplied with diaphragms to prevent reflection of stray radiation from the walls.   In the higher grade instrument, tubes have been eliminated in later years, and the entire instrument is encased in a large sheet-metal box, fitted with partitions to prevent reflections and to isolate the prism and lens compartments from the slit and photographic plate.

With a spectrograph covering the range from 2000 to 7000A, a decidedly broad band of wavelengths, it is quite impossible to achromatize the lens systems.   As a result, the focal plane is invariably inclined sharply to the optical axis and is curved, concave toward the lens.   The degree of this curvature can be controlled to a certain extent in the design of the lens system, but

Fig. 82.—A "medium" quartz spectrograph by Bausch & Lomb.   The entire spectrum from 2100A to 7000A may be impressed on one 10- by 4- or 10- by 2-in. plate.   It uses the Cornu prism system.   Note the "backbone" type of construction and massive proportions.

it can never be entirely eliminated.   For instance, in a certain type of spectrograph using lenses of about 600 mm focal length and rendering the spectrum from 2000 to 7000A on a single 10-in. plate, the spectrum is curved to an extent that the sagittal height of the curve at the center of the spectrum is about 3 mm. Ordinary commercial plates available in 4- by 10- and 2- by 10-in. sizes can be readily bent to this extent, provided the plate holder is appropriately constructed.

Figures 82 and 83 are photographs of "medium" spectrographs, so called because they are smaller than the usual Littrow instruments, and their size is established by the ability to cover the entire spectrum from 2100 to 7000A on a single standard 4- by 10- or 2- by 10-in. plate.   They employ a Cornu prism and a collimator lens of a single piece of quartz.   The imaging lens (camera lens) is a doublet of quartz corrected in accordance with the requirements for definition and minimum curvature. The entire ensemble is mounted on a strong cast-iron base which forms a "backbone" for the instrument and assures constancy of adjustment.   The slit, collimator lens, prism, imaging lens, and plate-holder support are all on individual supports, each attached to this base.   The entire space between the slit and the plate holder is covered with a metal box to exclude radiation. S is the slit, completely enclosed; L is a simple flap shutter to be used in making exposures; F covers a knob by means of which the imaging lens may be focused and clamped; P is the removable metal plate

FIG. 83.—Another "medium" quartz spectrograph.   Note again the "backbone" base.   The tubes in this instrument are well baffled.   (*Courtesy Gaertner Scientific Corporation.*)

holder; H is the lever by means of which the wavelength scale may be brought into position for impression on the plate, with the help of a small electric lamp on the opposite side of the case; M is a drive handle by means of which the plate may be moved up and down to permit the exposure of several spectra on one plate; and N is a scale by means of which the amount of excursion of the plate holder may be read.

Figure 84 is a view of the central section of one of the instruments, with the top cover removed, showing the partitions segregating the lens and prism system from the slit and plate spaces. J is the collimator lens; P is the Cornu prism mounted on its table T.   This table is provided with locking leveling screws and a locking rotational adjustment, permitting rotation of the prism about the vertical axis. NM is the imaging lens and mount fitted with the locking focusing device and with a locking device permitting slight rotation about the vertical axis.   Referring back to Fig. 82, *A, A, A, A* are four covered screws, with locks also, which permit the inclination of the plate-holder support with respect to the optical axis.   The angle between the plate and the optical axis in the horizontal plane must be exactly right to assure sharp focus from end to end of the spectrum, and the plate must be vertical to insure sharp focus and equal width of the spectrum lines from top to bottom, and to assure accurate juxtaposition of spectra when it is desired to make multiple

FIG. 84.—The prism and lens compartment of the medium spectrograph shown in Fig. 82.

adjacent exposures for comparison or for spectrophotometric work.

Littrow Spectrograph.   In cases where greater linear dispersion is needed, the second arrangement known as the Littrow type of instrument is ordinarily used.   Figure 85 shows schematically the fundamental optical system of this spectrograph.   Light passes from the slit, shown above, through the prism *p* to the lens *L* to the dispersing prism *P*.   The rear surface of this prism is coated with a mercury-tin amalgam, aluminum, or some other material that will reflect ultraviolet and visible radiation without absorption bands.   The optic axis of the quartz is perpendicular to this coated surface as in the Straubel prism.   The light is reflected and dispersed by this prism and, after passage again through L, forms the spectrum in the curved, inclined plane shown.

The prism p lies just under the optical axis and the spectrum just above, to avoid interference. With this instrument, the spectrum between wavelengths 2100 and 8000A may be divided into three parts, and each taken on a single plate 10 in. long. Since the total length of the spectrum is of the order of 700 mm, the partial spectra overlap somewhat. It would be feasible to place three plates successively in the positions shown by the three 10-in. lines, but as this would result in a bulky instrument, the arrangement is modified as follows; the lens and prism are

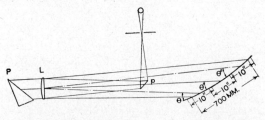

Fig. 85.—Fundamental schematic diagram of the Littrow spectrograph.

mounted on a carriage which moves along the axis, and means are provided to rotate the prism either automatically or manually; the plate holder is also provided with means to permit rotation about an axis perpendicular to the paper. It is seen that the system then resembles an autocollimating spectrometer of 180 deg. constant deviation. A very important added advantage of this system is that each of the three plates will lie with its center on the optical axis of the lens, instead of lying in the extra-axial positions shown in the diagram for the two ends of the spectrum. The definition is markedly better.

The Littrow system is used in spite of the disadvantage of this type of instrument because it gives relatively high dispersion. The instruments described are of the order of 8 ft. in total length. A Cornu instrument of similar dispersion would be nearly twice as long—too long for use in a room of average size.

The diagram (Fig. 86) shows schematically the construction of one of the Littrow instruments to be shown below. The slit and prism are shown at the right near the plate. The latter rotates, as indicated by the dotted lines and the arrow. At the left is shown a carriage, which moves to the right and left, on which are mounted the lens in a fixed mount and the prism on a rotating table. This table has an arm which bears on an inclined track fixed to the base of the instrument in such a manner that, as the table moves back and forth, the prism automatically rotates the amount required to bring to the center

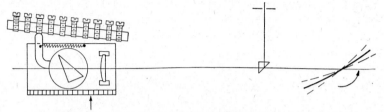

FIG. 86.—Schematic diagram of the Littrow quartz spectrograph.

of the plate the line which will be accurately in focus. It will be noted that the inclined track is provided with screws, against which the prism-table follower presses. Since the manufacture of a smooth cam of the exact curvature and inclination would be very costly, this expedient is used in order to provide nine individual points, along the excursion of the prism carriage, at which the rotation of the prism may be made precisely correct by adjust-

FIG. 87.—Front view of the Littrow spectrograph shown schematically in Fig. 86.
(*Courtesy Bausch & Lomb.*)

ment of these screws. The center and two end positions are sufficient to cover the entire spectrum, but the six other intermediate positions are provided in order that any line in the spectrum may be brought near the center of the plate. The positions are equally spaced throughout the spectrum. This is a unique and useful feature. A scale is attached to the carriage to inform the user as to the position of the prism.

Figures 87 and 88 show a front and rear view of this instrument. It will be noted that all levers and handles for manipulating the instrument are at the operator's end, so that all adjustments can be made without changing position. The hand wheel A operates the mechanism for changing the prism position, with a clamp at B. The button C rotates the plate holder by means of a tangent screw; it is provided with a scale for record purposes. D is a clamp for this rotation. E is the drive handle for raising and lowering the plate; a scale is provided to indicate its position. The scale on the prism table can be easily read from

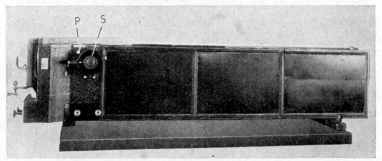

FIG. 88.—Rear view of the Littrow spectrograph shown schematically in Fig. 86.
(*Courtesy Bausch & Lomb.*)

the operator's position, with the help of the magnifier G. The slit is shown at S and the shutter lever at P.

The base of this instrument is made of pieces of U-shaped channel steel, and comprises a backbone which will not warp out of shape with time, as a casting would be apt to do; and temperature changes will not cause it to wind out of shape. The slit, the collimator lens, the prism, and the lenses are substantially mounted. The prism with its rotating mechanism is mounted on a carriage which moves on two parallel stainless-steel rods, and is fitted with two double conical steel rollers, operating on one of the rods, while the other rod carries a flat shoe, the entire carriage thereby being supported on a geometrically free bearing.

Figure 89 is a photograph of another instrument having an optical system 1,700 mm in focal length rendering a spectrum 600 mm long from 2000 to 8000A. The prism and lens system is similar to that described for the instrument above. Mechanically the instrument differs in that three individual and different plate holders are used for the different wavelength ranges.   They are so constructed that the angle of inclination of the plate to the optical axis is correct for the particular one-third of the spectrum to be photographed.

Adjustment of Spectrometers.   At most, only a few simple adjustments should be required before using a modern prism spectrometer or spectrograph purchased from a reliable manufac-

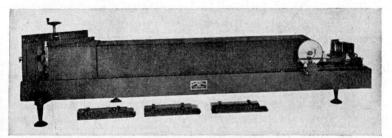

Fig. 89.—A Littrow spectrograph of similar characteristics to that one shown in Figs. 86 and 87.   (*Courtesy Gaertner Scientific Corporation.*)

turer, or made with due care in a well-equipped machine shop. Some of these adjustments have already been described.   Directions for adjusting optical instruments in common use in laboratories are to be found in various texts on optics.   Autocollimation provides a convenient means for lining up the telescope, collimator, and prism of spectrometers with a prism table which can be rotated until the telescope axis is normal to the prism face, or for

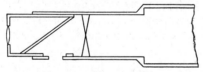

Fig. 90.—Gauss eyepiece.

checking the alignment of the telescope and collimator of constant-deviation instruments.   As shown in Fig. 90 the Gauss eyepiece, which replaces the regular eyepiece for this work, has cross hairs which can be illuminated from the side.   The intersection of these cross hairs should have the same position with reference to the telescope tube as the intersection of the cross hairs, or the center of the slit, when the instrument is in regular use.   If the focus setting is correct and the axis of the telescope is perpendicular to the face of the prism, the image of the cross hairs reflected from this prism face will coincide with the cross hairs themselves. This fact forms the basis of the adjustment and calibration of spectrometers of this type.

First, the eyepiece is focused on the cross hairs. Then, the image of the cross hairs reflected from one prism face is made to coincide with the cross hairs by turning the prism table to the proper position, leveling it, and adjusting the level and focus of the telescope. This last step of bringing the image of the cross hairs into focus at the cross hairs themselves focuses the telescope for parallel light. The telescope can also be focused for parallel light by focusing it on some distant object (several hundred yards away). Now the prism table is rotated until another one of the faces of the prism as near 90 deg. to the first as possible is presented to the telescope. In general, the image of the cross wires will be too high or too low to coincide with the real cross wires. Adjust half the error by leveling the prism table and half by adjusting the level of the telescope. Return to the first face of the prism and repeat the leveling adjustments half with prism leveling and half with telescope leveling. Continue this, working with two faces of the prism until coincidence of image and real cross lines is obtained in both positions. Do not alter the position of the prism on the table and do not rotate the telescope about its vertical axis bearing during this operation. This adjustment results in the placing of the planes of two of the prism faces parallel with the axis of rotation of the prism table and placing the axis of the telescope perpendicular to it. Now without rotating the prism table, rotate the telescope about its vertical axis from one to the other of these two prism faces. If coincidence between image and cross line is not maintained, the axes of rotation of the prism table and of the telescope are not parallel. Some instruments are provided with means for this adjustment and some are not. If the means for adjustment are provided, it can be carried out by observing alternately on the two prism faces and adjusting the prism-axis level without changing the prism-table level, without disturbing the position of the prism on the table, and without disturbing the telescope level. If means for the adjustment are not provided, the instrument can only be returned to the maker.

Now leaving the telescope fixed in position and level, rotate the prism table successively to the remaining faces of the prism, without disturbing the position of the prism on the table. If coincidence of image and crosslines is not maintained for all the faces, the prism has "pyramidal" error.

Leaving the level and focus of telescope undisturbed, rotate the telescope about the vertical axis (after having removed the prism from the table) until it is approximately coaxial with the collimator. Now focus and level the collimator until the center of the slit, or the collimator cross wire, coincides with that of the telescope.

The accuracy of the scales of the spectrometer and the concentricity of the scales with the axes may be checked by any of the methods described in handbooks on surveying.

In spite of the simplicity of the spectrograph, it is extremely difficult to adjust, especially when a wavelength scale is used. A purchaser should insist upon delivery of the instrument in a condition of good adjustment, accompanied by a specimen exposure showing what may be expected of the instrument. The user should choose a location for the instrument that will be permanent, and should not be content with the condition of the instrument until plates equal to the specimen supplied by the maker can be produced. In general, this will be found true immediately. If it is not true and a representative of the maker cannot be called to make the adjustment, the user must be reconciled to a tedious process of trial and error adjustment that can be accomplished only at the cost of repeated exposures of plates. Preliminary adjustments may be made visually in the visible part of the spectrum, by using a fogged and developed plate on which the wavelength scale has been printed. A false sheet-metal back for the plate holder with a slot through the center to expose the spectrum may be used. If a piece of ground uranium glass is available, lines in the ultraviolet may be seen by fluorescence.

The actual process of adjustment must be largely by trial and error, but the following will, in general, be found true: If the lines flare on one side, either the imaging lens or the prism or both should be rotated about a vertical axis; if the spectrum is the same length as the scale but is displaced laterally, the scale should be moved by means of the adjustment provided (lock nuts at H, Fig. 82); if the spectrum is not in focus at either end, the plate holder should be inclined about a vertical axis; if the lines are wedge-shaped or out of focus at top or bottom, the plate holder should be tilted about a horizontal axis, and if this is not effective, the jaws of the slit should be inspected for parallelism; if the entire spectrum is out of focus, the imaging lens should be adjusted to bring it to focus. When all of these adjustments have been carefully executed, full advantage of the resolving and defining powers of the optical system may be achieved. It will be readily understood why so much emphasis has been placed on the desirability of ruggedness and ability to maintain these adjustments, once they have been tediously executed—and also why it is desirable to disturb the instrument as little as possible.

Wavelength Scales. To be able to set a spectrometer to pass radiation of a definite frequency, a numerical statement of the relative positions of the entrance and exit slits and the dispersing means must be obtainable. This number may be a measure of the angular position of the telescope or prism table; it may be the corresponding frequency or wavelength of the radiation; it may even be a number on a purely arbitrary scale. Whatever the type of scale, it may be calibrated in terms of frequency or wavelength by using a source giving a known line spectrum (see Table 12, page 79).

Many spectrometers and monochromatic illuminators are provided with wavelength scales engraved on cylindrical drums or disks. Such drums or disks should be large enough in diameter to give a scale that can be read to the accuracy desired, and should be so located and oriented as to be easily readable from the observer's position. The numbers and lines should be sharply defined and stand out strongly against the background, to permit legibility in a semidark room. For the same reason the numbers should be as large as possible. In carefully wrought instruments, electric illumination is provided for these drums and suitable reading glasses of low magnification are either made a part of the instrument or may be added as accessories.

Spectrographs are sometimes provided with wavelength scales engraved on transparent plates that can be moved against the photographic plate, so that the wavelength scale may be photographed on the plate before the exposure of the spectrum, with the help of a small electric lamp. The figures on these scales should be large enough to be easily read on the final plate. It is appropriate to note here and to emphasize that such a wavelength scale can, in its very nature, be only approximate, and cannot even approach the exhaustion of the possibilities of accuracy of wavelength measurements on the spectrogram. It can be used only for comparatively rough approximations in wavelength determination. The most accurate wavelength scale is the impression upon the photographic plate of a known spectrum, rich in lines, with which the operator has become thoroughly familiar by experience. With such a spectrum impressed upon the plate simultaneously with the impression of the spectrum of unknown characteristics and adjacent to it, wavelength determinations may be made to the highest possible degree of accuracy.

THE WADSWORTH MOUNTING

L. B. Aldrich*

The Wadsworth mounting[6] is a type of constant-deviation spectrometer, the first application of which was in the spectrobolometer of the Smithsonian Astrophysical Observatory at Washington.

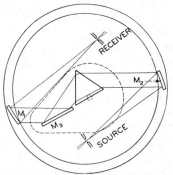

Fig. 91.—Wadsworth mounting showing prism, lenses, and mirrors.

For certain work with prism spectroscopes, particularly in cases where the source and the observing arm are difficult or impossible to move, the Wadsworth mounting (Fig. 91) is a simple and adequate form of constant-deviation single-prism spectrometer. The essential added feature in this mounting is a plane mirror fixed rigidly beside the prism. Unlike the Littrow mounting, the beam traverses the prism but once, emerges parallel to and may continue in the same direction as the incident beam. Slit and observing arms being fixed, different wavelengths are brought to the cross hairs of the observing arm by rotation of the spectrum table upon which the prism-mirror rests. Minimum deviation for the central ray in the field is automatically maintained for all wavelengths, by a preliminary adjustment of prism and mirror, as described below.

To insure that the emergent beam be parallel to the incident, that minimum deviation be maintained for all positions, and that

* *Assistant Director of Astrophysical Observatory, Smithsonian Institution.*

there be no lateral displacement of the beam as the table rotates, it is essential:

1. That the plane mirror be perpendicular to the plane bisecting the refracting angle of the prism, and parallel to the refracting edge.

2. That the line of intersection of the plane of the mirror and the plane bisecting the refracting angle of the prism be the axis of rotation of the spectrometer table.

For ease of adjustment, the prism-mirror table is fitted with leveling screws which rest one in a conical hole, one in a slot, and the third on a plane, the hole and slot being so placed on the spectrometer table that requirement (2) in the preceding paragraph is fulfilled. There is also an independent screw back of the prism, capable of moving the prism about a horizontal line parallel to the mirror face, so the refracting edge may be brought parallel to the mirror. The mirror should be as tall as the prism and the width, for a 60-deg. prism should be about twice that of the prism face. This will insure that all ordinary wavelengths traversing the prism at minimum deviation will fall upon the mirror. Angular deviations are easily determined by doubling the angles as read from the spectrometer circle, since, because of the single mirror reflection, the angular rotation of the prism is exactly one-half the angle swept out by the refracted-reflected ray.

The following adjustments are needed:

1. Make both the slit and the axis of rotation of the table accurately vertical.

2. Place the prism-mirror combination on the spectrometer table in the approximate position of minimum deviation. With the adjusting screws, the mirror and prism faces must be made vertical. This may be done as follows: Set up a theodolite at about 10 ft. distance and level its telescope. Adjust the leveling screws of the prism-mirror mounting until the image of the theodolite object glass reflected by the mirror falls centrally on the theodolite cross hairs. Turn the spectrometer table until one face of the prism reflects the object glass back to the theodolite. Screw adjustments are now made until both faces of the prism (first one face and then the other) reflect the theodolite object glass centrally on its cross hairs. This is sometimes a little troublesome. Each change should be made with two screws, half with one and half with the other, or somewhat that way.

Care must be taken not to alter any screws which would spoil the previous mirror adjustment.

3. Measure the perpendicular distance from the axis of rotation to the path of the incident beam. Temporarily removing the prism-mirror table, set the observing telescope (or the focusing mirror, as the case may be) at twice this distance to the side of the path of the incident beam, since this is the displacement suffered in traversing the prism-mirror combination. Likewise a point or slit may be set up this same distance to the side of the slit, and the image of this brought to the center of the observing telescope field. The purpose of this is to make the beam which leaves the plane mirror parallel to the incident beam.

4. Replacing the prism-mirror table, adjust the prism to minimum deviation, thus: Turn the spectrometer table until the image of the theodolite object glass, as reflected from the mirror, is central on the theodolite cross hairs. Read the circle and then turn the spectrometer table through an angle equal to 90 deg. minus one-half the refracting angle of the prism. Then slightly adjust the prism until the reflection of the theodolite object glass from the prism face is again central on the cross hairs.

These adjustments suffice for ordinary spectroscopic purposes. At the Smithsonian Observatory it is customary to drive the spectrometer table by clockwork, the same clock also moving a photographic plate in front of the galvanometer spot so that a continuous record of spectral intensities is obtained. A counter is attached so that known settings in the spectrum may be made and repeated at will. With ordinary precaution, when once adjusted, the Wadsworth mounting may be used for an indefinite period without readjustment.

DOUBLE MONOCHROMATORS

B. T. Barnes*

With an ordinary monochromator, stray radiation from more intense portions of the spectrum is usually present in appreciable amounts in the weaker spectral regions. Unless it is partially eliminated, or its effect reduced by use of a selective receiver, it may cause large errors in measuring intensities. One method of

* Physicist, *Incandescent Lamp Department, General Electric Company, Cleveland, Ohio.*

eliminating the major part of the stray radiation is to place two monochromators in series. Such a combination is quite effective but ordinarily inconvenient to use. Furthermore, it is difficult to couple the monochromators rigidly enough for accurate measurements. A better solution is to use a double monochromator. This is essentially two monochromators in series, with a single base and generally a single adjustment for wavelength. Prisms are used as dispersing agents in these instruments.

Zero-dispersion Instruments. A diagram of the optical parts of the simplest type of double monochromator is given in Fig. 92. If the two halves are identical, this is a zero-dispersion, constant-deviation instrument, since the second prism neutralizes the dispersive effect of the first. The entrance and exit slits, the

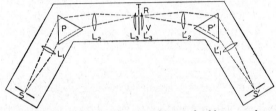

Fig. 92.—Schematic diagram of a Van Cittert double monochromator.

lenses and the prisms are all fixed except for slit width and focusing adjustments. The center slit may be moved laterally. The wavelength band received at the exit slit is determined entirely by the position and width of the middle slit. With several slits in the central plane, one obtains at the exit slit a mixture of radiation of several different wavelengths. If the center plane is unobstructed, all the radiation from the source which is transmitted by the instrument is received undispersed at the exit slit. The spectral distribution of this radiation may be measured by putting the center slit at successive positions throughout the spectrum and measuring the radiant flux at the rear slit with a thermopile. With the center slit removed and suitable diaphragms placed in the spectrum in the central plane of the instrument, one obtains at the exit slit radiation with certain portions of the spectrum removed. These unique features make the zero-dispersion instrument particularly useful.

Double-dispersion Instruments. Several types of double monochromator have been so designed that the second prism adds to the dispersive effect produced by the first one. One instrument[7] (Fig. 93) employs constant-deviation prisms. Additional dispersion may be obtained by using two prisms in the first half.

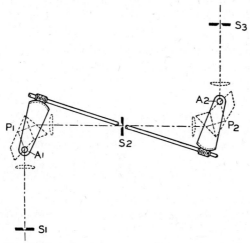

Fig. 93.—Double-dispersion instrument using constant-deviation prisms.

Another monochromator[8] (Fig. 94) of this type has two autocollimating systems side by side with both lenses and both prisms on a single sliding mount. Motion of this mount orients the prisms and focuses the lenses simultaneously.

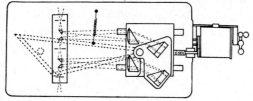

Fig. 94.—Double-dispersion instrument with autocollimating system.

In a third instrument[9] (Fig. 95), only one lens tube is fixed. A system of lever arms automatically orients the movable members and keeps the prisms at minimum deviation.

All double-dispersion double monochromators are set for wavelength by a rotation of the prisms, or of the collimator and telescope tubes, or both. The center slit is permanently located on the optical axis and serves only to limit the amount of direct and stray radiation entering the second half of the instrument.

Comparison of Types.   The respective advantages of the zero- and the double-dispersion types of instrument depend a great deal on the purposes of the user.   With either, the greatest efficiency is obtained[10] when all the slits are the same width. We shall assume the latter to be true in comparing the instruments.   For the same purity, the zero-dispersion type must have slits half as wide as the other type.   With a continuous spectrum the amount of radiant flux which gets into the second half of the zero-dispersion instrument is only a fourth as much as in the

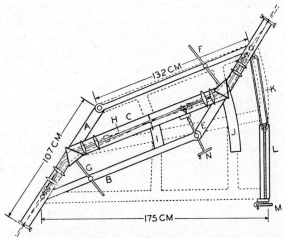

Fig. 95.—Diagram of mounting and movable parts of double monochromator with quartz optical parts.

case of the double-dispersion instrument with slits set for the same purity.   However, in the case of the zero-dispersion instrument, all of it will pass through the exit slit.   With identical lenses and prisms, the same slit height, and the same purity, the double-dispersion type transmits twice as much radiation to the receiver, regardless of whether line or continuous radiation is being measured.

With the double-dispersion type, the wavelength band entering the second half of the instrument is twice as wide as that passing through the exit slit.   Thus, radiation from the adjacent spectral regions may be brought by a single scattering into the exit slit. Also a single scattering in the first half of the instrument may bring[11] radiation from the spectral regions adjacent to the transmitted band into the exit slit.   This is not the case[11] with the zero-dispersion instrument. The latter is thus much superior when one wishes to measure a line which is quite close to a much stronger one. The two types are equally efficient in excluding stray radiation from more distant portions of the spectrum.

Adjustment of Instruments. If it is to be used for radiation measurements, a double monochromator must be so made that the two halves are practically identical, and it must be adjusted very carefully. With a zero-dispersion instrument, the image of the entrance slit must be centered in the exit slit, no matter what wavelength is being transmitted through the center slit. With the double-dispersion type, a monochromatic image of the entrance slit must center in the middle and exit slits irrespective of the wavelength. With either instrument, the focus at the center and exit slits must be quite sharp when a line spectrum is being measured. All of these adjustments should be tested in the extreme portions, as well as in the center of the spectrum. Outside the visible region, this may be done by placing a steady source with a line spectrum in front of the entrance slit, mounting a photoelectric tube or thermopile behind the exit slit, and finding the focus settings and slit positions which give maximum deflection.

In measuring line-spectrum intensities, it is ordinarily best to have the center and exit slits of a double monochromator a little wider than the entrance slit, to allow for any inaccuracy in the construction, adjustment, or calibration of the instrument. With a continuous spectrum, this procedure eliminates the necessity of measuring the width of the exit slit of the zero-dispersion or the center slit of the double-dispersion type. For accurate measurements of a continuous spectrum, it may be necessary to measure the other two slits with a micrometer microscope each time the widths are changed.

INSTRUMENTS FOR INFRARED SPECTRORADIOMETRY

E. F. Barker*

Spectroradiometry in the infrared, as in any other region of the spectrum, involves three essential factors, each subject to more or less modification and adaptation for particular problems.

* *Professor of Physics, University of Michigan.*

They are (1) the source, (2) the dispersing system, and (3) the detecting instrument.

Infrared radiation extends some 10 or 12 octaves before encroaching upon that of ultrashort radio waves. This region may be subdivided for convenience upon the basis of transparency of materials used for windows and prisms. For wavelengths less than 2.5μ, glass prisms function satisfactorily, and, when higher dispersion is required, reflection gratings may be used. These should be ruled with 15,000 or more lines per inch, but the demand for perfection is not quite so high as in photographic work, as the complete theoretical resolving power can seldom be utilized. Between 2.5 and 16μ, prisms of rock salt are generally employed, although fluorite, if available, has higher dispersion out to its limit of transmission, which is near 9μ. From 16 to 24μ KBr serves admirably, but for greater wavelengths no material sufficiently transparent for prisms is known. For these regions gratings must have coarser rulings: in practice the limit is about 1,500 lines per inch for a grating to diffract 16μ radiation and about 250 lines per inch for 50μ.

Energy is very much at a premium throughout the spectrum, and particularly so as wavelengths increase, owing to the rapidly diminishing intensities of all sources. For this reason the *prism spectrometer* has a distinct advantage, since it concentrates the dispersed radiation in a single spectrum. Randall and Strong[12] have described a most satisfactory instrument, equipped with prisms of glass, NaCl, KCl, KBr, and KI, which gives fairly good resolution throughout the range from 1 to 24μ, and particularly in the region beyond 10μ. This spectrometer is completely enclosed in a heavy case permitting evacuation. The energy selected from the spectrum by a narrow adjustable slit is focused upon a vacuum thermopile through a thin KBr window. This actuates the primary galvanometer of a photoelectric amplifier. The prism is driven by a small motor through a train of gears, its motion being precisely correlated with that of a large drum carrying photographic paper, upon which the variations in intensity of the spectrum are recorded automatically. The resolution is determined by the dispersion available and by the minimum usable slit width. The latter depends, of course, upon the sensitivity of the detecting system when energy is at a premium, but, in the range of shorter wavelengths, the limit may be set by the degree of impurity of the spectrum.   Because of diffraction, aberration, and optical defects, little is usually gained by narrowing the slits beyond about 0.1 mm.

The feature which particularly recommends the above-mentioned prism spectrometer is the availability of large perfect prisms of the potassium halides.   Although such prisms are remarkably transparent, some scattering does occur at their surfaces, and also at the surfaces of the mirrors and windows. This may become troublesome when long waves are under observation, since the intensity at 20μ of an incandescent source is a very small fraction of that at 1 or 2μ, and the quantity of short-wave radiation scattered into the receiver may exceed in intensity the beam being focused.   Various devices have been employed to eliminate this difficulty, such as the use of a fore prism to exclude short-wave radiation, or rough-surface mirrors to scatter it out before it reaches the prism.   Often a shutter of some material such as rock salt is used, which permits the short-wave radiation to fall upon the thermopile all the time, but intercepts the longer waves, thus indicating the differential effect which they produce.

Since the beam is not directed exactly along the optical axes of the mirrors, the image of a straight filament is somewhat curved, and considerable energy is lost if it is focused upon a straight slit, to say nothing of the impairment of spectral purity.   The introduction of slightly curved slits* has been found advantageous.

Grating Spectrometers.   Grating spectrometers, involving plane gratings and mirrors with metallic surfaces, have long been used for the study of infrared emission spectra.[13,14,15] With this arrangement, the overlapping of successive orders sometimes presents a problem, although it is not serious when the spectrum consists of sharp lines.   There is no suspicion of higher order diffraction, unless the observed frequency of a line is very precisely an integral factor of the frequency of some other correspondingly intense line.   For isolating certain regions, absorption screens or shutters with selective transmission may be used, but not many substances are available which cut off sharply at appropriate wavelengths.[16]

To avoid the overlapping of different orders of spectra, the *prism-grating-combination* spectrometer has come to be widely

* See p. 175.

used, particularly in the study of absorption. An arrangement of this type, in which the prism precedes the grating, was first applied by Sleator,[17] under Randall's direction, to the examination of water-vapor absorption. The optical system employed was very compact and has been widely copied. It is shown schematically in Fig. 96. The beam from a Nernst glower is focused upon a slit, then collimated by a spherical mirror, and directed toward a thin salt prism silvered on the back. The

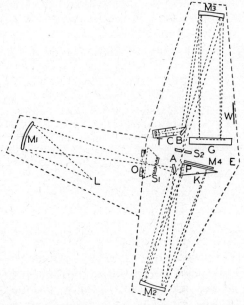

Fig. 96.—Prism-grating combination spectrometer.

returning beam falls upon the same mirror at a slightly different angle and is focused at the second slit, where a narrow spectrum is formed. Here a short range of wavelengths, including not more than one octave, is selected, and, having traversed a similar path to the grating, returns widely dispersed, to be focused upon the thermopile slit. Since the entrance and exit slits cannot be coincident, the spherical mirrors are used slightly off their axes, and a certain amount of astigmatism results. Hence, no great improvement in resolution is obtained when the slits are narrowed beyond a certain limit (about 0.2 mm). The situation is improved somewhat by increasing the size and focal length of the mirrors, the effective aperture remaining the same, since the minimum angle between the beams and the mirror axes may then be reduced.   Changes in the optical system making it possible to place the slits exactly upon the mirror axes have been suggested by Randall[18] and by Pfund.[19]

An instrument recently set up at the University of Michigan by Hardy[20] utilizes Pfund's method very successfully, according to the scheme indicated in Fig. 97.   The entrance slit is placed before a slot at the center of a plane mirror and exactly upon the axis of a collimating mirror which is parabolic.   A parallel beam

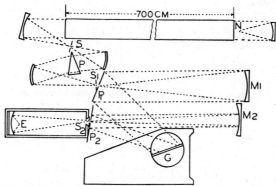

FIG. 97.—Prism-grating spectrometer using Pfund's method of mounting the mirrors.

is returned to the plane mirror and may be reflected toward the grating without astigmatism.   After diffraction, the beam traverses a similar path and forms a very sharp image upon the slit. A vacuum thermopile is enclosed in a small glass tube provided with a thin KBr window, and placed upon the optical axis where an image of the slit is formed upon it by an elliptical mirror with properly selected conjugated foci.   The beam already lacks a small central portion because of the apertures in the plane mirrors, and the thermopile intercepts very little useful energy. The magnitude of the deflections obtained reaches a sharp maximum when the optical system is precisely focused.   While making adjustments the grating is usually replaced by a plane mirror, and a microscope is focused upon the exit slit.   The concave mirrors are then moved backward and forward until the edges of the image are perfectly sharp.

The number of reflections involved in this system is not a great handicap, as the reflecting power of most metals is very high for infrared rays.   Even badly tarnished silver mirrors function satisfactorily beyond 4 or 5μ.

The thermopile is connected to an amplifier which, as ordinarily used, increases the deflections by a factor of about 100.   The fore prism is of salt, and the source is a Nernst glower which may be placed in various positions depending upon the length of the absorption cell to be used.   The arrangement illustrated permits cells as long as 7 m but requires windows so large that salt plates are out of the question.   Thin sheets of mica serve well when the observed radiation has a wavelength less than 8μ: for longer wavelengths films of nitrocellulose are employed, although somewhat permeable to most gases.   Evacuation of the cell is, of course, impossible, and it must be filled by displacement.   If the gas is easily obtainable, it is simply allowed to flow slowly through the cell for several hours.   Otherwise traps are placed at each end and alternately immersed in liquid air, the flow of gas being backward and forward until most of the air has escaped. Short absorption cells of glass with salt windows are more convenient.   They are usually arranged so that the rays cross within the cell to minimize the window area.

The working limit of this instrument is fixed by the transparency of the available prisms and at present is around 24μ. Regions of longer wavelength could be studied by utilizing residual rays from various crystals to isolate narrow spectral regions for presentation to the grating.   Wright and Randall[21] have employed this method which is quite successful in so far as appropriate residual rays can be found.   A list of available materials showing selective reflection may be found in Table 6 of the treatise "Das ultrarote Spektrum," by Schaefer and Matossi.[22]

Gratings for use in the infrared are usually of the type called by Wood echelette gratings.   The grooves are V-shaped with plane surfaces, and deep enough so that no flat strip is left between them. Except for the coarsest gratings, no mechanism could be relied upon to cut such grooves with uniform depth; hence the ruling tool is allowed to float over the surface forming a depression, the width and depth of which depend upon the load applied.   The angles between the resulting surfaces and the original flat may be determined at will and are selected so as to concentrate the desired wavelength as nearly as possible in a single order.   Obviously this procedure requires relatively soft and ductile material for the surface to be ruled, with consequent difficulties in the way of preparing the flats.   Surfaces of nickel, and of an alloy of nickel and copper, have been used for ruling gratings with 4,800 or more lines per inch.   A very special technique is required for polishing them, especially for the pure nickel, and care must be taken not to charge the surfaces with abrasive material which would be fatal to the ruling point.   The latter is a small diamond ground to a very fine edge where two plane surfaces intersect at an angle of about 85 deg.   Wood has prepared some excellent gratings upon copper, with a thin plate of chromium applied as a final finish after ruling.

Wider and much deeper grooves are required in gratings for use at greater wavelengths, and for them the most satisfactory material found thus far is an alloy of tin and lead on a hard metal base.   Polishing such a surface is out of the question, but a reasonably good finish may be obtained by cutting with a suitable steel tool.   At the University of Michigan the ruling machine is so arranged that it may be operated as a shaper.   Consequently a plate may be prepared by cutting, and subsequently ruled without any change in its position upon the ruling table of the machine. The surfaces obtained in this way are sufficiently flat, and the final cut is always made with the tool progressing at intervals exactly equal to those later used while ruling, so that the phase relation between successive cuts and the grooves ruled upon them is constant.   A polished flat would probably give no better result. The area of the surface which it is worth while to rule depends upon the size of the collimating mirrors available.   Thus, with 6-in. mirrors, a surface 5 by 8 in. is adequate.   However, some of the very coarse gratings for use at 20μ and beyond have been made as large as 10 by 18 in. and used with correspondingly large mirrors.

SPECTROMETER AND SPECTROGRAPH SLITS

Gustave Fassin[*]

A properly mounted and adjusted slit is one of the most important of the mechanical parts of a spectrometer.   Although

[*] *Physicist, Bausch & Lomb Optical Company.*

numerous slit mechanisms have been invented and applied in the construction of the spectrographic apparatus since Kirchhoff and Bunsen, they can all be listed under four types.

1. The fixed slit, in which the width is not variable.
2. The unilateral slit, in which one blade is fixed and the other movable.
3. The bilateral slit, in which both blades move symmetrically.
4. The curved slit, in which the jaw edges, instead of being straight, are curved to compensate for the curvature of the spectrum lines, produced by the prism.

With the exception of the fixed slit the requirements are:

1. The slit should open with its jaw edges strictly parallel.
2. These jaw edges should be optical straight lines or smooth curves (in case of the curved slit).
3. The slit should close under spring tension.
4. The mechanism of opening and closing should be extremely sensitive.

The Fixed Slit.   When high precision is not required, a simple saw cut of the required width will constitute the simplest type of

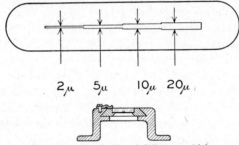

2μ 5μ 10μ 20μ

Fig. 98.—Fixed slits of different width.

fixed slit.   Thin sheet brass or steel about 0.4 mm thick can be used in this case; if it is necessary to have sharp edges, a slight bevel on one side of the saw cut will answer this requirement. This type of slit is suitable only for crude setups, of course, as the obtainable precision is only 0.05 to 0.1 mm.   To improve on this type of slit, two separate jaw blades can be made of the same materials as mentioned above and screwed down on to a holder with the fixing holes in one of the blades drilled large enough to permit some adjustment for width or parallelism.

One of the most accurate and most practical slit devices is the fixed slit represented in Fig. 98, which consists of about a 1-mm thick quartz plate silvered on one side and slits of different widths

cut in the silver by a dividing engine.   With the plate mounted
as shown in Fig. 99 and an observation microscope, provided with
filar micrometer, under the table, the operator can determine
very accurately the width of the slit cut into the metallic layer.
This unit is to be mounted, with the silver toward the spectrograph, in a dovetail slide provided with stops to line up the different slit widths in front of a diaphragm cutting off the other
openings and determining the required slit height.   If dust particles collect on the slit surface, a camel's-hair brush can be used
to remove them without any danger of damaging the slit proper.

The advantages of the fixed slit are its simplicity and the
obtainable accuracy in parallelism.   Such a slit requires, of
course, the least care and will
never lose its precision.   The
disadvantages, however, are
obvious and are directly an
outcome of its lack of adjust-
ability in width.   It is practically impossible to determine
the critical slit width, for the
greatest resolving power, in
all cases.   The slit width to

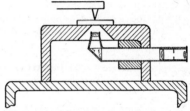

Fig. 99.—Schematic setup for the
cutting of a fixed slit of a given width.

be used will depend upon the
energy of the source and the nature of the spectrum one wishes
to obtain.   For high-precision work it takes painstaking effort
and a great number of spectrograms to determine the best slit
width to use in each particular case, and there, of course, the fixed
slit is of less practical value.

The Unilateral Slit.   The main advantage of a unilateral slit
is its great precision for the simple mechanism required.   Its
disadvantage, which becomes serious in case of accurate wavelength determination, is that the center of the density gradation
in the spectrum line is shifted every time the slit width is changed
so that the printing of a wavelength scale on the spectrogram is
impractical.

To fulfill the requirements mentioned above, the unilateral
slit has, of course, the simplest mechanism.   Figure 100 represents
such a slit mechanism where A is the slit mount made in cast
brass or bronze.   In the front part B is milled the dovetail slide
C, undercut at the middle part of the slide, as shown in Fig. 101,
to reduce the friction.   This slide must be lapped very carefully,

after fine milling, starting with pumice powder, the final lapping being done with rouge, using a cast-iron or brass lap, of twice the length of the female slide.

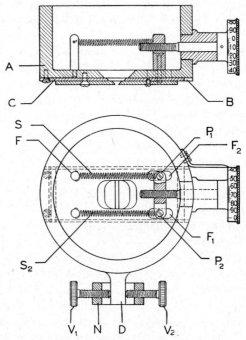

Fig. 100.—The unilateral slit.

During the process of lapping, which requires skill and patience, it is necessary to pass the lap completely through the slide and turn it around from time to time.   Next, the male slides are made

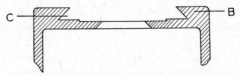

Fig. 101.—Dovetail slide for slit blades.

using a material which has about the same coefficient of expansion as the slit housing, as otherwise a slight change in temperature may cause the slide to stick or give it lost motion which will result in a slit of which the jaws are not parallel.   The fixed jaw holder of a unilateral slit should be made about 1 mm smaller than the movable slide and fixed in the center of the dovetail, by means of one screw A (see Fig. 102) and the back end of the slide beveled so that two bevel-headed screws, S_1 and S_2, as far as possible apart, provide some rotational adjustment. The movable slide should be fitted, with great precision, into the dovetail so that it will move with a minimum of pressure or spring tension. Upon these slides the slit jaws are mounted.

In this sliding jaw two posts P_1 and P_2 (see Fig. 100) are mounted entering the slit housing through two slots F_1 and F_2. Two light coil springs S and S_2 (No. 30 B and S. gage) about 3 mm in diameter and each having the same number of coils and attached to the posts P_1 and P_2 pull the movable slide in contact with the fixed slide. A screw of steel fitting in a nut of bronze or brass with a thread of 0.5 mm (finer threads are not recommended) is generally used to move this slide away from the fixed jaw. A trace of lubrication can be admitted; vaseline or a mixture of equal parts of vaseline and lanolin will give a good sliding motion almost independent of the temperature at which the instrument is used. If the drum on the end of the screw is divided into 100 divisions, each will give approximately 5μ change in slit width. For finer settings, the screw can be made to operate a lever system instead of being connected directly to the movable slide.

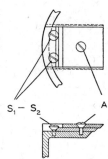

Fig. 102.—Rotatable-slit blade carrier to adjust parallelism.

A rotational adjustment of all slit housings should be provided to permit adjusting the slit exactly in alignment with the prism. A good method of doing this is shown in Fig. 100, where the tail end D of the slit housing and the two screws V_1 and V_2 with the nut bracket N fixed to the spectrograph proper provide this adjustment.

A great number of other schemes have found their way into the laboratory, but all are very similar in the simplicity of their mechanism.

The Bilateral Slit. The bilateral slit presents a more difficult mechanical problem. Sometimes one is made as an extension of the unilateral slit just described. Both of the male parts are made movable and pushed apart with a screw consisting of two parts, sometimes one a right-hand, the other a left-hand thread,

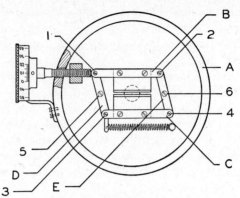

Fig. 103.—Simple mechanism for a bilateral slit.

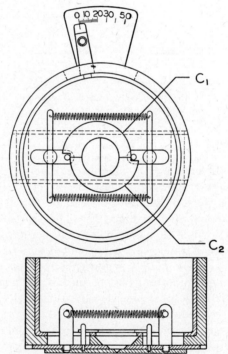

Fig. 104.—Bilateral slit with cam arrangement.

and sometimes two right-handed threads one with twice the pitch of the other.   This requires that the slit away from the screw support be moved by a frame to keep the screw from in front of the slit opening.

One of the most common and simplest slit mechanisms is represented in Fig. 103.   On a back plate A is mounted a parallelogram of which the two arms B and C are the jaw blades of the slit and D and E the two links which connect them together. To make this slit successful for precision work, the center distances 1-2 and 3-4 must be drilled with the greatest precision, also the centers of rotation 5 and 6 must be perfectly in the middle

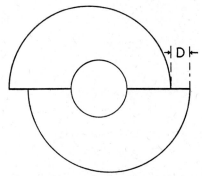

FIG. 105.—Construction of cam for bilateral-slit construction.

between 1 and 2 and 3 and 4.   This slit is in general used only on demonstration instruments for spectrum projectors and the like.

A simple device, which, however, can be made with greater accuracy, is represented in Fig. 104.   The two slit blades are mounted in a dovetail slide and pulled together by means of two coil springs with a simple cam arrangement which, by rotation, pushes these two slit blades symmetrically apart.   The cam, which is the most important part of the slit mechanism, can be made with relatively great precision by using a steel disk about 1.5 mm thick very carefully turned and ground on the periphery. After this operation, the disk is cut in two pieces and reassembled, as shown in Fig. 105 where D represents the greatest slit opening obtainable.   These two parts are screwed down on a separate bushing which will fit very accurately in the slit housing.

An old scheme designed by Merz around 1860 and still in use today has proved to be very successful.   Figure 106 represents

this original design.   Here the slides have been replaced by two
planes O_1 and O_2 finished optically, with springs S_1 and S_2 to hold
the jaw carriers in contact with these planes and also to furnish

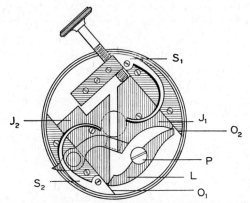

Fig. 106.—Bilateral slit as designed by Merz in 1860.

a means of closing the jaws.   Lever arm L, with pivot P very
accurately made, transmits the motion from J_1 to J_2.   In this
design the shape of the springs is somewhat difficult for ordinary
manufacturing.

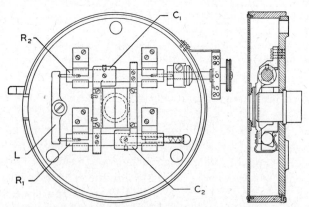

Fig. 107.—The Bausch & Lomb spectrograph slit.

The Bausch & Lomb slit (Fig. 107), in principle the same as the
Merz design, presents some interesting points.   Here the slides
have been replaced by two perfectly ground and lapped cylindrical rods R_1 and R_2 which slide in bronze bearings shaped in

such a way as to assure a minimum of friction and keep the two rods accurately parallel to each other.   On these rods are fixed the slit-blade carriers C_1 and C_2 with weak springs to keep the slides in contact with the opposite rods.   A micrometer screw pushes one of the jaw carriers in one direction against the lever arm L which moves the second jaw carrier in the opposite direction.   Here also, the location and the fitting of the axle of the lever arm L require the highest precision.

A somewhat different design[23] is shown in Fig. 108.   Here the difficulty of accurate slide fitting is eliminated as the two

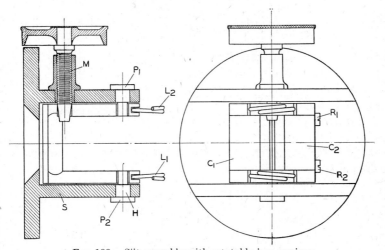

FIG. 108.—Slit assembly with rotatable jaw carriers.

U-shaped jaw carriers rotate around a main axis fixed in the slit support.

The jaw carriers are held together by means of springs and they are wedged open by a cone at the end of a micrometer screw. The slit support S, after being machined, is fixed on to a surface plate with 90-deg. angle support and the hole H drilled and reamed so that both steel pins P_1 and P_2 are accurately centered. These slit jaw carriers C_1 and C_2 are machined together so the distance from the grooves V_1 and V_2 (Fig. 109) to the surface S_1 is very precisely the same in both pieces. C_1 and C_2 are mounted on to the pins P_1 and P_2 and kept in contact by means of two springs, L_1 and L_2.   The ends of these springs are set in two little cavities drilled into C_1 and C_2 a little below the centerline of the

V grooves, and the middle of the spring fits in a small groove milled into C_1 and C_2 to keep them in place.

Screw M (1 mm), mounted in a spring nut, is tapered on the lower end concentric with the screw head and wedges between the two jaw blade carriers C_1 and C_2 in which two inclined planes are provided. The jaw blades are made of stellite and are

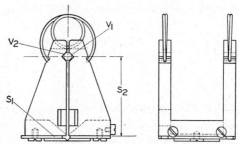

Fig. 109.—Jaw-blade carriers.

optically lapped. One blade is attached to the carrier C_2 with a screw in the middle and, by means of the two screws R_1 and R_2, adjusted to parallelism with the other blade which is fixed on to carrier C_1 (Fig. 108). By this construction the danger of damaging the jaws in use and in cleaning is greatly reduced.

The slit jaws on any spectrometer should be made a little longer than the maximum useful slit height and means should be

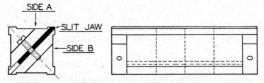

Fig. 110.—Holder for the grinding of slit jaws.

provided for adjusting the slit height to any desired value. The maximum useful slit height and the optimum slit dimensions are discussed on page 172. The thickness of the blade depends merely on the mechanical construction; a thickness of 1.5 mm will be sufficient in most cases.

The finishing or lapping of a pair of slit blades requires a very skilled hand. However, by using a fixture as shown in Fig. 110 a very accurate edge can be obtained with a minimum of skill or difficulty. This fixture consists of a brass or bronze block split in two parts A and B and held together by means of two screws. The slit blades to be finished are clamped between these two halves in such a way that the edge protrudes a few tenths of a millimeter. On an optical lap, perfectly flat, the blades are ground with fine emery powder (No. 20) on the side A. After the inserted slit blades have all acquired the same finishing, the edges are polished with rouge on a pitch lap. The side A of the slit blade will now have a sharp edge of 45 deg. and if it is

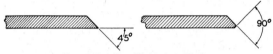

FIG. 111.—Bevels for jaw blades.

turned over in the holder and the side B polished so as to create a bevel of about 0.3 mm, the blade will have an edge as shown in Fig. 111. The angle of 90 deg. will make the knife edge much more resistant and still keep the same precision on a 45-deg. bevel.

In some prism spectrographs and monochromators a curved slit is used to compensate for the curvature of the spectrum lines.

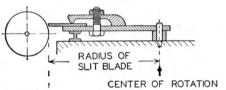

FIG. 112.—Fixture for generating a convex slit jaw.

The grinding of these slit blades is a more difficult problem. The determination of this curve can be made by computation, or much easier by experimental* methods. It is always possible to find an approximate circle for this curve so as to make a mechanical reproduction possible. For short radii the slit blades are fixed on an arm which rotates around a center point, so as to describe a circle of the radius required. By means of a fine grinding wheel (about 160J Norton ⅛ in. wide and rounded on the edge) the curvature is ground, then the wheel is placed about 45 deg. below the center (Fig. 112), and in this position the bevel is ground. After grinding, this emery wheel can be replaced by a fine cast-iron lap, and rouge can be used for finishing. The

* See p. 176.

procedure for the concave slit blade is the same except that the fixture is slightly different, see Fig. 113.

Materials Used for Slit Blades. The earlier slit blades were made of nickel or nickel silver which takes a reasonably sharp edge, but of these the first is too brittle and the second is too soft. For ordinary spectrometers nickel silver, however, is satisfactory. Stainless steel is not satisfactory as the crystal structure of this material makes it impossible to obtain a sharp edge.

In Europe platinoid (Cu, 61 per cent; Zn, 24 per cent; Ni, 14 per cent; W, 1 to 2 per cent), a noncorrosive alloy which can be

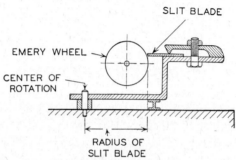

FIG. 113.—Fixture for generating a concave slit jaw.

machined satisfactorily and takes an optically straight edge, is generally used. Stellite blades made from sheet stellite, ground to the correct shape and soldered to brass carriers, are most successful, but the hardness of this material makes it difficult to shape the slits. This method is not free from criticism, since the difference in expansion coefficients may bend the slit out of shape. Slots can be ground in the blades so as to permit fixing by screws, but in this case reasonably thick material should be used.

Quartz blades have been suggested by Crookes.[24] These jaws are cut in the same way as the metal ones and optically polished so that the beveled sides form prisms and refract the light which falls on them so that their transparency offers no objection. It may be said, however, that their edges are extremely fragile and cleaning is very difficult.

Accessories. In the study of absorption spectra it is often desirable to print several spectra adjacent to each other on the same photographic plate; in this case it is of great advantage to provide the slit with a Hartmann diaphragm, as shown in Fig. 114.

Successive exposures are made through the apertures 1-2-3 and a series of spectra is obtained which will line up in such a way as to make comparison simple and accurate.   The square aperture must have a knife-sharp edge as close to the slit as possible; reflection of this edge will spoil the definition on the top and bottom of the lines.   The top and bottom of each consecutive

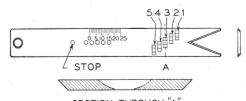

SECTION THROUGH "A"

Fig. 114.—The Hartmann diaphragm.

surface must be perfectly lined up to overcome superposition of spectra lines.   Stops are provided to bring each aperture centered in front of the slit.   On one side is provided a V opening, also beveled toward the slit of the spectrograph.   This V aperture permits the use of different slit heights.

Sometimes a comparison prism is mounted in front of the slit covering half the height.   This prism is carried on a rotatable arm and can be swung out so that the full slit can be used in the ordinary way.   This prism, however, can be used only for rough visual work.

References

1. Uhler, *Astrophys. Jour.*, **47,** 65 (1918).
2. De Laszlo, *Jour. Sci. Inst.*, **7,** 292 (1930).
3. Straubel, *Ann. Physik*, **7,** 905 (1902).
4. C. A. Young, *Jour. Franklin Inst.*, **62,** 348 (1871).
    L. Thollon, *Compt. rend.*, **86,** 595 (1878); "Spectroscopy," E. C. C. Baly, vol. 1, p. 53, 1924.
5. Féry, *Jour. phys.*, 762 (1910); *Astrophys. Jour.*, **34,** 79 (1911); "Spectroscopy," E. C. C. Baly, vol. 1, p. 121, 1924.
6. F. L. O. Wadsworth, *Phil. Mag.*, **38,** 337 (1894).
7. K. Leiss, *Zeitschr. Physik*, **69,** 680 (1931).
8. *Hilger Publication* 169.
9. Forsythe and Barnes, *Rev. Sci. Inst.*, **4,** 289 (1933).
10. P. H. van Cittert, *Zeitschr. Instrumentenk.*, **46,** 557 (1926).
11. P. H. van Cittert, *Rev. d'optique*, **5,** 393 (1926).

12. RANDALL and STRONG, *Rev. Sci. Inst.*, **2**, 585 (1931).
13. PASCHEN, *Ann. phys.*, **27**, 537 (1908); **29**, 625 (1909).
14. RANDALL, *Ann. phys.*, **33**, 739 (1910); *Astrophys. Jour.*, **34**, 1 (1911); **42**, 195 (1915).
15. RANDALL and BARKER, *Astrophys. Jour.*, **49**, 42, and 54 (1919).
16. PFUND, *Phys. Rev.*, **36**, 71 (1930); *Jour. Optical Soc. Am.*, **23**, 375 (1933).
17. SLEATOR, *Astrophys. Jour.*, **48**, 125 (1918).
18. RANDALL, *Rev. Sci. Inst.*, **3**, 396 (1932).
19. PFUND, *Jour. Optical Soc. Am.* and *Rev. Sci. Inst.*, **14**, 337 (1927).
20. HARDY, *Phys. Rev.*, **38**, 2162 (1931).
21. WRIGHT and RANDALL, *Phys. Rev.*, **44**, 391 (1933).
22. Strukten der Materie in Enzeldarstellung X, "Das Ultrarote Spektrum," Berlin: J. Springer, 1930.
23. G. FASSIN, *Jour. Optical Soc. Am.*, **23**, 186 (1933).
24. *Chem. News*, pp. 71–175 (1895).

CHAPTER V

THE SPECTROMETER AS AN OPTICAL INSTRUMENT

B. T. Barnes*

Spectrometers ordinarily are designed to serve in the analysis of radiant energy as precision instruments for determining the wavelengths of spectral lines or for measuring spectral intensities. Yet automatic adjustments or sufficiently detailed instructions for their use and adjustment are rarely supplied. Since accurate results can be obtained with any instrument only through proper use, the function of each part of the spectrometer and the path of the beam of radiation from the source to the receiver must be considered carefully. On account of the varied uses of spectrometers, very few universal rules may be laid down. One such rule, however, is that for best results both the source and the receiver should be symmetrical, and should be centered on the collimator axis and the telescope axis, respectively. Other points of importance in connection with the use of spectrometers are discussed in the following paragraphs.

Magnification and Intensity. If the entrance slit of a spectrometer is so wide that diffraction effects are negligible, the spectrum formed by the instrument consists of a series of monochromatic images of the slit. The dimensions of the slit image and those of the slit are in the same ratio as the focal lengths of the telescope and the collimator. The intensity at any point in the slit image is equal to the intensity at the corresponding point of the slit multiplied by both the transmission of the instrument and the square of the ratio of the focal length of the collimator to that of the telescope.

With a narrow slit, diffraction effects spread the slit image. Then the intensity is maximum at the center of a spectral line and falls off gradually toward either side. The diffraction pattern depends on the width of the slit and on the aperture and focal length of the collimator. If these are fixed, the area of the slit

* Physicist, Incandescent Lamp Department, General Electric Company.

image is directly, and the intensity at corresponding points in the slit image is inversely proportional to the square of the focal length of the telescope.

Irradiation of the Slit. When the entrance slit of a spectrometer is wide enough to make diffraction effects negligible, one can obtain the greatest spectral intensity with a given source by filling the collimator lens completely with radiant flux from the brightest portion of the source. If the source can be placed close enough to the slit to do this without use of a lens, any setup with a condensing lens gives less intensity. For if ω is the solid angle subtended at the slit by the collimator aperture, A the area of the slit, $\mathcal{B}$ the radiant flux per unit area per unit solid angle emitted by the source, and d the distance from the slit to the source, then the radiant flux striking the collimator lens comes from an area ωd^2 (approximately) of the source and is emitted within a solid angle A/d^2. Assuming the source uniform over the area ωd^2, the radiant flux received at the collimator lens is $\mathcal{B}\omega A$. With an image of the source focused on the slit by a lens of transmission τ at distance x from the slit and y from the source, the collimator lens receives radiation from an area $A\,y^2/x^2$ and from a solid angle $\omega\,x^2/y^2$ from the source, provided the lens between the source and the slit is sufficiently large. The radiant flux reaching the collimator lens is then $\mathcal{B}\omega A\tau$, that is, τ times that obtained when no lens is used. Focusing an image of the source on the slit is of advantage only when one has a small source which cannot be moved close to the slit or when one wishes to obtain the radiation from a small area of the source.

In measuring the spectral distribution of the radiation from a large nonuniform source, the latter should be placed far enough from the slit that the collimator lens is not quite filled. When it is not convenient to locate the source at the proper distance, the angular aperture of the beam from the source may be reduced or increased by placing a suitable diverging or converging lens at the proper distance in front of the slit. In the case of a converging lens this distance must be less than the focal length. The lens should subtend a greater angle at the slit than the collimator lens. Let x be the distance of the slit image,* y the distance of the slit from the corresponding principal planes of the lens, and τ the transmission of the lens. Then the radiant flux entering the slit

---

* This image is virtual.

is $\tau x^2/y^2$ times the amount which would enter the slit if no lens were used and the slit were as far from the source as the slit image actually is when the lens is used. To correct measured radiant flux for the effect of the lens, one may divide by the lens factor given above or one may assume that the lens is replaced by a filter of transmission τ and the slit dimensions changed to those of the slit image. In either case the distance from the source to the slit image is to be considered as the distance at which spectral intensities are being determined.

When the entrance slit is very narrow, diffraction plays an important part in determining the intensity and width of spectral lines. These diffraction effects depend on the method of irradiation, the width of the slit, and the horizontal aperture and focal length of the collimator. To obtain very narrow spectral lines,[1] the beam of radiation striking the collimator should be centered and should be less than half as wide as the horizontal aperture of the collimator. When high intensity is desired and considerable broadening of the lines is permissible, the horizontal aperture of the collimator should be three-fourths filled[2] by the beam entering the instrument. Filling the vertical aperture completely does not broaden the lines much.

Resolving Power. Spectroscopic resolving power is defined as the ratio of the average wavelength λ of two neighboring spectral lines to the minimum separation $\delta\lambda$ for detecting that the two lines form a doublet. Rayleigh found that with a very narrow entrance slit, monochromatic lines, and visual observation, $\delta\lambda$ was roughly a separation such that the first minimum of the diffraction image of one line coincided with the maximum of the central image of the other line. In practice $\delta\lambda$ is assumed to be exactly the above separation. This fixes the resolving power arbitrarily, making it independent of the observer and the method of observation.

For a prism spectrometer the resolving power for very narrow lines[3] is $-T\ dn/d\lambda$, where n is the refractive index of the prism material and T the difference in the aggregate thickness of dispersive material traversed by the extreme rays. This holds true for a series of prisms of the same material.

For any spectrometer the resolving power for very narrow lines observed visually[4] is $bd\theta/d\lambda$, where b is the width of the beam at the telescope lens or mirror and θ is the angle through which the radiation of wavelength λ is deviated by the dispersing system.

The foregoing formulas for resolving power apply only to the case of strictly monochromatic lines and an infinitely narrow entrance slit. For entrance slits of appreciable width, two lines are assumed to be just resolved when the separation between them is twice the distance from the center of a single line to the point where its intensity is 0.405 times that at the center. The ratio of the mean wavelength to the separation of these lines which are just resolved is called the purity of the spectrum. The purity of a spectrum is proportional to the resolving power of the instru-

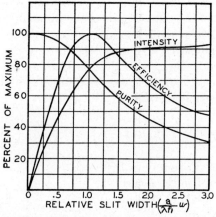

Fig. 115.—Variation with slit width, of purity and intensity of spectral lines and efficiency of instrument, for "noncoherent" radiation.

ment, but it also depends on the width of the slit. The relationship has been worked out in detail for the case of a slit which is a source of radiant energy and has been presented in tabular form by Schuster.[5] Figure 115 gives Schuster's results.

Resolving power and purity were calculated by Rayleigh and Schuster on the assumption that the slit was a source of radiant energy. However, a source narrow enough to serve as the slit of any ordinary spectrograph is not practical. With external irradiation the diffraction pattern obtained with a narrow slit, and consequently the resolution of neighboring lines, depend on the method of irradiation.[1,2]

Efficiency of Spectrographs. The entrance slit of a spectrograph is ordinarily so narrow that diffraction effects play an important part in determining both the purity of the spectrum and the intensity at the center of spectral lines. The diffraction pattern obtained depends on the method of irradiating the entrance slit and on the dimensions of the optical system. The relationship between all the variables has never been worked out completely except for two limiting cases, *viz.*, for strictly "noncoherent" and for strictly "coherent" radiation. By the latter is meant radiation which has the same phase at all of a series of points extending across the slit. It is approximated satisfactorily in practice by placing a narrow source on the axis of the collimator at a relatively great distance from the slit with the long axis of the source parallel to the slit. By noncoherent radiation is meant radiation reaching all parts of the slit in all possible phases. It can theoretically be realized by a perfectly diffusing source of adequate extent placed in front of the slit or by a slit which is a source of radiant energy. In this case the ratio of the intensity at the center of a spectral line to the radiant flux density of the same wavelength at the entrance slit is

$$I = C\tau\left(\frac{a}{f_1}\right)^2\left(\frac{f_1}{f_2}\right)^2\varphi\left(\pi\frac{wa}{\lambda f_1}\right) = C\tau\left(\frac{a}{f_2}\right)^2\varphi\left(\pi\frac{wa}{\lambda f_1}\right) \qquad (42)$$

where τ = transmission of instrument.

  f_2 = focal length of telescope.

  f_1 = focal length of collimator.

  C = constant.

  w = width of slit.

  a = aperture of collimator lens.

The function[*2]

$$\varphi\left(\pi\frac{wa}{\lambda f_1}\right) = \int_0^x\frac{\sin x}{x}dx - \frac{1 - \cos x}{x} \qquad (43)$$

where $x = \pi\dfrac{wa}{\lambda f_1}$

The purity of the spectrum of a slit as a source of radiant energy has been computed for various slit widths[†] by Schuster.[5] It may be expressed as

$$P = r\Psi\left(\frac{wa}{\lambda f_1}\right) = a\frac{d\theta}{d\lambda}\Psi\left(\frac{wa}{\lambda f_1}\right) \qquad (44)$$

* See p. 164.
† See p. 164.

where r is the resolving power for very narrow slits and $d\theta/d\lambda$ the dispersion of the instrument. A satisfactory mathematical expression for the function Ψ has never been worked out. Numerical values may be obtained from Schuster's tables or from Fig. 115.

The usefulness of a spectrograph in recording line spectra depends on the purity of the spectrum it gives and on the ratio of the intensity at the center of a line to the radiant flux density of this wavelength at the entrance slit. We may define the product of these two quantities as the efficiency of the instrument. Then the efficiency of a spectrograph with a slit which is a source of radiant energy is given by

$$E = C\frac{a^3\tau}{f_2{}^2}\frac{d\theta}{d\lambda}\varphi\left(\pi\frac{wa}{\lambda f_1}\right)\Psi\left(\frac{wa}{\lambda f_1}\right) \tag{45}$$

Figure 115 shows the variations[5] of intensity, purity and efficiency (*i.e.*, of φ, Ψ, and their product) with the quantity $wa/\lambda f_1$. The efficiency is maximum when the slit width is equal to $\lambda f_1/a$. The maximum efficiency is

$$E_m = \text{const.} \times \frac{a^3\tau}{f_2{}^2}\frac{d\theta}{d\lambda} \tag{46}$$

Thus, to obtain both high intensity and satisfactory purity of spectrum, one should choose a spectrograph with high transmission and dispersion, with optical parts as large as is practicable, and with a relatively short focus telescope. The finite size of the grains of a photographic plate will, however, set a limit to the gain in efficiency obtainable by shortening the focal length of the telescope. The difficulty of correcting lenses or mirrors for various types of aberration also increases as the ratio of the focal length to the aperture is decreased.

The maximum efficiency obtainable with a spectrograph is, theoretically, independent of the focal length of the collimator. It is also independent of the slit height, provided the latter is made great enough to prevent vertical diffraction or astigmatism from affecting the intensity at the center of a spectral line.

The theoretical case of noncoherent radiation discussed above is more or less approximated in practice when a broad source is used for irradiating the slit. If an image of the source is focused on the slit, and the slit width is of the order of one wavelength, diffraction may make the irradiation more or less coherent even if the focusing lens or mirror subtends a wide angle at the slit.

The optimum slit width for a laboratory setup giving an approximation to noncoherent irradiation is of the order of $\lambda f_1/a$ but is best determined by trial.[1] The maximum efficiency is obtained when the horizontal aperture of the collimator is three-fourths, and the vertical aperture completely, filled.[1,2] The efficiencies actually obtained are, however, always considerably less than the theoretical values.

With coherent radiation the optimum slit width[1,2] is $2\lambda f_1/a$. The purity of the spectrum obtainable in practice is relatively high,[1] but the intensity is low because the source must be placed quite far from the slit.

Efficiency of Monochromators. If a spectrometer is to be used as a monochromator, the efficiency is ordinarily determined by the purity of the spectrum and by the ratio of the radiant flux in a given line or wavelength band at the exit slit to the radiant-flux density of the same radiation at the entrance slit. Considering the product of these two quantities as representing the efficiency of the instrument, spectrometers of different types can be compared. For simplicity, assume that the entrance slit is wide enough to make the widening of spectral lines by diffraction negligible; that lines are not appreciably widened by spherical aberration or other imperfections in the optical system; and that the slit heights, optical parts, and apertures are so chosen that the only limiting diaphragm is at the collimator lens. Assume also that with a given slit area the radiant flux through the collimator lens is proportional to the square of the angular aperture of the collimator lens. This obtains in practice if the source is used without a focusing lens or mirror and its distance is inversely proportional to the angular aperture of the collimator lens, or if one focuses an image of the source on the slit with a lens or mirror of sufficient aperture to avoid limiting the amount of radiation passing through the spectrometer.

With the above conditions satisfied, the ratio R of the radiant flux in a given wavelength band of the spectrum to the radiant-flux density of the same spectral region at the entrance slit, the purity P of the spectrum, and the efficiency E are given by the following equations:

$$R = \text{const.} \times hw\left(\frac{a}{f}\right)^2 \tau \qquad (47)$$

$$P = \text{const.} \times \frac{f}{w} \cdot \frac{d\theta}{d\lambda} \qquad (48)$$

$$E = \text{const.} \times \frac{h}{f} \cdot a^2\frac{d\theta}{d\lambda} \cdot \tau \qquad (49)$$

where h = height of entrance slit.

w = width of entrance slit.

τ = transmission of instrument.

a = aperture of collimator.

f = focal length of collimator.

$d\theta/d\lambda$ = dispersion of instrument.

The dispersion, the transmission of the instrument, and the focal length of the collimator are all functions of the wavelength.

The optimum height of the entrance slit depends on the design of the monochromator and on the use for which it is intended. It is, however, roughly proportional to the focal length of the collimator lens. In designing or choosing an instrument of a given type we may assume

$$h = \text{const.} \times f \qquad (50)$$

Then

$$E = \text{const.} \times a^2\frac{d\theta}{d\lambda}\tau \qquad (51)$$

This means that, for monochromators of the same type to be used for the same purpose, the efficiency as we have defined it is proportional to the area of the collimator aperture, the dispersion, and the transmission of the instrument. It is independent of focal lengths or slit widths, so long as the latter are wide enough to make diffraction effects negligible.

Since the assumptions we have made as to slit height, irradiation of the entrance slit and diaphragming correspond approximately with the best practice, the efficiency as we have derived it is a fair measure of the utility of a monochromator. It does not take into consideration the linear spread or height of the spectrum. These may be varied at will, by changing the focal length of the telescope lens, without affecting the efficiency of the monochromator.

Stray Radiation. Radiation which reaches the spectrum by some route other than direct passage from the entrance slit

through the optical system is called stray radiation.   If a monochromator or spectrograph is light-tight, and if the insides of the
collimator and telescope enclosures have dull black radiation-
absorbing surfaces and a suitable system of diaphragms to stop
reflection of the stray radiation from the walls, there will be
practically no stray radiation except that coming directly from
the optical parts.   Prisms should be sufficiently large to permit
radiation to pass without impinging on non-optical surfaces.
If the instrument is built without tubes, it should be divided by
light-tight partitions into at least three chambers: one corresponding to the collimator, a second enclosing the lens and prism sys-

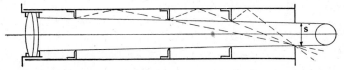

FIG. 116.—Diagram showing the method of placing diaphragms in a collimator
tube to prevent reflection of stray light from the interior surface.   They should
be similarly placed in a telescope or camera tube, except that the bevels should
be reversed, *i.e.*, the flat sides of the diaphragms should always be adjacent to
the source of light.

tem, and a third corresponding to the telescope or camera.
These three chambers should be properly fitted with diaphragms.
Figure 116 shows one method of locating the diaphragms.   All
diaphragms and slits should have sharp bevels with the sharp
edge toward the oncoming radiation.   The diaphragm nearest
the entrance slit should be close enough to it and of such size as
to stop all the radiation coming through the ends of the slit at
angles too great to allow it to strike the collimator lens, but its
aperture should be large enough to clear all of the rays joining the
margin of the objective with the ends of the slit.   Probably still
more care should be exercised with the telescope diaphragms to
avoid having dispersed radiation of other wavelengths scattered
onto the receiver.

The stray radiation coming directly from the optical parts
consists of radiation reaching the spectrum after being scattered
by imperfections in the optical parts or after suffering one or more
reflections other than those incidental to regular passage through
the optical system.   The scattered radiation of a given wavelength is usually distributed more or less uniformly throughout
the spectrum.   It should of course be kept at a minimum by

using optical parts as nearly perfect as one can obtain. The reflected radiation of a given wavelength is usually concentrated in the spectral regions near the regularly transmitted beam. A spectrometer using lenses for focusing always has some reflected radiation in the spectrum.

In the strongest portions of a spectrum the amount of stray radiation is ordinarily negligible. On the other hand, it may be more intense than the regularly transmitted radiation in regions where the intensity is a small fraction of the maximum spectral intensity. If one wishes to make intensity measurements in a very weak portion of the spectrum, it is necessary to use a double monochromator,* or to use a filter which has a much higher transmission for the spectral region under investigation than it does for the most intense portions of the spectrum, or to use a selective receiver which is much more sensitive to the radiation being measured than it is to the most intense parts of the spectrum.

Stray radiation can be partially suppressed by use of a spectrometer with constant-deviation prisms[6] if the reflection angle at the back of the prism is such that total reflection is obtained for radiation of the wavelength being measured but not for that of greater wavelengths. Such a device is particularly valuable for ultraviolet measurements where most of the stray radiation will be visible and infrared.

Choice of Slit Widths. Formulas for the optimum slit width for a spectrograph have already been given.† These formulas also apply to a spectrometer used for separating spectral lines which are so close together that the instrument can barely resolve them. The relative widths of the entrance, center, and exit slits of a double monochromator have also been discussed.‡ If the collimator and telescope have the same focal length, a single monochromator should have entrance and exit slits of the same width for a continuous spectrum and should have the exit slit a little wider than the entrance for a line spectrum. The optimum entrance and exit slit widths for either a double or a single monochromator are proportional to the focal lengths of the collimator and telescope, respectively, and to the angular dispersion

* See p. 137.
† See p. 167.
‡ See p. 141.

of the instrument.   It is not sufficient to give the slit width in millimeters without giving the focal length of the lens and the dispersion of the instrument.   Ordinarily data concerning slit widths, focal lengths, and dispersion are more easily applied to the interpretation of spectral-intensity data if they are combined to give the wavelength interval transmitted in different parts of the spectrum.   For this reason the width of a slit is often expressed in terms of the width (in wavelength units) of the band of a continuous spectrum which it would transmit if it were the exit slit of the spectrometer, if the entrance slit were made infinitely narrow, and if the spectrometer were set for a certain specified wavelength.   Then the sum of these "slit widths," *i.e.*,

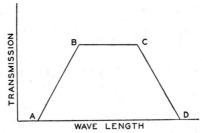

Fig. 117.—Relative spectral transmission of slits of a simple spectrometer. Spectral ranges *BC* and *AD* are $b - a$ and $b + a$, respectively, where b and a are widths of exit and entrance slits in terms of wavelength range of a pure spectrum each would transmit.

the widths of the bands of a pure continuous spectrum each slit would transmit, gives the total wavelength interval of a continuous spectrum transmitted by the instrument.   The relative transmission of the slits for radiation of wavelengths within this interval is given by Fig. 117.

The absolute magnitudes of the optimum slit widths vary greatly with the type of work.   For accurate measurements of the intensities of spectral lines, the slits should be kept so narrow that any continuous radiation or weaker lines included in the measurements may be neglected, or eliminated by corrections.   Where less accuracy is required, it is often desirable to open the slits as wide as possible without causing overlapping of important lines in the spectrum.   Sometimes some overlapping of strong lines is permissible, provided the exit slit is made wide enough to allow a group of overlapping lines to pass through it.

For measurements of spectral intensities in continuous spectra, relatively wide slits are satisfactory.   If the slit-width correction computed by the methods outlined in a later section of this chapter* is negligible, then the slits are certainly sufficiently narrow. If, on the other hand, the correction is many times the permissible error, the slits should be made narrower because such methods give only approximate corrections.   In general the slits should be made narrower if more than one of the quantities involved in the measurement—spectral intensity, instrument transmission, dispersion, or receiver sensitivity—vary a great deal over the wavelength band being transmitted, or if one of these is not approximately a linear function of wavelength over the wavelength interval being transmitted.   Ordinarily slits 100 to 400A wide (so to speak, *i.e.*, each capable of transmitting a band this wide if the other were infinitely narrow) will prove satisfactory for measuring intensities in a continuous spectrum, such as that of a tungsten-filament lamp, except for wavelength regions for which the glass bulb has strong absorption.   For a spectrometer with one 60-deg. quartz prism used at minimum deviation and with lenses 10 to 15 cm in focal length, the corresponding widths in millimeters would be roughly 0.02 to 0.12 mm for λ 1.3μ, and 0.1 to 0.6 mm for $\lambda = 0.5\mu$.   If the lamp is provided with a quartz window, a slit width of 1 mm will be satisfactory for λ 0.25μ.

If this same spectrometer were used in determining the spectral transmission of a filter whose transmission varied rapidly with wavelength, it might be desirable to use slits only 10A wide.   In this case the slit width would be 0.002 to 0.003 mm for λ 1.3μ and 0.010 to 0.015 mm for $\lambda 5000A$.

Choice of Slit Height.   The height of the entrance slit of a spectrograph ordinarily is determined solely on the basis of the height of spectrum desired.   For microphotometry and for identification of spectral lines, a spectrum height of 5 mm is ample.

In the case of a monochromatic illuminator, the entrance slit ordinarily is made as high as possible without introducing excessive nonuniformity in the slit image.   Nonuniform brightness of the image of a uniformly irradiated slit of uniform width results whenever the radiation passing through the ends of the slit is diaphragmed more than the radiation passing through the

* See p. 182.

center of the slit.   This difficulty may be avoided by making one aperture in the optical system sufficiently smaller than the others. Then this aperture serves as the only limiting diaphragm, provided that the slit height does not exceed $(a_2 - a_1)\dfrac{f}{d}$, where a_1 and a_2 are the respective heights of the limiting aperture and of any other aperture,* d is the optical path (in terms of the equivalent air path) between the two apertures, and f focal length of collimator.

If it is important to transmit the greatest possible amount of radiation irrespective of the length and the nonuniformity of the slit image, then the apertures should all be set at their maximum height and the entrance slit height should be increased until it becomes equal to $(a_1 + a_2)\dfrac{f}{d}$ for some pair of apertures, provided that the source is long enough to illuminate the entire collimator lens aperture through each point of a slit of this length and that the receiver has a vertical aperture sufficient to take in all the radiation leaving the exit slit.   Any further increase in slit height would increase the stray radiation, but it would not increase the radiation reaching the plane of the exit slit by a direct optical path because radiation from top and bottom of the slit would all strike the diaphragms at the apertures in question.

The above are only approximate formulas applying to relatively simple optical systems in which the lenses or mirrors have their optical axes in the same horizontal plane and in which the apertures and the entrance slit are symmetrical about this plane. If a lens is used in front of the slit, its optical axis should be in this same plane, its aperture should be symmetrical about this plane, and the relationship between the height of its aperture, that of the collimator aperture and the entrance slit height should be taken into consideration.

In practice, other factors besides the height and the uniformity of the slit image must ordinarily be taken into account in choosing the height of the entrance slit of a spectrometer.   For example, the variation with wavelength of the curvature of spectral lines produced by prism spectrometers makes it desirable to use relatively short slits, even though a curved exit slit is used.   A suitable height for making a certain set of measurements with a

---

* Limited to aperture in parallel beam between telescope and collimator.

certain instrument can be determined only by tests or computations for the particular case. For example, the diaphragming
action of the various apertures may be studied by making a
diagram showing the paths of the rays which are in the extreme
positions at each aperture. It is often advantageous to use a
more open scale for distances measured perpendicular to the
optical axis than for those measured along the axis.

If such a diagram shows a portion of the beam cut off at one of
the apertures, the fraction of the radiation lost may be obtained by
drawing on cross-section paper the outline of the beam as it falls
on the aperture and making a graphical integration. This procedure applies only to a uniform beam, unless relative intensities
are used in the integration. The latter procedure is tedious and
may often be avoided by outlining the beams from several points
on the slit, obtaining the percentage transmission for each of
these beams, plotting a curve of transmission vs. distance from
center of slit, and determining by graphical integration the net
transmission of the aperture for all the radiation passing through
the entrance slit. All this computation may be avoided, however,
by making certain that the entire optical system has only one
limiting vertical aperture besides the entrance slit and that the
uniform portion of the source is sufficiently long to fill this aperture through each point on the slit. If this second condition
cannot be satisfied, or if a measurement of the radiant flux from
a nonuniform source is desired, it is best to make the entrance
slit the only limiting vertical aperture.

Location of Receiver. If a bolometer is used for measuring
spectral intensities in a spectroradiometer, it is ordinarily used
in place of an exit slit in the focal "plane" of the telescope lens.
With a thermopile, this procedure is unsatisfactory unless the
cold junctions are very massive or are otherwise protected from
the effects of the portion of the spectrum adjacent to that falling
on the hot junctions. Ordinarily the thermopile is used either
very close behind the exit slit or at such a distance that an image
of the slit may be focused on the receiver with a lens. The latter
procedure makes it possible to use a smaller receiver, makes the
area receiving radiation independent of the angular aperture of
the beam of radiation, and makes it possible to have uniform
intensity over a certain definite part of the thermopile. Whenever it is possible to keep the slits set at the same width for all

measurements, the last two features increase the accuracy obtainable because the area of the thermopile exposed to radiation should be the same when it is used for measurements as when it is calibrated. However, the use of a lens is successful only if the slit image is accurately focused and centered on the thermopile whatever the wavelength of the radiation being measured. This means that both the thermopile and the lens must be rigidly mounted on the arm or base which supports the telescope tube of the spectrometer. If the lens is not strictly achromatic over the entire range for which it is to be used, a suitable focusing mechanism must be provided. This focusing device must keep the lens centered on the optical axis of the telescope lens.

With a photoelectric tube or cell as receiver, the variation in sensitivity over the cell surface is often so great that it is necessary to keep the distribution of intensity over the sensitive surface the same during any intensity measurements as during the cell calibration. If sources of different types are used without a lens between the source and the entrance slit, it may be impossible to keep the distribution of intensity over the cell surface constant except by focusing an image of the exit slit on the sensitive surface. Since the sensitivity of photoelectric cells is often changed by very moderate heating, it is best to make the exit slit image large enough so that the temperature of the irradiated portion of the sensitive surface does not rise more than 5°C. when exposed to the radiation.

When a lens is used for focusing an image of the exit slit on the receiver, the relationship of its aperture to that of the other apertures in the optical system must be taken into account.* Ordinarily this lens should have a principal focal length equal to about half that of the telescope lens and should have an aperture sufficiently large that it will have no diaphragming action on the beam of radiation passing through the exit slit. Of course, the losses due to reflection and absorption by the lens should be considered in computing spectral intensities.

Curvature of Spectral Lines. Any prism-dispersing instrument with a straight entrance slit, except a double monochromator of the zero-dispersion type, forms curved spectral lines at the exit slit or in the exit image "plane." Rays passing through a prism obliquely suffer greater deviation than the corresponding

* See p. 173.

ones in a principal plane. To a first approximation, the spectral
lines are parabolic in shape.* The vertex of the parabola lies in
the plane which passes through the centers of the lenses perpendicular to the refracting edge of the prism. If the normal to this
plane at the vertex of the parabola be taken as the y-axis, and the
line in this plane passing through the vertex perpendicular to
the ray from the center of the lens to the vertex be taken as the
x-axis of coordinates, then the equation defining the position of
the spectral line is

$$x = \frac{n^2 - 1}{2nf} \frac{dD}{dn} y^2 \tag{52}$$

where n = refractive index.
$\quad$ f = focal length of lens.
$\quad$ D = angular deviation (in radians) produced by prism
$\quad\quad$ system.
This holds both for minimum deviation and for the case in which
the entrance angle is fixed, as in a spectrograph. In the more
general case, dD/dn is to be replaced by the corresponding partial
derivative.

The radius of curvature ρ at the vertex of a spectral line is

$$\rho = \frac{nf}{(n^2 - 1)(dD/dn)} \tag{53}$$

for minimum deviation or fixed entrance angle. In other cases
the same equation holds except that dD/dn is to be replaced by
the corresponding partial derivative.

If a spectrometer with a single prism of refracting angle β is
used at minimum deviation, the curvature at the vertex of a
spectral line is given by

$$\rho = nf \frac{\left(1 - n^2 \sin^2 \frac{\beta}{2}\right)^{1/2}}{2(n^2 - 1) \sin \frac{\beta}{2}} \tag{54}$$

The table below gives the radius of curvature at the vertex of a
spectral line formed at minimum deviation by a spectrometer with

* The general equation defining the shape of spectral lines was worked
out by Ditscheiner. Many others have made contributions to the theoretical study of this feature. See H. Kayser, *Handbuch der Spectroscopie*, vol. 1,
p. 319, for references to literature on this subject up to 1895.

a single 60-deg. crystalline-quartz prism and a crystalline-quartz telescope lens having a focal length of 100 cm for λ5,893.

TABLE 16. RADIUS OF CURVATURE AT VERTEX OF SPECTRAL LINES FORMED
BY SPECTROMETER WITH 60-DEG. QUARTZ PRISM AND TELESCOPE OF
INDICATED FOCAL LENGTH

Wavelength, A	2,300	5,893	27,000
Focal length, cm	89	100	107
Radius of curvature, cm	53	71	85

It is usually desirable to furnish a monochromator with a curved exit slit. If one wishes to have the spectral lines straight, the entrance slit should be made curved. Ordinarily it suffices to make one of the slits circular with its radius of curvature equal to that at the vertex of a spectral line near the middle of the range over which the instrument is to be used. One may, of course, obtain the same result by giving both the entrance and exit slit jaws half this curvature. In this case the proper orientation of the entrance slit may be found by tracing the course of the radiation through the instrument. If the number of times that the beam forms a real image of the entrance slit (not at infinity) plus the number of times it is reflected is odd, then the curvature of the entrance and exit slits must be toward the same side of the beam with respect to the direction of travel of the radiation. If this sum is an even number, then the entrance and exit slits must curve toward opposite sides. In any case the curvature of the exit slit must be in the direction in which the beam would move if the index of refraction of the prism material were increased.

Transmission of Prism Spectrometers. The transmission of a monochromator is defined as the ratio of the radiant flux in a given wavelength band at the exit slit to the radiant flux of the same wavelengths entering the collimator. Losses in transmission include radiation stopped by diaphragms and that reflected, absorbed, or scattered by the optical parts. Diaphragm losses may, of course, be eliminated by making the angular aperture of the beam entering the collimator sufficiently small. Scattering is usually negligible in fairly homogeneous crystals whose faces have been given a high polish. Reflection losses are given by optical theory. With normal incidence the fraction reflected at each interface is $(n - 1)^2/(n + 1)^2$, where n is the refractive index.   At any other angle of incidence i, with a corresponding angle of refraction r, the fraction reflected is $\dfrac{\sin^2 (i - r)}{\sin^2 (i + r)}$ for the component vibrating perpendicular to the plane of incidence and $\dfrac{\tan^2 (i - r)}{\tan^2 (i + r)}$ for the component parallel to the plane of incidence. As a consequence, the transmission of a prism spectrometer depends on the state of polarization of the radiation entering it.

Absorption losses in the optical parts may be computed roughly from published data on similar material.   With natural crystals

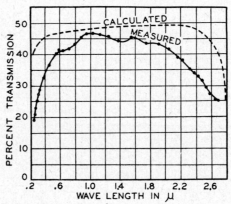

Fig. 118.—Measured and calculated spectral-transmission curves for central ray in spectrometer with two crystalline-quartz prisms each 7 cm thick at base and two quartz-fluorite achromats.

the presence of impurities in unknown amounts makes the results of such a computation unreliable.   This is evident from Fig. 118. It is best to determine the transmission experimentally over the entire wavelength range for which the instrument is to be used. This gives a correction factor for the combined effect of all losses.

If there is appreciable absorption in the optical system, the transmission depends on whether or not the center of the beam of radiation passing through the instrument coincides with the optical axis.   It also depends somewhat on the width of the beam.   If α is the coefficient of absorption of the prism material and T the thickness traversed by the central ray, the transmission (apart from reflection losses) for this ray will be $e^{-\alpha T}$.   If a centered uniform beam traverses thicknesses ranging from $T - a$ to $T + a$, the average transmission will be[7]

$$e^{-\alpha T} \cdot \frac{\sinh \alpha a}{\alpha a}$$

In the case of a triangular prism completely filled at minimum deviation the thickness traversed ranges from 0 to $2T$. The average transmission for a uniform beam is[7]

$$\frac{1 - e^{-2\alpha T}}{2\alpha T}$$

Figure 119 gives the ratio of the average transmission to that for the central ray when the beam completely fills the prism and also

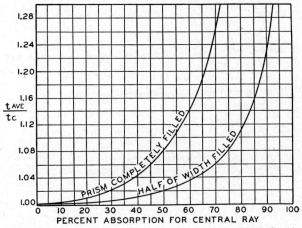

FIG. 119.—Ratio of average transmission t_{ave} to transmission for central ray t_c for uniform centered beam passing through triangular prism at minimum deviation.

when it covers half the width of the prism face. In the latter case this ratio does not exceed 1.02 unless the prism absorbs more than 50 per cent of the flux in the central ray. If more than half of the flux in the central ray is absorbed, the average transmission for a beam of radiation naturally varies a great deal with the width and position of the beam and the distribution of intensity in the beam.

The transmission of lenses also varies slightly with the width of the beam and depends on whether or not the latter is centered.

Both absorption and reflection losses vary with the distance from the center of the lens. However, unless the lens material has a much higher absorption coefficient than the prism material or unless the angular aperture of the lens is unusually large, the variations in the transmission of a spectrometer lens with the width and location of the beam are ordinarily negligible (of the order of 1 per cent).

Determination of Transmission. The transmission of a spectrometer for radiation of a given wavelength usually is determined by sending a measured flux of approximately monochromatic radiation into the instrument and measuring the flux which reaches the exit slit or the photographic plate. The monochromatic radiation may be obtained from a source of line radiation with a suitable filter[3] or from another spectrometer. It must be relatively free from stray radiation of wavelengths which would be measured at the entrance slit but not by the final receiver. To satisfy this condition it may be necessary to use as the preliminary dispersing instrument a double monochromator or a single monochromator with a source of line radiation. In the latter case only the strongest lines in the spectrum are apt to be sufficiently free from stray radiation.

When using a prism spectrometer as a preliminary dispersing agent for transmission measurements, one must remember that it furnishes partially polarized radiation. When this radiation is sent through a second prism spectrometer, the transmission may be several per cent higher than that for unpolarized radiation. The difference can be computed from the equations given above.*

In using filtered line radiation for transmission measurements, one must be certain that the filters transmit no radiation in the wavelength band to which the first receiver is sensitive except that used in the measurements. Often two or three filters must be used together to fulfill this requirement. When a thermopile is used to measure the radiant flux transmitted by a relatively thin filter, the two should be separated by a distance many times as great as the average diameter of the illuminated area of the filter. Otherwise the thermopile will receive an appreciable amount of energy reradiated in the far infrared owing to heating of the filter each time the shutter is raised.

* See p. 178.

A continuous source with filter may be used in transmission measurements[9] if the spectral distribution of the radiation transmitted by the filter is accurately known. Similarly a directional candlepower standard may be used as source and the amount of light transmitted by the spectrometer determined by measuring the visible spectrum step by step. In either case errors due to stray radiation are more apt to occur than when monochromatic radiation is used.

In any transmission measurements, the passage of the beam through the instrument should be carefully checked to see that it is unobstructed. For the highest accuracy the beam should have the same cross section, the same distribution of intensity, and the same location with respect to the optical axis when the transmission is being measured as it does when the instrument is used for radiation measurements. However, the transmission for an axial beam is nearly the same as that for any symmetrical centered beam unless the absorption is quite high (> 40 per cent, p. 179). The difference may be determined by trial, or it may be computed if one knows separately the amount of absorption by the prisms and that by the lenses.

Atmospheric Absorption. The earth's atmosphere may be considered perfectly transparent for radiation of wavelengths between 2900 and 10,000A if the length of the total path in air traversed by the radiation does not exceed a few meters. When measuring radiation of wavelengths outside this range, or when using optical paths longer than 10 m, absorption in the atmosphere should be taken into consideration.

Atmospheric absorption for infrared radiation is due chiefly to the water vapor and CO_2 present. There are a number of broad absorption bands throughout the range from 1 to 50μ[10]. In a warm humid laboratory the magnitude of the absorption for each maximum and minimum of the absorption curve 0.25 to 13μ is approximately that given in Table 17.

TABLE 17. ABSORPTION FOR 1-m PATH IN AIR AT 76 CM PRESSURE, 30°C. AND 70 PER CENT HUMIDITY WITH CO_2 CONTENT 2 g/m³

λ (μ)	0.25–1.00	1.13	1.25	1.40	1.60	1.89	2.20	2.62	3.8
Per cent absorption	0	1	0	5	0	7	0	23	4

| λ (μ) | 4.3 | 4.9 | 5.9 | 6.3 | 6.5 | 8–13 | | | |
| Per cent absorption | 33 | 4.5 | 25 | 14 | 35 | 0 | | | |

Over this wavelength range the absorption is almost entirely due to water vapor. CO_2 absorbs strongly radiation of wavelengths 14 to 16μ; water vapor also has strong absorption for this range of wavelengths and for radiation of wavelengths 16 to 50μ.[10]

Since measurements of the water vapor and CO_2 contents of the atmosphere and correction for their absorption are troublesome procedures, it is best to enclose spectrometers used for measuring radiation of wavelengths greater than 1.3μ and keep them filled with air from which the water vapor has been removed (also the CO_2 in cases where its absorption would be appreciable). Two methods have been used for the enclosure of the spectrometer. It may be fitted to the completed spectrometer, as was done at Wisconsin,[11] or a case of suitable dimensions may be chosen, as at the University of Michigan,[12] and the spectrometer built in this case. Of course, any gas having negligible absorption in the region under investigation would be satisfactory for filling the spectrometer case.

In the ultraviolet, absorption for 1-m path length in air at atmospheric pressure is negligible for λ's $> 2300A$; it is about 1 per cent at 2200 and 3 per cent at 2050A and increases rapidly toward shorter wavelengths.[13] This absorption is due to oxygen (O_2). It sets a lower limit of about 1850A to the wavelength of the ultraviolet which can be recorded by a spectrograph in which the beam traverses 50 cm of air at atmospheric pressure. For measuring ultraviolet of wavelengths less than about 2000A, one needs a vacuum spectrometer or one filled with a suitable gas. Nitrogen is considerably more transparent than oxygen for radiation of wavelength 1860A.[14] With nitrogen, argon, helium, and hydrogen, used at pressures of 2 or 3 mm in a spectrograph with a path length of about 2 m, ultraviolet spectra extending to wavelengths shorter than 1000A (to 600A in the case of helium) have been obtained.[15]

SLIT-WIDTH CORRECTIONS

Willibald Weniger*

Correction for Dispersion. In spectroradiometric investigations, the different parts of a spectrum are, of course, located as to wavelength, and in addition a measurement is made of the

* *Professor of Physics, Oregon State Agricultural College.*

rate of energy reception. Since prisms are frequently used, the dispersed spectrum is not normal, *i.e.*, distances in the spectrum are not directly proportional to wavelengths. When the spectrum is made to pass over the receiving strip of the instrument (bolometer, thermojunction, or radiometer), the wavelength interval incident on the strip is not constant. Consequently, the wavelength distribution of the energy flux striking

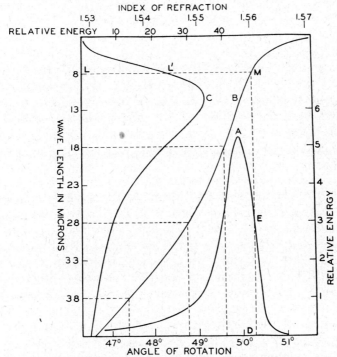

FIG. 120.—Graphical method of correcting for dispersion of prism spectrometer. *A*, energy curve as obtained; *B*, dispersion curve of prism; *C*, normal energy curve.

the entrance slit of the spectrometer is not correctly represented by a curve showing the deflection for different positions of the strip in the spectrum.

The transformation of the experimental curve to a normal curve can be accomplished either numerically or graphically. Let Δq be the energy flux in the wavelength interval λ to $\lambda + \Delta\lambda$ in a normal spectrum. Then the mean intensity in this interval is $\Delta q/\Delta\lambda$. In the limit the intensity J_λ of wavelength interval

λ to $\lambda + d\lambda$ is $J_\lambda = dq/d\lambda$. Let the receiving strip be at an angular distance θ from some fixed point in a prismatic spectrum; the deflection d for this point will be proportional to $dq/d\theta$. Hence for proportionality factor unity,

$$d = \frac{dq}{d\theta} = \frac{dq}{d\lambda} \cdot \frac{d\lambda}{d\theta} = J_\lambda \frac{d\lambda}{d\theta},$$

or

$$J_\lambda = d \cdot \frac{d\theta}{d\lambda}$$

The value of $d\theta/d\lambda$ can be determined at any point in the spec-

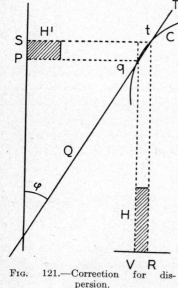

Fig. 121.—Correction for dispersion.

trum from the dispersion curve of the prism material. Hence, in order to transform from the prismatic to the normal spectrum, each deflection must be multiplied by the corresponding value of $d\theta/d\lambda$ obtained from the dispersion curve.

The process can sometimes be done more readily by a graphic method due to Langley.[16] In Fig. 120 B is the dispersion curve of the prism material plotted with either angle of rotation of prism or the index of refraction as abscissas and wavelengths as ordinates, the wavelength scale being an equally spaced or normal scale. A is the experimental curve plotted with the same abscissas as B and with deflections (intensity) as ordinates. Corresponding points on the two axes are indicated by the dotted lines. On the axis of ordinates as base, the normal energy-flux curve C will be constructed by the following process: Select a wavelength on the axis of ordinates and draw the dotted lines to find the corresponding point on the experimental curve A. At point M draw a tangent to B, making an angle ϕ with the axis of ordinates. Multiply the intercept DE by tangent ϕ and lay off this length as LL'. The point L' is one point of the desired curve.

To prove that this construction agrees with the preceding theory, choose two points S and P (Fig. 121) on the axis of ordinates a distance $\Delta\lambda$ apart. By drawing the dotted perpendiculars locate t and q on C and points V and R at a distance $\Delta\theta$ from each other, on the axis of abscissas. Draw the chord TQ, which as $\Delta\lambda$ becomes smaller will approach the tangent, making an angle φ with the axis of ordinates. Evidently $\tan\varphi = \Delta\theta/\Delta\lambda$. The energy in the interval $\Delta\theta$ is represented by the area $H \cdot RV$, or $h\Delta\theta$. The energy in the interval $\Delta\lambda$ must be equal to this; denoting the length of the ordinate of the interval by H',

$$H' = \frac{H\Delta\theta}{\Delta\lambda} = H \tan\varphi.$$

Correction for Overlapping. Owing to the finite width of the slit and to diffraction, there will be overlapping of the slit images which introduces an error even in a normal spectrum. This source of error can be partly corrected for by the methods to be described. It must be pointed out, however, that the accuracy of the final results obtained depends upon the magnitude of the error introduced by the width of the slit that it is necessary to use. A much better procedure when possible is to use a large dispersion and a slit so narrow that the error introduced will be negligible.

The following method of correcting for this overlapping is due to Runge, but was first published in a paper by Paschen.[17]

Let the position in the spectrum be denoted by x. This may signify wavelength, refractive index, angle of minimum deviation, or angle of rotation of the prism from some fixed position. Let the intensity at point x be $f(x)$. Then the energy at x, in a strip of width dx is $f(x)dx$, and the energy centering at x in a portion of the spectrum extending from

$$\frac{-a}{2} \text{ to } \frac{+a}{2} \quad \text{is} \quad \int_{x-\frac{a}{2}}^{x+\frac{a}{2}} f(x)dx,$$

where a is the width of the receiving strip of the energy-measuring instrument. Let the slit be adjusted so that its image has the width a. Then $f(x)$ is no longer restricted to an infinitesimal part of the spectrum, but is distributed over a width a. If the spectrum is continuous, the intensities of neighboring points overlap. The image of intensity $f(x)$ just covers the strip and heats it, but parts of adjacent images are also heating it at the same time. To ascertain the effects of these, consider a point somewhat close to x, say, $x + v$; the total intensity at the point is $f(x + v)$. Of this energy the fraction $\dfrac{a - v}{a}$ falls on the strip. For all points v lying on one side of x, the energy falling on the strip is

$$\int_0^a \frac{a - v}{a} f(x + v) dv,$$

and for all points v on the other side of x, the energy falling on the strip is

$$\int_0^a \frac{a - v}{a} f(x - v) dv.$$

Hence the total energy warming the receiving strip,

$$F_x = \int_0^a \frac{a - v}{a} [f(x + v) + f(x - v)] dv.$$

The galvanometer deflection when the strip is centered at x will be proportional to F_x. Runge gives the following series for computing $f(x)$ from F_x.

$$a \cdot f(x) = 2 \left\{ \frac{F_x}{2!} - \frac{1}{4!}\Delta^2 F_x + \frac{(2!)^2}{6!}\Delta^4 F_x - \frac{(3!)^2}{8!}\Delta^6 F_x + \right.$$
$$\left. \frac{(4!)^2}{10!}\Delta^8 F_x - + \cdots (-1)^n \frac{(n!)^2}{(2n + 2)!}\Delta^{2n} F_x \cdots \right\} \quad (55)$$

where

$$\Delta^2 F_x = \{F_{x+a} - F_x\} - \{F_x - F_{x-a}\}$$
$$\Delta^4 F_x = \{\Delta^2 F_{x+a} - \Delta^2 F_x\} - \{\Delta^2 F_x - \Delta^2 F_{x-a}\}$$
$$\Delta^{2n} F_x = \{\Delta^{2(n-1)} F_{x+a} - \Delta^{2(n-1)} F_x\} - \{\Delta^{2(n-1)} F_x - \Delta^{2(n-1)} F_{x-a}\}$$

If the values of the energy F_x have been measured at intervals of $x = a$, $\Delta^2 F_x$, etc., can be computed readily by taking successive differences.

If, however, the data have not been taken at these intervals, or if they have been plotted, the following form of the series is handier,

$$af(x) = F_x - \tfrac{1}{6}F_{1(x)} + \tfrac{2}{45}F_{2(x)} - + \cdots \qquad (56)$$

where

$$F_{1(x)} = \frac{F_{(x+a)} + F_{(x-a)}}{2} - F_x$$

$$F_{2(x)} = \frac{F_{1(x+a)} + F_{1(x-a)}}{2} - F_{1(x)}$$

. . . .

TABLE 18.   ILLUSTRATION OF THE COMPUTATIONS TAKEN FROM PASCHEN'S
PAPER[17]

$(a = 7')$

δ observed...............	29° 49, 4′	59, 4	30° 9, 4′	14, 3	19, 3	22, 3	25, 3
$F(\delta)$ observed..............	207, 2	254, 9	314, 8	350, 9	385, 8	398, 0	413, 0
$\dfrac{F(\delta + a) + F(\delta - a)}{2}$	210, 0	257, 8	319, 2	348, 5	378, 8	409, 0	450, 0
$F_1(\delta)$......................	+2, 8	+2, 9	+4, 4	+2, 4	−7, 0	+11, 0	+37, 0
$-\tfrac{1}{6}F_1(\delta)$...................	−0, 4	−0, 5	−0, 7	+0, 4	+1, 2	−1, 8	−6, 2
$\dfrac{F_1(\delta + a) + F_1(\delta - a)}{2}$	+1, 5	+3, 9	+1, 7	+3, 9	+21, 8	+18	+22
$F_2(\delta)$......................	−1, 3	+1, 0	−2, 7	+1, 5	+28, 8	+7	−34, 8
$+\tfrac{2}{45}F_2(\delta)$..................	−0, 1	+0, 1	−0, 1	+0, 1	+1, 5	+0, 3	−1, 5
$af(\delta)$......................	206, 7	254, 5	314, 0	351, 4	388, 5	396, 5	405, 3

The same correction can be made graphically.   Let the curved
line in Fig. 122 represent the
energy curve F_x.   Let x be the
point under discussion.   When
the energy XB was measured,
the edges of the receiving strip
were at $X - A$ and $X + A$.
Draw the chord DC, intersecting
XB at A.   Then $AB = F_1(x)$.
Similarly if $F_1(x)$ be plotted,
$F_2(x)$ can be obtained by an
exactly similar process.

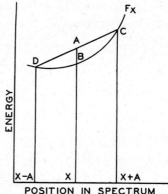

FIG. 122.—Graphical determination
of correction for overlapping.

The effect of this correction is
to deepen the minima of absorption bands and make their sides
somewhat steeper; it may shift
maxima.   With a receiving strip of fixed width, the corrections
are larger for small dispersion.

A similar, but more approximate correction, is given in Preston's "Theory of Heat."[18]   It is based on approximating the
experimental curve near a maximum or minimum by a parabola.

For a maximum draw a chord, the difference of whose abscissas represents the width of the bolometer. Erect the middle ordinate and add to it one-third of the length of the intercept between the curve and the chord.

A second application of the same process would furnish a correction for the width of the slit.

References

1. D. C. Stockbarger and L. Burns, *Jour. Optical Soc. Am.*, **23,** 379 (1933).
2. P. H. van Cittert, *Zeitschr. Physik*, **65,** 547 (1930).
3. Schuster and Nicholson, "Theory of Optics," 3d ed., p. 159.
4. E. C. C. Baly, "Spectroscopy," 3d ed. vol. 1, pp. 65, 152, 170.
5. A. Schuster, *Astrophys. Jour.*, **21,** 197 (1905).
6. F. Benford, *Jour. Optical Soc. Am.*, **26,** 99 (1936).
7. P. H. van Cittert, *Zeitschr. Physik*, **73,** 252 (1931).
8. H. Alterthum and M. Reger, *Das Licht*, **3,** 69 (1933).
9. H. E. Krefft and M. Pirani, *Zeitschr. tech. Physik*, **14,** 400 (1933).
10. F. E. Fowle, *Smithsonian Misc. Coll.*, **68,** No. 8 (1917).
11. McCauley, *Astrophys. Jour.*, **37,** 166 (1913).
12. Randall and Strong, *Rev. Sci. Inst.*, **2,** 587 (1931).
13. L. H. Dawson, L. P. Granath, and E. O. Hulburt, *Phys. Rev.*, **34,** 136 (1929).
14. H. Kreusler, *Ann. Physik*, **6,** 419 (1901).
15. T. Lyman, *Astrophys. Jour.*, **43,** 89 (1916).
16. Kayser, "Handbuch der Spectroscopie," vol. 1, p. 752.
17. *Wied Ann.*, **60,** 712 (1897).
18. Preston, "Theory of Heat," 2d ed., p. 606.

CHAPTER VI

RADIOMETRY

Radiometry is the science of measuring radiant energy. Such measurements fall into different classes, according as (a) the detector is selective or nonselective with respect to radiation of different wavelengths (more precisely, frequencies) and (b) the radiation falling on the detector is a representative sample, (total radiometry) or a selection, with respect to frequency, (spectral radiometry, or spectroradiometry) of the total radiation of the source. Nonselective detectors generally depend for their response upon the heating effect of radiation, so they respond equally well to a given amount of radiant energy regardless of its wavelength. They are, consequently, particularly sensitive to change in temperature of the surroundings. Therefore the shutter and screens, and particularly the last limiting diaphragm, must either be maintained at a constant temperature as by water cooling, or be of high enough heat capacity not to change in temperature significantly between the test and blank readings. It is also essential that in all cases the detector be protected (by well-designed and properly placed screens and diaphragms) from radiation from other sources, or from the source itself by undesired paths. The nonselective type of radiation detector is exemplified by a well-blackened* vane radiometer, radiomicrometer, thermopile, or bolometer.

Among the selective detectors or receivers may be mentioned the human retina, photographic plate, selenium cell, photo e.m.f. cell, and the photoelectric tube. The sensitivity of these selective receivers may vary enormously with the wavelength; therefore they have to be calibrated in terms of a known radiation intensity, at the different wavelength intervals, obtained from the characteristics of the source and the dispersing instrument used, or calibrated by comparison with one of the nonselective receivers. Each type of receiver has its advantage and disadvantage so each in general finds its own sphere of usefulness.

* See p. 210.

In total radiometry, not only must the receiver be nonselective, but any reflecting or transmitting means of directing the radiation, or windows for either the source or receiver, must likewise be nonselective—a condition difficult to satisfy well enough for the purpose at hand, and impossible to satisfy for all possible frequencies of radiation. If windows are necessary, they should be made of quartz or other material of high transmission for the range of frequencies studied (see section on prism materials),* or blown from glass or vitreous silica to a thickness of 20 to 50μ.

Measurements of the total radiation from a source with a sufficiently selective receiver would correspond to measurements made at the appropriate frequency with a receiver of any sort, but most selective receivers have a selectivity less pronounced than this. The indications of moderately selective receivers are comparable among themselves and, in the case of the human eye, additive at intensities sufficiently high, or sufficiently low, to avoid the Purkinje effect, but are not comparable with the indications of a nonselective receiver, or of a differently selective receiver. The addition theorem for photographic effectiveness is somewhat more complicated.[1]

For analyzed radiation and a nonselective receiver, a single absolute calibration of the receiver in units of energy, or power, is needed. With a selective receiver a point-by-point calibration is needed. This may be made either by direct comparison with a nonselective receiver, or by using a previously calibrated comparison source. This latter method—that of the spectrophotometer—has the advantage that any error due to the selective transmission of the instrument is avoided.

Beams of radiation analyzed by reflection, transmission, or optical rotation are uniform in spectral quality, so that the effective position of the receiver is not critical, so long as it is wholly in the beam, or the beam wholly in the receiver. In analysis by refraction or diffraction, the effective position of the receiver in the resulting more or less impure spectrum formed at the focal "plane" of the telescope lens determines the effective frequency. In the photographic method a considerable region of the spectrum is allowed to fall on the plate, and the effective frequency prescribed by the region of the plate whose optical density (after development, etc.) is measured. When it is neces-

---

* See page 92.

sary to use a spectrometer for analysis, there are some precautions necessary which are outlined in Chap. V.

Sometimes one of the nonselective measuring devices, *i.e.*, a bolometer or thermopile, is made of such dimensions that it may be used in the place of the telescope slit of the dispersing device. However, most workers in the field prefer to place the detecting device just back of the slit. This in general is necessary for the nonselective receivers since it is not easy to make them of definite dimensions. The sensitivity of modern detecting devices with their galvanometers and amplifying systems is such that measurements can now be made using narrower slits than formerly. This makes it possible to avoid in part the troublesome corrections for overlapping of energy of different wavelengths. Of course, such corrections are always in order, but by using a narrower slit the error due to this correction can be reduced until it is of the order of other errors in this kind of work. When such narrow slits are used, care should be taken to make observations close enough together to obtain a fair representative value of the distribution of energy from the source that is studied. Several of the standard methods for measuring radiation, with both nonselective and selective receivers, will now be described.

THERMOPILE CONSTRUCTION AND USE

W. W. COBLENTZ*

One of the earliest devices used in measuring radiant energy was the thermopile. The Melloni thermopile, in use almost a century ago, consisted of blocks of bismuth and antimony, which, in spite of the large heat capacity, rendered good service in the type of investigations in progress at that time.

With the general advance in physical science, demands arose for a radiometer having a quick action in attaining temperature equilibrium. A thermopile of this type was made by Rubens[2] who used fine wires of iron and constantan, with junctions of hard solder, which were hammered flat for receivers. Paschen[3] produced a quick-acting thermopile of iron-constantan by rolling the thermocouple wires thin, after soldering the junctions. Moll's surface thermopile[4] made of thin sheets of copper-con-

* *Chief, Radiometry Section, National Bureau of Standards.*

stantan had the defect that the "cold junctions" were soldered to relatively heavy posts.

Theory. The first real advance in the art of thermopile construction began about 1910 when fine pliable bismuth wire became available commercially.

About this time two important theoretical papers were published; one by Altenkirch[5] relating to thermopiles for use as thermoelectric generators to replace the dynamo, and the other by Johansen[6] relating to thermopiles for measuring radiant energy. Later, Firestone[7] discussed thermopile design and suggested improvements in construction.

Johansen's conclusions, which do not differ radically from those of Altenkirch, are that (1) the galvanometer resistance should be equal to the resistance of the thermo-elements; (2) the radii of the two wires of the thermo-element should be so chosen that the ratio between the heat conductivity and the electrical resistance is the same in both; (3) the heat loss by conduction through the wires must equal the heat loss by radiation from the junctions (a question that can be answered only by direct experiment with the material to be used); and (4) the radiation sensitivity is proportional to the square root of the exposed surface. In his experimental instrument, the "cold" (unexposed) junctions are joined directly to the binding posts. This is likely to cause a "drift" of the zero reading, owing to the fact that the air is warmed by the incident radiation and the "cold" junction cannot quickly assume the temperature of the surrounding air. In a subsequent paper he recognized this defect and gave a symmetrical design with circular receivers as used in the Rubens thermopile.

Materials for Thermocouples. Some years ago a commercial thermopile made of fine iron and constantan wires was tried.[8] The iron wire being short-lived, experiments were begun in the construction of thermocouples, for radiomicrometers and thermopiles, by using narrow pliable bismuth strips, cut from wider plates and "wires" made by dropping the molten metal from a height upon a sloping surface of plate glass.

The advent of fine bismuth wire (diameters 0.025 to 0.15 mm) solved this problem. Experimental tests[8] showed that thermocouples made of Bi wires 0.15 mm in diameter (even when pressed flat between glass plates) are slow in attaining temperature equilibrium, whereas a thermocouple made of Bi wire 0.1 mm in diameter was satisfactory in that respect and yet was sufficiently strong to withstand shipment as a commercial instrument.

The silver wire (diameter 0.035 to 0.04 mm) was selected because it reduces the resistance of the thermopile; and because it is easily annealed and rendered bright by heating on a thin sheet-iron plate. In the completed thermopile these wires are protected from corrosion by means of a thin coat of shellac. Such thermopiles (in air) have been in use for 15 years or longer without corrosion of the silver wire.

Thin sheets of pure tin (thickness 0.18 to 0.20 mm), such as are used in telephone condensers, can be readily cut into the sizes desired for continuous-surface linear-thermopile receivers by means of a dividing engine and can be easily rubbed bright and clean on a pad of paper. Moreover, the use of tin for a receiver seems to be advantageous since tin alloys readily with the bismuth wire and makes a better contact than a receiver of pure silver. The optimum size of such a receiver is about 2 by 2 mm,[9] under which conditions the difference between the thermal conductivity of a receiver of tin and of silver seemed inappreciable. Single long receivers are used in spectroradiometry.[6,10]

By coating the overlapping edges of the individual receivers with a thin layer of an alcoholic solution of shellac, for electrical insulation, no difficulty is experienced in assembling a linear thermopile having a continuous surface, produced by overlapping the edges of the receivers of the individual thermocouples. In this manner linear thermopiles are produced that permit accurate calibration in absolute value, against a standard of radiation.[11]

A strong thermocouple of bismuth can be made by using pure tin as a solder, instead of the low-melting alloys ("Wood's" or "Gray's" alloy), which already contain bismuth, and become more brittle in combining with the bismuth wire. By attaching a globule of pure tin (0.05 mm) to the end of the silver wire and then bringing the end of the bismuth wire in contact with the globule of tin and applying heat, the two combine into an alloy which readily adheres to the tin receiver. By using untarnished silver wires tipped with globules of tin, no soldering fluid or rosin is required in making the thermojunctions, and hence there is no possibility of occlusion of acids to cause corrosion.

Construction and Use of Thermopiles. Figure 123 shows a satisfactory device for soldering the thermojunctions. This consists of a wire of nichrome (or iron) bent into a V-shape, the rounded end of which is hammered thin (over a length of about 15 mm) and filed smooth, providing a heating area 1 to 2 mm wide, as desired. By keeping this heated area bright and polished, the temperature is easily controlled, no molten metal adheres to it, and there is no danger of injury to the thermo-junction during the soldering process.

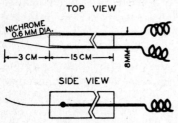

Fig. 123.—Electric heater for soldering thermocouples.

The temperature of this soldering device is easily controlled by a rheostat and should be somewhat higher for attaching the tin to the silver wire than for making the bismuth-silver junction. The latter is best made by touching the silver wire near the tinned end.

All work of this type is done under a reading glass with the fine wires, etc., resting upon a pad of clean white paper. The silver wires (length 10 to 15 mm as required) are lifted with flexible brass tweezers (kept for this purpose), the tips of which are polished and accurately matched.

The bismuth wires, cut in suitable lengths and pressed flat between pieces of plate glass, are lifted by means of a rounded wooden toothpick, the end of which is cut thin and pliable to prevent injury to the bismuth wire.

The tin is attached to the silver wire by stroking the molten material into an oblong bead, the most of which is cut off after solidifying, leaving a cone-shaped mass with a flat base which is brought end to end with the bismuth wire to form the junction. To accomplish this, the silver wire is held in place by means of a small brass weight, the end of the bismuth wire is held (by means of the wooden toothpick) in contact with the tin bead which is then touched with the heating device. By means of the toothpick the tin receiver is then pushed under the junction which is then touched with the heater. In Fig. 124 are shown two thermocouples constructed in this manner.

The underside of the part of the receiver that is to overlap is covered with shellac. The finished thermocouples are then assembled upon a cardboard template, which is covered with a thin layer of glue to secure the elements, during the process of mounting upon the support, illustrated in Fig. 124. After the elements have been mounted upon the template, the rear side of the central line of "hot" junctions is touched with alcohol or a weak alcoholic solution of shellac to cause them to adhere. After the thermocouples have been attached to the mounting, the template is removed by immersion in warm water which dissolves the glue.

For measuring stellar radiation, and planetary radiation from different portions of the disk of Mars, some of the thermocouple

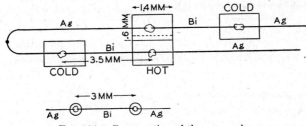

Fig. 124.—Construction of thermocouple.

receivers were only 0.12 mm in diameter. They were made by attaching a fine globule of pure tin to a thin (0.01 mm) platinum wire, pressing it to the desired diameter between small sheets of plate glass, placing over this receiver the end of a fine bismuth wire (0.025 mm pressed flat), covering both with a thin lamina of mica, and touching it momentarily with the herein described heater. Such a thermocouple is illustrated diagrammatically in the lower part of Fig. 124.

Thermopiles of alloys of Bi-Sb and Bi-Sn have been tried, but owing to brittleness and great heat capacity, they have not come into general use.

Linear Thermopiles. Another type of linear thermopile which has proved very satisfactory is made of 1.5 mil (0.037 mm) copper wire, and of No. 38 or No. 40, B. S. gage "Advance" (constantan) wire, which is rolled and hammered to 0.01 mm (or less) in thickness.

The tips of the copper wires are dipped into a drop of dilute zinc chloride solution (on a glass plate) and then covered with a thin coat of a good quality tinner's solder. The solder-covered tip of the wire is again moistened with soldering solution, and the end of the Advance (constantan) ribbon is laid over it and touched with the heater (Fig. 123). After this, the tin receiver is pushed under the junction which is then touched lightly with the heater, forming a good soldered junction of low heat capacity and quick response. The acid is removed by washing in water.

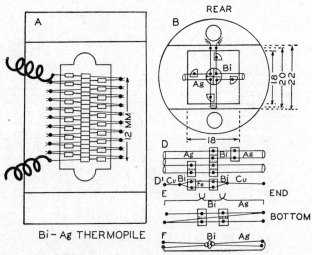

Fig. 125.—Various forms of thermopiles.

Surface Thermopiles. Surface thermopiles made of three rows of linear thermopiles have also been made[9,12] and used in several problems. They are, of course, more difficult to construct than the Moll type in which both the "hot" and the "cold" junctions (the latter on heavy metal supports) are exposed to radiation.

Special Thermocouples and Thermopiles. Numerous forms of thermocouples and thermopiles for special problems under investigation have been constructed during the past two decades. They include the circular receiver *B*, applicable to many problems; the U-shaped, trough-like receiver *E*, for use in a biological problem (production of heat by nerve); and a thermopile *F*, of two elements, for the eyepiece of a polarization photometer—

all illustrated in Fig. 125.   Among other forms are the portable
vacuum thermopile for measuring the solar corona[13] and the
absolute thermopile for evaluating the Stefan-Boltzmann
constant.[14]

Vacuum Thermopiles.   Attention may be called also to the
portable vacuum thermopile (Figs. 126 and 127, rear view),
which has been in service for a long while.   The degree of evacua-

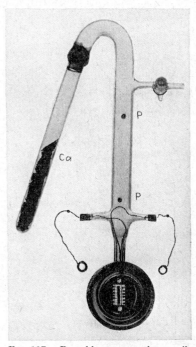

FIG.   126.—Vacuum
mounting   for   thermo-
piles.

FIG. 127.—Portable vacuum thermopile
(rear view).

tion is tested by means of the potential terminals P, shown in
Fig. 127.

The method of maintaining a vacuum by means of metallic
calcium[12] contained in a quartz-glass test tube is the simple
procedure that has made it possible to transport vacuum thermopiles to the remotest stations (*e.g.*, the eclipse station at
Benkoelen, Sumatra).

Summary.   From the foregoing brief description, it may be
seen that the thermopile is both an old and also a very recent

development for measuring radiant energy, competing with the bolometer in sensitivity and applicability, and indeed, functioning successfully in problems (*e.g.*, the measurement of the radiation from different parts of the disk image of the planet Mars), to which other radiometers are not readily, if at all, adaptable.

THE VANE RADIOMETER

B. J. SPENCE *

The history of the radiometer effect dates back, perhaps, to the time of Fresnel when he observed the repulsion of a small

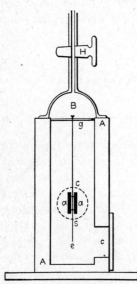

body subjected to a beam of light. Later Sir William Crookes[15] undertook a study of the phenomenon and this led to the construction of the vane type of radiometer such as is commonly seen in the optician's window.

Toward the end of the last century, there was considerable activity in attempts to measure the pressure of electromagnetic radiation and to study the various aspects of the infrared spectrum. It was during this period that E. F. Nichols[16] developed the vane radiometer to a point where it became a reliable instrument in the study of infrared radiation.

Nichols Radiometer. The following is a brief description of the Nichols radiometer as shown in Fig. 128. The outer case consisted of a bronze cylinder

FIG. 128.—Diagram of Nichols vane radiometer.

bored to within a few millimeters of the bottom. A glass cover *B* fitted with a stopcock was ground to fit the top of the case. The suspended vane system consisted of two mica vanes *a* and *a* held together by small glass rods and the whole fastened to a vertical glass staff *s*. At the bottom end of the staff was a small mirror. This system with a mass of a few milligrams was hung from a glass strip placed across the top of the case. The bronze case was provided with two openings for windows: that indicated

* *Professor of Physics, Northwestern University.*

by the dotted circle was covered with a fluorite plate and that at c was covered with a glass plate to admit light for the illumination of the small mirror. The assembly was then pumped out to a pressure of about 0.02 mm Hg.

Radiation was allowed to fall on one vane only while the other was shielded and served as a compensator for stray radiation. Nichols found with this instrument that the radiation from a candle at a distance of 6 m gave a deflection of the vane system of 60 mm as registered on a scale at a distance of 1.3 m from the instrument. He claimed for the instrument freedom from electric and magnetic disturbances, and from air currents, and felt that it could better compensate for stray radiation than the bolometer. With an instrument of this type Nichols carried out many researches in infrared spectrum analysis.

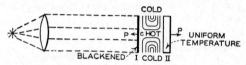

Fig. 129.—Diagram showing action of Nichols vane radiometer.

The action of the radiometer of the Nichols type appears to be explained by the theory of Hettner and Czerny,[17] as indicated in Fig. 129. The blackened vane is subjected to radiation from a given source. In front of the vane is a plate P (the radiometer window) kept at uniform temperature. Gas currents flow along both surfaces from the edge to the center opposite to the temperature gradients in the plate and build up a pressure repelling the vane. Marsh[18] has made quantitative measurements for such blackened radiometer vanes which are in agreement with the theory of Hettner and Czerny.

Modified Forms of the Nichols Radiometer. Almost all successful forms of vane radiometer in use today for radiation measurements are modifications of the Nichols radiometer. These modifications consist usually in vane construction leading to lower moment of inertia, shorter period, and higher sensitivity. The earliest and best known of these modifications is that of Coblentz.[19] In comparing the effect of sensitivity with the area Coblentz found that as the width of the exposed portion of the vane increased from 0.3 to 1.3 mm at pressures of 0.02 and 0.04 mm Hg there was a linear increase in the sensitivity.

The most sensitive of his instruments had a period of 150 sec. and gave a deflection of 71 mm/mm² of exposed surface, the source being a candle at a distance of 1 m, and the scale at a distance of 1 m.

About 15 years after the work of Coblentz, Tear[20] developed a type of vane radiometer of unique construction. The chief

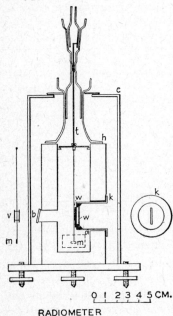

departure was in the design of the suspended system whose vanes were of pearled mica. The mica was pearled, after cutting it to the desired dimensions, by placing it between heavy plates and heating it to redness. In this manner innumerable cleavage planes were developed which lowered the thermal conductivity of the mica. The following is a description of a typical suspended system. A vane of pearled mica 1.5 by 0.1 mm was placed in front of a shield of mica 1.5 by 0.3 mm and separated from it by a distance of 0.05 mm. Two such sets of vane and shield were fastened together by means of a crossarm of fine quartz rod to the middle point of which was fastened an axial quartz rod

RADIOMETER

Fig. 130.—Vane radiometer constructed by Coblentz.

carrying a mirror for purposes of observation. This system was suspended by a quartz fiber in a double-walled chamber with suitable windows, and the pressure lowered (that is somewhere between 0.02 and 0.03 mm Hg) to give the maximum sensitivity.

Tear studied the two very important points in connection with radiometer construction, *viz.*, the effect of vane width and the effect of the lever arm of the system. With regard to the vane width he constructed two suspension systems to one of which was fastened in turn a series of vanes without breaking the quartz fiber keeping the dimensions of the shield and also the distance between shield and vane constant. To the other system was fastened a vane without the shield present.

With his system he found roughly a fourfold increase in sensitivity per unit area of vane surface as the result of the shields. He found also that the relative sensitivity per unit area remained practically constant as the width of the vane increased, and that the deflection of the system was proportional to the width of the vane. The following table is taken from the paper by Tear:

TABLE 19.—VANE RADIOMETER SENSITIVITY

Vane, mm	Shield, mm	Deflection, mm	Relative sensitivity per unit area
1.0 × 0.1	None	6	60
1.0 × 0.3	None	18	60
1.0 × 0.5	None	28	56
1.5 × 0.002	1.5 × 0.3	0.5	250
1.5 × 0.1	1.5 × 0.3	32.5	216
1.5 × 0.2	1.5 × 0.3	68	226
1.5 × 0.3	1.5 × 0.3	100	222

With regard to the lever arm, Tear found, as a matter of practice, that the choice of the distance of the vane away from the axis of rotation depended almost wholly upon the damping of the system. When the distance of the vane from the axis was 3 mm or better, the mechanical stability became good at the expense of the sensitivity. For the vane having dimensions 0.5 × 1.5 mm, a distance between 1 and 2 mm was satisfactory.

In 1926, Sandvik[21] described a sensitive vane radiometer of very simple design. The vane system was enclosed in a thick-walled steel chamber with the necessary windows for observation and for entrance of radiation. The system was suspended from a tapered-steel plug ground to fit into the top of the chamber and which could be sealed with mercury. In the use of such a plug a zero adjustment of the instrument could be made and the system could be removed quite readily if desired.

The novel feature of the construction lies in the vane system. The vanes were made of aluminum leaf about 4.5μ thick cut into narrow strips 50 mm long and ranging in width from 0.15 to 0.4 mm. These strips were laid flat on a brass plate, fastened down with shellac, and then blackened with camphor soot. A pair of strips was then selected, and their ends fastened to two parallel capillary tubes about 25 mm apart. After placing them about 3 mm apart with their blackened faces downward, very fine capillary tubes about 3 mm long were laid across the vanes about 15 mm apart and fastened to the vanes by means of a trace of dilute shellac. A straight, very fine glass capillary was fastened to the mid-point of the crosspieces and parallel to the vanes. The system was completed by the addition of a mirror about 1 mm² at the end of the glass staff.

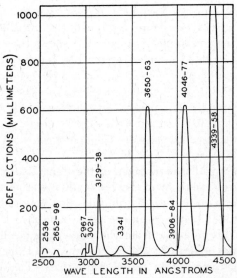

Fig. 131.—Results of measuring intensity of mercury lines with vane radiometer.

Sandvik described one of his systems as having a mass of 1.63 mg with approximately 80 per cent of the total mass of the system in the glass staff which contributed practically nothing to the moment of inertia of the system. The assembled system was suspended by means of a very fine quartz fiber in the steel chamber and then pumped out to a pressure close to 0.02 mm Hg.

Sandvik includes in his papers data on the sensitivity relative to the intensity of radiation from a standard Hefner lamp. For example, he cites the performance of one of his radiometers as giving in 2 min. its maximum deflection of 15,000 mm/mm² of exposed vane surface for the Hefner lamp at a distance of 1 m and scale at 1 m. The author has sought a material less difficult to handle than aluminum leaf and one of considerably less thermal conductivity in order to develop a larger temperature gradient between front and back surface. A very thin but high grade paper was finally used and essentially the same mode of construction of the vane was employed as that used by Sandvik. The radiometer is otherwise identical with that of Sandvik. Recently it was found that the radiometer of this type could be used for measurements in the ultraviolet down to a wavelength of approximately 2500A. The radiation from a quartz mercury arc carrying 4 amp. of current was sent through a Gaertner single-prism quartz monochromator and the intensities of the various radiations examined. Figure 131 shows the results.

Abbot[22] constructed a radiometer using vanes of house flies' wings. A very light system of vanes of 0.4 by 1.0 mm weighing only 0.95 mg resulted. This was mounted in hydrogen in order to reduce damping. The period of the swing was about 12 sec. Some trouble was experienced with electrostatic charges but the instrument was used to measure the spectrum of a number of stars.

Advantages and Disadvantages of the Vane Radiometer. In summing up the behavior of the vane radiometer as a device for studying spectral intensity distribution, one may list its disadvantages and its advantages in use.

It is comparatively free from the customary mechanical disturbances in the laboratory which make the use of the thermopile galvanometer combination quite impossible. The use of the compensating vane makes for freedom from drift and for zero stabilization. There is no necessity for the use of a slit before the radiometer because the vane can be made as narrow as desired: for most purposes a vane width of 0.2 mm is sufficiently narrow for the use to which the instrument is usually put. The use of a slit may lead to trouble owing to the heating of the jaws and reradiation to the vanes. In regard to sensitivity, almost any desired sensitivity may be obtained providing an aperiodic deflection of long time is not detrimental in the use to which the instrument is put. When, however, the sensitivity is pushed to extremes for a given system, the zero becomes unstable. The problem of design resolves itself in the last analysis into designing a system with small enough moment of inertia to bring the

period within the desired range and with a long enough torque
arm to give the desired sensitivity.

The vane radiometer has the disadvantage over the galvanometer used in conjunction with either the bolometer or thermopile
in that its period is long. It is furthermore not so portable as
other types of radiation measuring instruments, but with care
it can be transported about a laboratory without breaking the
quartz fiber.

The vane radiometer has recently been used as a measuring
instrument in the determination of energy of radiation in absolute
units. It was first used in the problem on the photoelectric
properties of pure and gas-contaminated magnesium to measure
the energy from a Hilger monochromator in the range from 4000
to 7000A.[23]

Later,[24] it was used in the determination of the temperature
coefficients of the work function of the alkaline earths. Here
it was necessary to determine the spectral-energy distribution
with the radiometer of high sensitivity. The following procedure was resorted to: Light from a 70-watt linear tungsten
filament was resolved by means of a van Cittert glass-prism double monochromator whose three slits were set at approximately
0.2 mm. The wavelength band at 4000A was 8A wide. The
exit radiation was focused by means of a short focused lens on
the vane of the radiometer. The interception of the radiation by
the vane was checked by a microscope mounted behind the vane.
In a typical case the radiometer sensitivity was 4.6×10^{-9}
watt/mm at a meter-scale distance. The area of the vane was
0.0502 cm.[2] The error made in the energy measurements of
the resolved light was estimated to be less than 1 per cent.

The Radiomicrometer. The radiomicrometer is essentially a
moving-coil galvanometer of the d'Arsonval type, the coil consisting of a single loop and a thermojunction at the bottom.
The instrument appears to have been invented by d'Arsonval[25]
and by Boys[26] for radiation measurements on moon and stars.
d'Arsonval used a loop one-half of which was palladium and the
other half was of silver. Boys used a bismuth-silver junction
soldered to a loop of copper. Boys overestimated the sensitivity
of his instruments as has been indicated by later observations.
Nichols (*loc. cit.*) found that his vane radiometer was about
twelve times as sensitive as the radiomicrometer. It gave a

deflection of 1 cm/mm² of exposed vane for a candle and scale both at a distance of 1 m from the vane.

Paschen[27] improved the instrument in an attempt to map the distribution of intensity of the blackbody. The following-(Fig. 132) is a brief description of the instrument as modified by Paschen.

Two alloys were prepared, one of bismuth and antimony in the ratio of 10:1, and the other of equal parts of cadmium and

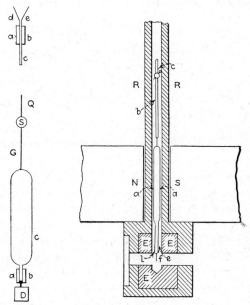

Fig. 132.—Paschen radiomicrometer.

antimony.   A strip 0.3 by 0.5 by 5 mm was made from each of the alloys.   One of each of these (*a* and *b*) is soldered to each end of a silver band 0.5 mm wide and 0.03 mm thick and sufficiently long to make the galvanometer loop.   The loop was formed and the strips of alloy soldered together to form a thermojunction just above *D*, the damping vane of thin mica.   A very thin glass rod *G* is fastened to the upper end of the loop and carries a mirror *S*.   The whole ensemble was supported by a fine quartz fiber.   The thermocouple was suspended in an iron block *E*, which in turn was enclosed in a copper block.   A hole was drilled in the blocks to admit radiation.   The silver loop was hung inside of a copper tube R which had a window for illumination of the mirror. Powerful magnetic pole pieces were placed up against the copper tubing, but it was soon found that there was an optimum field strength for a particular instrument which gave the highest sensitivity. Traces of diamagnetic and paramagnetic substances led to difficulties and Paschen was never able to make the moving part free from magnetic effects, and at best he could obtain only about three times the sensitivity of the Boys radiomicrometer.

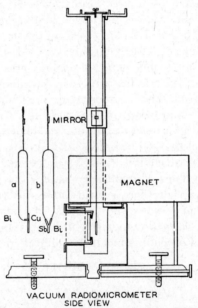

VACUUM RADIOMICROMETER
SIDE VIEW
Fig. 133.—Coblentz vacuum radiomicrometer.

Later Coblentz[28] undertook the construction of a vacuum radiomicrometer-radiometer with better success. The instrument (Fig. 133) merits a brief description. The thermocouple consisted of either a bismuth-copper or antimony-copper combination. The dimensions of the components of each were about 3.5 by 0.2 by 0.1 mm. The loop was of No. 40 copper wire about 4.5 cm long, blackened with copper oxide. The magnet was without pole pieces since they carried too much damping. The metal case of the instrument was made of Swedish iron and the vertical tube housing the system was of brass. As a vane radiometer the time required for maximum deflection was about 25 sec., and the sensitivity was roughly 4 cm/mm² of exposed vane for a candle and scale distant 1 m; used as a radiomicrometer the period was about 8 sec. with a sensitivity a little better than when used as a radiometer.   Coblentz states that the combination of the two was no better than the radiomicrometer owing simply to the fact that the periods were different and the magnetic moment of the radiomicrometer masked the radiometer effect.   Figure 133 indicates the type of construction of the loop when the instrument is used primarily as a radiomicrometer. When the instrument was assembled and the pressure reduced the period dropped from 25 to 14 sec. and the sensitivity increased from a deflection of 3.6 cm/mm² of exposed surface for candle and scale at 1 m, to 6 cm/mm² of exposed area.

Coblentz remarks that his purpose in describing the instrument is not so much to show its sensitivity as to show directions in which further improvements are possible.   Curiously enough very little has been done to improve radiomicrometer construction since Coblentz's publication.   By the use of metals which can now be obtained free from magnetic materials, the construction of systems of small mass, and a better knowledge of galvanometer design, there is little reason why the radiomicrometer should not become a more useful instrument.   In the present form of its development it is not equal to the vane radiometer and probably much more difficult to control.

THE BOLOMETER

L. B. ALDRICH[*]

The bolometer was devised by Langley[29] in 1880.   It consists of two nearly identical, very thin strips of metal, usually platinum, which form two arms of a Wheatstone bridge.   The strips are blackened on one side.   One strip is hidden and the other is exposed to the radiation which it is desired to measure.   These strips may be wide or narrow, depending upon the width of slit used and the purity of spectrum desired.   The radiation absorbed by the blackened strip increases the temperature of the strip.   This changes its electrical resistance and destroys the balance of the bridge so that a deflection of the galvanometer results.   The shape of the absorbing surface

* *Assistant Director of Astrophysical Observatory, Smithsonian Institution.*

of the bolometer, the narrow strip similar to a slit image, is decidedly favorable for spectroradiometry.

In early work the bolometer was difficult to manipulate because of very large uncontrolled drift of the galvanometer spot. Many improvements, mainly introduced by Abbot, have now made the bolometer a docile and easily handled instrument. One improvement—placing the bolometer strips inside a glass enclosure which is evacuated to less than 0.001 mm pressure—produced nearly tenfold increase in sensitiveness. A type of vacuum bolometer used in recent years by the Smithsonian Astrophysical Observatory is described below (Fig. 134).

Construction of Bolometer. *A* is a general view of the bolometer within its mounting, shown in section. *B* is a longitudinal cross section of the copper bolometer frame. *C* is the end view of this frame looking from above. *a* is a glass flask. Its side tubes *t* and *t'* end in optically figured glass plates. At *b* are sealed in three platinum wires (one not shown in the figure) to make electrical connections to the bolometer. A copper piece *c* was constructed having upon it the two electrically insulated pieces *d*, *d'*, and having slots e^1, e^2, e^3, to allow the piece *c* to be shoved down the neck of the flask, *a*, past the platinum wires *b*. The piece *c* has both a longitudinal round hole and a transverse rectangular hole *g*, 16 by 10 mm. The two bolometer strips are soldered across the rectangular hole *g* so as to expose lengths of 16 mm each. The upper ends of the bolometer strips are attached to the insulated pieces *d*, *d'*. Thus when the whole copper piece *c* is slid into the neck of the flask past the three platinum wires *b*, it can be rotated slightly so that the wires can be soldered to the piece *c* and to the two insulated parts of it, *d* and *d'*, and so be in proper connection with the bolometer

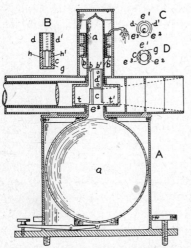

Fig. 134.—Smithsonian vacuum bolometer.

strips h and h'. This soldering is done by reaching the soldering iron down the neck of the flask, being careful not to overheat and break the glass. While soldering, the copper block is held in place by a special long-handled clamp which is inserted through the longitudinal hole in c and removed after soldering is completed.

The bolometer strips h and h' are made from platinum wire 0.025 mm in diameter, hammered out to a width of 0.12 mm. The resistance of each strip 16 mm long is very close to 3 ohms. Slipped over the neck of the flask is a wooden spool upon which are wound two coils of silk-covered manganin wire of 54 ohms each, to form the remaining two arms of the Wheatstone bridge. After connecting up the bridge (see the bolometer-circuit diagram, Fig. 135), the length of one of these coils is adjusted until the bridge balances when a shunt of about 7,000 ohms is connected around one or the other of the coils. The neck of the flask is now drawn down and sealed off,

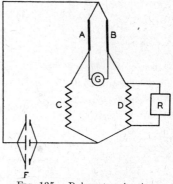

Fig. 135.—Bolometer circuit.

after having been evacuated and warmed repeatedly for several days with drying material in close proximity. The vacuum is as high as can be obtained with a mercury-vapor pump, certainly 0.0001 mm or less.

The instrument as mounted in the brass case has provision for examining the spectrum by means of an eyepiece. The spectrum is admitted through a vestibule with screens to reduce stray radiation. A battery of three storage cells in parallel is applied directly, giving a total current of 0.07 amp., or 0.035 amp. through each bolometer strip. A discussion of the theory of the vacuum bolometer is given in the *Annals of the Astrophysical Observatory.*[30]

Bolometer Technique. To prepare platinum wire for strips, a piece long enough for both strips is held as straight as possible between steel flats and hammered out to the desired width. For very thin strips of high-resistance, silver-coated Wollaston wire may be used and the silver removed with nitric acid after the wire is hammered out.   Strips should not be less than five times as wide as they are thick.   They are soldered in place with ordinary solder and rosin as a flux.   In soldering, the strip should be kept straight but not too taut or it will break with change of temperature.   The resistances of the two strips should be equal within less than 1 per cent.   After being soldered in place they are blackened on one side only.   The other two arms of the bridge are coils of manganin wire, non-inductively wound and placed as close to the strips as may be.   The current should be sufficient to raise the strip temperature as much as 50°C above the surrounding temperature, as roughly determined by computation.   Too large a current must be avoided, otherwise the strips will be injured or the blacking burned off.   Always apply the current as shown in the diagram so that it divides, part going through each strip.   A shunt resistance between 3,000 and 10,000 ohms is convenient to use.   The size of shunt necessary to balance is easily altered by a slight change in the length of either manganin coil.   To minimize galvanometer drift, mount the bolometer in a nearly constant temperature chamber, wrapping in cotton the battery and galvanometer leads and even the bolometer case.   The current circuit should be closed at least 1 hr. before using the bolometer.   A well-constructed bolometer once balanced remains so day after day with no change in shunt needed other than a very small change to set the galvanometer spot where desired.

THE BLACKENING OF RADIOMETERS

A. H. Pfund*

Most radiometers are made of selective materials so it is necessary to black their receiving surfaces, *i.e.*, to give them a coating of some nonselective material, if they are to absorb and thereby measure the radiation that falls upon them.   The ideal conditions imposed on the black coating for radiometers are as follows:

1. The coating must absorb all incident radiations completely.
2. The thermal capacity must be negligible.
3. The heat conductivity must be high.
4. The act of applying the coating must not subject the thermopile, etc., to the danger of breakage.

* *Professor of Physics, Johns Hopkins University.*

While it is not possible to fulfill these conditions simultane-ously to an ideal degree, it is possible to reach a very fair approxi-mation provided the spectral range to be covered is not too great.

Soot as a Blackener.   In the earliest experiments on radiom-etry, the radiation-absorbing surfaces were coated with soot from a candle flame.   Later on, soot from burning camphor or acetylene was used for the same purpose.   While it has long been known that soot becomes increasingly transparent with increasing wavelength, the use of soot persists to this day.   To

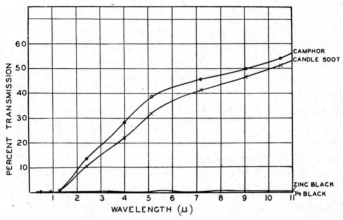

Fig. 136.—Transmission of materials used for blackening radiation receivers.

test anew the effectiveness of soot as an absorber, a polished plate of rock salt was coated over half of its area with the soot from a burning candle—the film thickness being such that the filament of a 100-watt tungsten lamp (with a clear bulb) could just barely be recognized.*   Transmission measurements were then carried out with an infrared spectrometer and the experi-ment was repeated for camphor soot.   The results, presented in Fig. 136 show that but for the fact that the film of camphor soot was slightly the thinner, the two curves are essentially the same. At 11μ the transmission exceeds 50 per cent† and, according to

---

* Thicker films applied to thermopiles or bolometers cause increasing sluggishness of response.

† While it is true that the absorbing film on actual receivers is twice trav-ersed by the incident radiation, it is evident that any film yielding a (single) transmission of more than 10 per cent must be considered unsatisfactory.

Rubens and his coworkers, the transparency is virtually complete at 50μ and beyond.

Fine Metallic Powders as Blackeners. The behavior of metallic blacks is strikingly different. Some platinum black, so coarse as to appear grayish black, was mulled with butyl alcohol containing a few per cent of linseed oil (serving as a "binder"); the resultant paste was spread uniformly over a polished plate of rock salt and the butyl alcohol was allowed to evaporate. Even though the lamp filament could be seen distinctly, the transmission for this material never became as large as 1 per cent. Similar results were obtained with distilled films of zinc black. It may therefore be stated that if an absorbing film in thin layers appears brownish or reddish, it will become increasingly transparent to greater wavelengths. If, on the other hand, the transmission is nonselective (grayish), it is highly probable that the absorption in the infrared will likewise be nonselective. The reflection factor of any of these substances, candle soot, camphor soot, platinum black, or zinc black is very small for normal incidence, being much less than 1 per cent.

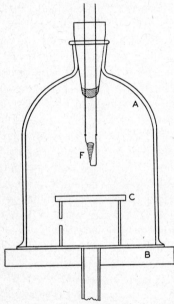

Fig. 137.—Apparatus for blackening receivers with metal powders.

It has been found that in the interval extending from the ultraviolet to beyond 14μ a coating of zinc black[31] will absorb 98 per cent of the incident radiation.

Methods of Applying Metallic Powders. The apparatus used for the deposition of such coatings is shown in Fig. 137. Here, A is a bell jar resting on a cast-iron base plate B which is connected to an oil pump. A tapered glass tube is ground to fit snugly into the neck of the bell jar. A pair of heavy leads is sealed into the lower end of this glass tube and a conical spiral of tungsten wire (0.18 mm diameter) is attached at F. A bit of the metal to be distilled (1 mm³) is dropped into the spiral, the latter having been previously oxidized in a gas flame to avoid short-circuiting by the fragment of metal.   Pure zinc is unsatisfactory since it is liable to "explode" and disappear from the spiral before a satisfactory coating has been deposited.   More satisfactory is an alloy of four parts of zinc to one part of antimony. The thermopile is laid on a metal plate C about 2 cm away from the spiral and the air pressure in the bell jar is reduced to about 3 mm.   If the tungsten filament is raised to yellow heat, the distillation is complete in about 1 min.   The color of the coating on the walls of the bell jar (seen in transmitted light) ought to be bluish gray.   If the film appears reddish brown, the particles are too fine.   An increase in the temperature of the tungsten filament as well as an increase in gas pressure tends to increase the particle size.   If, after the first distillation the film is too thin, the process is to be repeated until the image of a tungsten lamp cannot be seen through the bell jar.   As a result of this procedure an intensely black film ought to result.   Such a film will absorb 98 per cent of the incident radiations out to 14μ. Even at 51μ the absorption is 85 per cent.

Blackening for the Extreme Infrared.   While nonselectivity is desirable in most cases, the situation is different in case long heat waves ($\lambda > 50\mu$) are to be studied.   Owing to the weakness of these radiations in comparison with those of shorter wavelength, it is desirable to have a selective receiver which will absorb the radiations of great wavelength and ignore those of shorter wavelength.   It has been found[32] that powders of quartz, calcite, etc., become intensely black within the regions of selective absorption in the infrared if the particle size is small in comparison with the wavelength.   If then, the receiver is coated with a film consisting of a mixture of $NaCl$, KBr, and $TlCl$ (distilled as before, at a pressure of 3 mm), the desired condition for selectivity will have been attained.   These films are rather fluffy and therefore of poor heat conductivity, a condition favorable to the (Nichols) radiometer but unfavorable to the thermopile.

The following quotation, relative to the blackening of receivers, is taken from an article by J. Strong:[33]

The receivers are blackened in the welding position by inverting a wide-mouth bottle over the housing.   In this bottle, the blackening material is suspended in air from which it settles onto the receivers. Several applications of the bottle are usually necessary. The thickness of the material may be judged by an examination of the deposit on the microscope stage outside of the housing. ThO_2, NaCl, CaF_2, soot, and copper powder may be used for blackener. The material is sealed in place by atomizing a thin solution of colorless lacquer above the receivers. This settles gently and seals the blackener in place. By this blackening technique it is possible to assemble the thermopile and test it between successive coats of blackener until it gives maximum deflection. It is important that the blackener should have the proper thickness. If it is too thin the radiation is not absorbed and if it is too thick the thermocouple is unnecessarily sluggish.

References

1. Toy, *Proc. Roy. Soc.*, **A 100**, 109 (1922); Adams, Barnes, and Forsythe, *Jour. Optical Soc. Am.*, **21**, 213 (1931); van Kreveld, *Zeitschr. Wiss. Phot.*, **32**, 222 (1934); Webb, *Jour. Optical Soc. Am.*, **26**, 12 (1936).
2. Rubens, *Zeitschr. Instrumentenk.*, **18**, 65 (1898).
3. Paschen, *Ann. Physik*, **33**, 330 (1910).
4. Moll, *Inaug. Dissertation Utrecht*, 1907, *Arch. Néerlandaises des Sci.*, Série II, Tome XIII, p. 100.
5. Altenkirch, *Phys. Zeitschr.*, **10**, 560 (1909).
6. Johansen, *Ann. Physik* (4), **33**, 517 (1910); *Phys. Zeitschr.*, **14**, 998 (1913).
7. Firestone, *Rev. Sci. Inst.*, **1**, 11 (1930).
8. Coblentz, *Bur. Standards Bull.* (S.P. 85), **4**, 398 (1907).
9. Coblentz, *Bur. Standards Bull.* (S.P. 188), **9**, 7 (1911).
10. Brackett and McAlister, *Rev. Sci. Inst.*, **1**, 181 (1930).
11. Coblentz, Standard of Radiation, *Bur. Standards Bull.* (S.P. 227), **11**, 87 (1914); Coblentz and Stair, *Bur. Standards Jour. Research* (R.P. 578), **11**, 79 (1933).
12. Coblentz, Various Modifications, *Bur. Standards Bull.* (S.P. 229), **11**, 131 (1914).
13. Stetson and Coblentz, Solar Corona Thermopile, *Astrophys. Jour.*, **62**, 128 (1925).
14. Coblentz and Emerson, Absolute Thermopile, *Bur. Standards Bull.* (S.P. 261), **12**, 503 (1916).
15. Crookes, *Phil. Trans.*, **11**, 166, 325 (1876).
16. Nichols, *Phys. Rev.*, **4**, 297 (1897).
17. Hettner and Czerny, *Zeitschr. Phys.*, **27**, 12 (1924).
18. Marsh, *Jour. Optical Soc. Am.*, **12**, 135 (1926).
19. Coblentz, *Bull. Bur. Standards*, **4**, 408 (1907–1908).
20. Tear, *Phys. Rev.*, **23**, 641 (1924).
21. Sandvik, *Jour. Optical Soc. Am.*, **12**, 356 (1926).

22. Abbot, *Contr. Mount Wilson Obs.*, No. 38; also *Astrophys. Jour.* No. 69, 293 (1929).

23. R. J. Cashman and W. S. Huxford, *Phys. Rev.*, **48**, 734 (1935).

24. R. J. Cashman and N. C. Jamison, *Phys. Rev.*, **50**, 568 (1936); N. C. Jamison and R. J. Cashman, *Phys. Rev.*, **50**, 624 (1936).

25. D'Arsonval, *Soc. franç. phys.* **30** (1886).

26. Boys, *Proc. Roy. Soc.*, **42**, 189 (1887); **44**, 96 (1888); **47**, 480 (1890); *Phil. Trans.* **180A**, 169 (1889).

27. Paschen, *Ann. Physik*, **48**, 272 (1893).

28. Coblentz, *Bull. Bur. Standards*, **2**, 479 (1906).

29. Langley, *Proc. Amer. Acad. Arts Sci.*, **16**, 342 (1881); *Researches on Solar Heat*.

30. *Ann. Astrophys. Observ.*, **4**, 45, and **5**, 75.

31. Pfund, *Rev. Sci. Inst.*, **1**, 397 (1930); *Jour. Optical Soc. Am.*, **23**, 375 (1933).

32. Pfund, *Phys. Rev.*, **36**, 71 (1930); **39**, 64 (1932); *Jour. Optical Soc. Am.*, **23**, 270 (1933).

33. Strong, *Rev. Sci. Inst.*, **3**, 68 (1932).

CHAPTER VII

MEASUREMENT OF SPECTRAL RADIATION BY MEANS OF THE PHOTOELECTRIC TUBE

Lewis R. Koller[*]

One method of measuring radiation in the visible, ultraviolet, and short infrared spectrum is by means of the photoelectric tube. The field of usefulness of this receiver extends from the high intensities involved in photometry to the very feeble illumination of fifteenth magnitude stars, a range of one thousand million fold. Since the photocell functions by a simple response to radiant energy, a discussion of its use very largely takes the form of a description of its operation and characteristics. Accordingly, its characteristics are described insofar as they pertain to the measurement of radiant energy and, in particular, the points are emphasized wherein the behavior of photoelectric cells differs from that of the ideal photoelectric effect. Many of these have been discussed previously by Ives and Kingsbury in a paper on the applicability of photoelectric tubes to colorimetry.[1]

The Photoelectric Tube. There are several different kinds of photoelectric cells, depending for their operation upon very different phenomena. We shall first consider those based upon what has been variously called the photoemissive, the external photoelectric or the surface effect. Such cells are usually referred to as photoelectric tubes.

One outstanding characteristic of the photoelectric tube is that it is selective, *i.e.*, its response is not the same for equal amounts of energy in different parts of the spectrum. Accordingly, a calibration for different wavelengths by means of a thermopile or other nonselective detector is necessary.

A second outstanding characteristic—and a very desirable one—is that its response at any given wavelength is directly proportional to the incident energy.

---

[*] *Research Physicist, General Electric Company, Schenectady, New York.*

216

Essentially the photoelectric tube consists of two metal electrodes in vacuum.   One of these (the anode) is maintained at a positive potential with respect to the other (the cathode) by an external source of e.m.f.   When radiation falls on the cathode, the emitted electrons are drawn across the space to the anode.   This constitutes a current in the external circuit from cathode to anode, as is shown in Fig. 138.   Electrons would likewise be liberated by radiation falling on the anode, but since this is maintained at a positive potential, they are unable to escape from it.

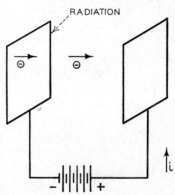

Fig. 138.—Schematic diagram of phototube.

The Photoelectric Current. The photoelectric current, *i.e.*, the number of electrons released, is directly proportional to the incident flux, from the highest to the lowest values that have been measured.   While this statement is correct for the photoelectric *effect*, there are some deviations from linearity in some

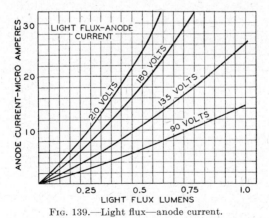

Fig. 139.—Light flux—anode current.

photoelectric *tubes*, due to little-understood phenomena.   These are not, for the most part, abrupt deviations, but a curvature in the irradiation-current characteristic.   A typical example is shown in Fig. 139.   This effect is usually larger, the higher

the anode voltage used.   It may be made very small by the choice
of the proper anode voltage.

The deviation from linearity is particularly noticeable in gas-
filled photoelectric tubes at high voltages and high radiation
intensities.   It is, however, also present to a smaller extent
in some vacuum tubes.   It is possible, by special forms of construction,[2] to achieve strict proportionality, but such tubes
are not readily available.

Where an accuracy of not greater than 1 or 2 per cent is
required, it is usually safe to assume that response of the vacuum
phototube is linear, if the range of irradiation is not too great.
For precision measurements, however, it is necessary to determine
the relation between current and irradiation by experiment for
the particular tube used under the exact conditions of operation.

In addition to the inherent nonlinearity of phototubes, deviations may also be introduced due to circuit conditions.   If a
tube is used with a high series resistance, as is the case where
the current is to be amplified, the IR drop across the resistance
lowers the potential across the tube terminals.   If the resistance
is of the order of megohms, and the current of the order of
microamperes, this drop in potential may become quite large
and may result in a characteristic tending to saturate with
increasing irradiation.   This condition is unlikely to be met
with in measuring spectral radiation, but it may occur with high
intensities of unresolved radiation.

Spectral Response.   Photoelectric emission is a quantum
process.   One quantum of radiation causes the emission of a
single photoelectron.   If the process
were 100 per cent efficient at all
wavelengths, the relation between
photocurrent and frequency would
be as is shown in Fig. 140.   This
represents the relative values of photocurrent which would be obtained
by illuminating a phototube with

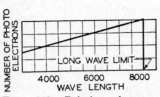

Fig. 140.—Relation between
photocurrent and wavelength.

equal amounts of energy at the various wavelengths.   Since the
energy of each quantum is $h\nu$, as we pass to the lower frequencies
(longer wavelengths), the energy of each individual quantum
becomes less and, accordingly, there are more quanta for any
given amount of energy.   Thus the photoelectric response would

increase with increasing wavelength. At the long-wave limit, which is the longest wavelength capable of causing the emission of a photoelectron, the photocurrent would drop to zero as is shown in the figure. Thus the device is inherently selective. Actually, a curve of this kind is never observed in practice. The efficiency of photoelectric emission is not uniform throughout the spectrum. A typical curve showing the relation between wavelength and photocurrent when a metal surface is irradiated with equal amounts of radiant energy of different wavelengths is shown in Fig. 141. This particular curve is for a sodium surface.

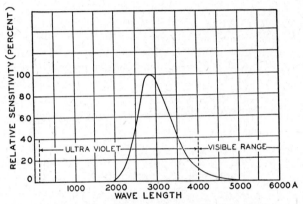

FIG. 141.—Characteristic response of sodium tube.

Instead of a linear increase in current with wavelength, as in Fig. 140, the curve rises quite sharply to a maximum, and then falls off until it reaches the axis asymptotically at the long-wave limit. From this curve it can be seen that a given radiant flux at wavelength $\lambda = 2900A$ will produce a larger photocurrent than the same flux at any other wavelength. Also, no wavelength longer than $\lambda = 5000A$ will cause any photoelectric emission. The shape of this "spectral-sensitivity" curve, the wavelength corresponding to the maximum, and the long-wave limit are each definite characteristics of the various elements, and are factors to be considered in choosing a phototube for any particular purpose.

For most of the metals the entire spectral-sensitivity curve lies in the ultraviolet. In the case of Zn, Cd and Mg, the curves lie in the near ultraviolet and, accordingly, these elements are useful for measurements in this region. The alkali metals are the only elements whose curves fall in, or extend into, the visible spectrum to any great extent. The pure alkali metals have similar spectral-sensitivity curves whose peaks and long-wave limits shift toward the red end of the spectrum as we pass from Li to Cs.

In the case of certain compounds, the shape of the spectral-sensitivity curve is radically changed. The general tendency in the formation of compounds is to shift the long-wave limit toward the red end of the spectrum, and to form additional maxima in the spectral-sensitivity curve. These maxima usually lie in the red end of the spectrum, and may be even higher than the

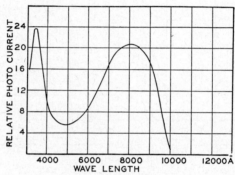

Fig. 142.—Characteristic response for Cs-CsO-Ag phototube.

maximum for the pure metal. The compounds which have been investigated are the oxides, sulfides, hydrides, and some complex organic substances.[3] The spectral sensitivity of metals is also affected by the thickness of the layer. A thin film of an alkali metal on a background of some other metal has very different photoelectric properties from the pure alkali metal in bulk. The thin layer shows a long-wave limit further toward the red than the bulk metal, and a generally increased sensitivity at all wavelengths. The nature of the underlying metal also influences the spectral sensitivity. In making highly sensitive phototubes, the effect of thin films and the effect of compounds are combined. The cathode surface consists of a conducting background, such as silver, upon which is formed a thin layer of the compound, and on top of this is a film of the alkali metal with a thickness of the order of atomic dimensions. Photocells of this type have a sensitivity to unresolved radiant energy of the order of one thousand fold that of the pure metal type. Their disadvantages are the lack of uniformity between cells of the same type and the instability of individual cells. Figure 142 shows the shape of the spectral-sensitivity curve for a Cs-CsO-Ag cell of this type. The chemical symbols here merely indicate that the cathode consists of a layer of caesium on a layer of oxides of caesium on silver. The exact nature of the compound is not definitely known.

Cells of this type are often described as "red-sensitive," owing to the relatively large response in the red end of the spectrum.

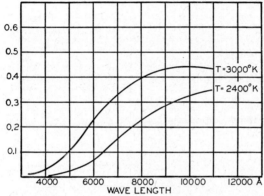

Fig. 143.—Spectral-energy distribution for tungsten filaments at temperatures shown.

This is particularly advantageous for industrial applications where the cell is to operate some control device according to the amount of light falling upon the cathode from an incandescent-lamp source.

Dependence of Response upon Spectral Character of the Incident Radiation. The spectral-energy distribution of the radiation from an incandescent tungsten lamp is shown in Fig. 143. From this figure it can be seen that 68 per cent of the energy of the lamp between 3000 and 10,000A is radiated at wavelengths longer than 6000A. A consideration of Fig. 142 will show that the tube is not greatly more sensitive to wavelengths in this region than in the blue end of the spectrum, but since the source radiates so *much* energy in the longer waves, the response of the tube will be greater to this than to the blue radiation. This can be seen from Fig. 144, which is obtained by multiplying the ordinates of Fig. 143 by those of Fig. 142.

That is, Fig. 144 shows the relative response of a phototube to the energy distribution of an incandescent lamp, instead of to an equal energy spectrum. A consideration of Fig. 144*B* shows that 94 per cent of the response is due to the radiation of wavelength longer than 6000A. The response of the same tube to a source at a temperature of 2400°K is shown in Fig. 144*A*.

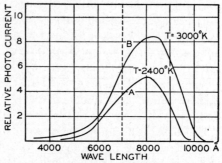

Fig. 144.—Response of Cs-CsO-Ag tube to radiation from tungsten filament at temperatures shown.

If we were to use the radiation source of Fig. 143 in conjunction with a filter which was opaque to radiation longer than 7000A, we would lose all of the response lying to the right of the dotted line in Fig. 144. Thus it can be seen that a consideration of the energy distribution of the radiation is just as important as that of the spectral sensitivity of the photoelectric tube.

Alkali Metal Tubes. Table 20 gives the response of some alkali metal vacuum phototubes to unresolved radiant energy

TABLE 20.—ALKALI METAL PHOTOTUBE RESPONSE

Cathode material	Photo-current, μa per incident lumen	Tempera-ture of light source	Reported by
Sodium..................	0.1 to 0.2	Not given	Selenyi
Potassium..............	1.0	2650	Campbell and Ritchie
Potassium hydride........	1.0	2848	Olpin
Rubidium..............	0.44	2650	Campbell and Ritchie
Caesium................	0.17	2650	Campbell and Ritchie
Caesium................ (thin film Cs-CsO-Ag)	88	2870	Gordon

from incandescent sources. The temperature of the source is indicated in column 2. In using this table, it must be remembered that these values have no significance for monochromatic radiation, since a large part of the response may be due to infrared radiation, as in the case of the Cs-CsO-Ag tube.

Dependence of Response upon Construction. The differences in tube characteristics due to differences in manufacturing technique, using the same cathode materials, may be much greater than the differences between tubes with entirely different cathodes. Furthermore, the common method of rating tubes in terms of microamperes per lumen may be very misleading. Tubes having very nearly the same overall sensitivity may differ greatly in their response in different parts of the spectrum. While published spectral-sensitivity curves are helpful in making the choice of the tube best suited for a particular task, it is necessary in any instance to determine the spectral sensitivity for the tube by experiment. Furthermore, it must be emphasized that the spectral response is not uniform over the entire cathode and that it may, and usually does, vary from time to time.

Tubes for Special Purposes. Figures 145 and 146 give the spectral sensitivity in the visible and ultraviolet spectrum for a number of elements. At the short-wave end of the spectrum, the characteristic is determined by the transmission of the glass rather than by the cathode material. By means of these curves, it is possible to choose the cathode material best suited to any particular investigation. The choice is necessarily limited to a few types. For many purposes, the response may be limited (at the expense of sensitivity) to broad spectral bands by the use of filters. In photometry,* in particular, it has been found convenient to correct the phototube spectral response curve by means of filters to approximate the visual-sensitivity curve.[4]

A mixture of solutions of copper chloride and potassium dichromate is very useful for correcting caesium tubes. The copper chloride cuts off the extreme red, and the potassium dichromate cuts off the blue end of the spectrum. The two solutions are mixable in all proportions and are stable over long periods of time. The exact concentrations, of course, must be adjusted for the particular phototube used. Many other

* See p. 404.

inorganic solutions and glass filters may be used for special purposes. The transmission curves for many materials are given in the International Critical Tables.

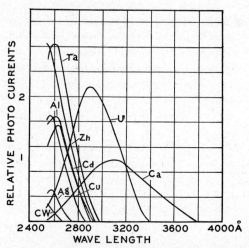

FIG. 145.—Spectral sensitivity for phototubes with different metals for cathodes, absolute values not comparable.

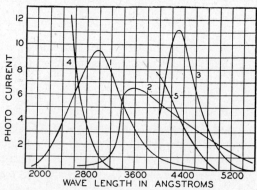

FIG. 146.—Spectral sensitivity for phototubes with different metals for cathodes, absolute values not comparable 1-Na; 2-Sodium hydride (*Hulburt, Phys. Rev.*, **32**, 593, 1928); 3-K (*Campbell and Ritchie*); 4-Cd (*Bonke, Ann. d. Phys.*, **10**, 576, 1931); 5-Mg (*Cashman and Huxford, Phys. Rev.*, **43**, 811, 1933).

A cadmium tube with a red-purple corex filter and a solution of picric acid has been used to give a sensitivity approximating the erythema curve.[5] Cadmium-magnesium alloys in corex bulbs have also been used for this purpose.[6]

A very ingenious method for correcting phototubes to approximate the visual-sensitivity curve has been devised by Dresler. According to this method two filters are used, green and orange, respectively. Instead of using them in series in the customary way, they are placed side by side and partly overlapping. By this arrangement a part of the cell surface is overcompensated and a part is undercompensated. The width of the overlapping portion is adjusted until good agreement is obtained with visual measurements. This method is discussed in R. Sewig's "Objektive Photometrie."

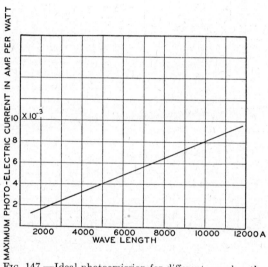

Fig. 147.—Ideal photoemission for different wavelengths.

Very few data are available giving spectral sensitivity in absolute values. It is possible, however, to form an approximate estimate of the order of magnitude of the maximum photoelectric current to be expected, as follows: the efficiency of photoemission is rarely more than 1 per cent, *i.e.*, 1 electron per 100 incident quanta, and it is usually far less than this. Figure 147 has been plotted on the basis of an efficiency of 1 per cent, giving the photocurrent per watt of incident flux throughout the spectrum. The photocurrent at any wavelength rarely exceeds the values shown here, and in most cases may be several hundred or thousand fold smaller. Nevertheless, such an approximation is a help in the choice of suitable measuring instruments.

Table 21 gives the spectral sensitivity in amperes per watt at the wavelength of maximum response for a few cases in which the data were available. Variations in the properties of the phototubes prepared by different investigators are very large, and data such as those in Tables 20 and 21 or Figs. 141, 142, 143, and 144 should be considered only as approximations.

TABLE 21.—SPECTRAL SENSITIVITY OF SOME PHOTOTUBES

Cathode material	Wavelength of max. response, A	Yield, amp. per watt	Reference
Sodium..........	3100	5.8×10^{-3}	St. Louis—Thesis
Potassium.......	4500	1.1×10^{-3}	Fleischer and Teichman
	3900	0.7×10^{-3}	Fleischer and Teichman
	4300	5.6×10^{-3}	Campbell and Ritchie
Cs-CsO-Ag..... $\{$	3500	4.0×10^{-3}	Benford
	8000	3.5×10^{-3}	
Magnesium.... $\{$	2536	13×10^{-3}	de Lazlo*
	2536 (not max.)	0.08×10^{-3}	Dejardin and Schwegler†
Cadmium........	2900	0.04×10^{-3}	Fleischer and Teichman

* *Phil. Mag.*, **13**, 1171 (1932).
† *Compt. rend.*, **196**, 1585 (1933).

Tubes for Measuring Ultraviolet Radiation. The usual practice for the measurement of ultraviolet radiation is to use pure metal surfaces in quartz bulbs or bulbs of ultraviolet transmitting glass.

Use of Fluorescent Screens. The range of usefulness of phototubes in glass bulbs may, however, be extended into the ultraviolet by the use of fluorescent screens. A fluorescent material may be used which, when excited by the ultraviolet radiation, will emit radiation of a wavelength in the visible spectrum to which the phototube will respond. The fluorescent material may be coated on the outside of the phototube instead of on a separate screen. Materials which have been used are quinine sulfate in alcoholic solution, esculin in gelatine, fluorescein, novocaine and sodium salicylate mixed with dextrin.[7] The last shows a constant response to equal amounts of energy over a wide range of wavelengths. Figure 148 shows the spectral-sensitivity curve of a potassium tube treated in this way. This procedure introduces the complicating effects of the characteristics of the screen, *i.e.*, its response to variations in intensity, temperature, fatigue, etc. Furthermore, the efficiency of the fluorescent material in transforming the radiation from ultra-violet to visible is involved, as well as the efficiency of the photo-electric transformation.

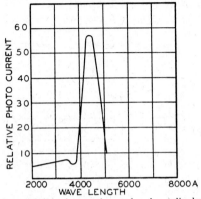

FIG. 148.—Spectral sensitivity of potassium tube plus salicylate of sodium screen (Dejardin).

Electrical Characteristics of Phototubes. The volt-ampere characteristic of a vacuum phototube is very similar to that of any other high-vacuum electronic device. At low voltages, the

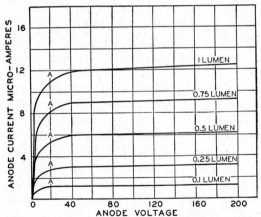

FIG. 149.—Volt-ampere characteristics for vacuum phototube.

current is limited by the electrode arrangement and spacing and the initial velocities of the electrons as in the region OA in Fig. 149; at higher voltages, the current saturates. The saturation voltage is of the order of 5 to 20 volts for most tubes at ordinary irradiations. The voltage used should be sufficient to give saturation for the highest value of irradiation to be used. Ninety volts is usually ample for this purpose. Higher voltages are not necessary and may be harmful, owing to bombardment by positive ions formed from the residual gases present. At voltages below or near the saturation voltage, the volt-ampere characteristic may also depend upon the wavelength of the radiation.

Gas-filled Phototube. In order to increase the sensitivity of phototubes, it is general practice to introduce a low pressure

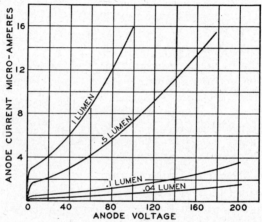

Fig. 150.—Volt-ampere characteristics for gas-filled phototube.

of an inert gas into the bulb. The primary electron current may be amplified several fold owing to impact ionization. Thus the current through the tube for any given value of irradiation depends upon the voltage. A volt-ampere characteristic for a gas-filled tube is shown in Fig. 150. From this figure, it can be seen that at the higher voltages and higher values of irradiation the tube becomes unstable. A very slight change in voltage here results in an enormous increase in photocurrent. When a tube is operating in this critical region, a very small increase in irradiation or voltage will cause the discharge to pass over into a self-sustained glow discharge. Under these conditions, the current is no longer a function of the irradiation but depends only upon the voltage and resistance of the circuit, and will continue even when the irradiation ceases.   If the glow current does not exceed, say, 100 to 200×10^{-6} amp., it will not necessarily damage the tube.   It will, however, alter the sensitivity, and this change may be either an increase or a decrease, depending upon the type of tube and other conditions.   After glowing, it usually requires a considerable period before the tube becomes stable again.   At low values of irradiation, the transition to the glow discharge is an abrupt one, but at high values the change is gradual, and the volt-ampere curve is perfectly smooth.   Under these conditions, it may not be possible to see the glow, but the condition may be readily ascertained by shielding the tube from the light, for, if the tube is glowing, the current will be maintained.   The characteristics of gas-filled tubes have been studied by N. R. Campbell and described in detail by Campbell and Ritchie in their book.

The increase in sensitivity of a gas-filled tube over that of a vacuum tube of similar construction is, under ordinary conditions, of the order of five or sixfold.   It is possible to exceed this greatly by operating on the steep portion of the characteristic, but the gain is at the expense of stability.   A high resistance of the order of $10^6 \Omega$ should be included in the circuit to protect instruments.   This will not affect the measurements under normal conditions, since the resistance of the tube is many megohms, but if the tube tends to go over into a glow discharge, the IR drop across the resistance will lower the voltage below the glow point.

The distinction between vacuum and gas-filled phototubes is, in the main, one of sensitivity.   The spectral response of the tube is not affected by the gas.   The response of the tube is directly proportional to irradiation, except at high values of irradiation or high voltages, where it tends to increase more rapidly than the irradiation.   In the case of very rapidly changing values of irradiation, however, there is an important difference between vacuum and gas-filled phototubes.   The vacuum tubes show no time lag other than that due to the electrostatic capacity of the system.   The gas-filled tubes, however, do show a time lag.   This is noticeable at frequencies above several hundred cycles per second, and results in a decrease in sensitivity with increasing frequency.   The effect is shown in Fig. 151, where the response of a gas-filled tube is shown as a function of frequency, when it is irradiated by an intermittent light source. The magnitude of this effect depends upon the cathode material, nature and pressure of the gas, and the applied voltage.[8]

In practically every respect, vacuum photoelectric tubes are more desirable than gas-filled tubes for purposes of measurement, and should be used whenever possible.

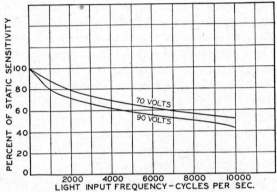

Fig. 151.—Dynamic sensitivity; sinusoidal variation of light flux. (Maximum value of light-flux constant at 0.05 lumen.)

Size of Active Surface. The response of a phototube depends upon the total quantity of radiant flux falling upon the cathode. Accordingly, the photocurrent from a surface will be the same for a given flux regardless of the intensity; *i.e.*, theoretically the same current will be obtained from a small intense beam as from the same beam dispersed over a larger area of the cathode. In practice, however, it is advisable to avoid a concentrated beam. A very intense spot on the photocell cathode may cause over-heating, whereas the same amount of energy distributed over a larger area would not have any harmful effects. Another reason for irradiating a large area is that the cathode is not always uniformly sensitive over its entire surface. Adjacent areas of the cathode may differ in sensitivity by a factor of two or more, even though there is no visible difference in their appearance. If two small beams are to be compared, therefore, it is quite important that they both be focused on the same portion of the cathode surface. It is even better to irradiate the entire surface so that these local irregularities are averaged out.

Since the response of a phototube depends upon the total radiant flux, the size of the tube is relatively unimportant, as the same current is produced regardless of whether the flux is concentrated on a small area or spread out over a greater area. Accordingly, the choice of the size of tube to be used will depend upon other conditions. In some cases, it may prove simpler to use a tube with a large window area than to concentrate the radiation by means of mirrors or lenses, and vice versa.

It is important always to introduce the radiant flux at the same angle of incidence with respect to the surface, since in many types of cathodes the photoelectric yield is a function of the angle of incidence, and varies with the angle of incidence to a much greater extent than would be expected from the optical properties of the surface. This is known as the selective effect.

Fatigue of Phototubes. Much of the older literature on the subject of phototubes contains references to "fatigue." By this was meant a gradual decrease in photocurrent with time, when the tube was exposed to constant radiation. This was largely, but not entirely, due to poor vacuum conditions. In well-exhausted tubes with pure metal surfaces, this effect is almost wholly absent. In the case of tubes with more complex surfaces than the pure alkali metals, these transient effects are much more complicated. Their exact nature varies with different

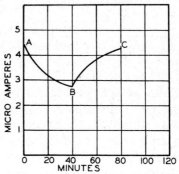

Fig. 152.—Transient effects in response of tube.

types of tubes, and even with individual tubes of the same type. One special case, however, will indicate the kind of difficulties which may be experienced. In Fig. 152, the point A represents the initial sensitivity (to unresolved radiant flux) of a tube when removed from storage. On exposure to strong radiation with the tube on open circuit, the sensitivity gradually decreased to the value B. In some cases B was found to be less than 50 per cent of A. Thus if such a tube were used for measurement while in the condition A, and then removed from its circuit and exposed to strong sunlight, it would give only half as large a current when again used under the same conditions as initially. Upon exposing the tube to moderate irradiation and applying an anode voltage, it gradually recovered to the condition C (practically the same as A). The rate at which the sensitivity changes from A to B to C depends upon the degree of irradiation, the wavelength of the radiation, and also upon the applied voltage. The decrease is facilitated by increasing the intensity, and is also greater and more rapid for blue than for red light. It is retarded by applying an anode potential, and the magnitude of the effect is a function of the applied potential. This is not the place for a detailed discussion of this effect other than to point out that the sensitivity of a phototube is not a definite fixed quantity, but depends upon the history of the tube, the irradiation to which it has been subjected, and the voltage at which it has been operated. Accordingly, in order to obtain consistent measurements, it is desirable to avoid large changes in the conditions of operation of the tube; *i.e.*, the anode potential should not be altered but should be kept at a constant value. The tube should not be exposed to extremely high intensities. A certain regularity should be observed in the procedure of taking data, and readings should always be taken in the same order, with approximately the same time intervals between them. A tube such as the example in Fig. 152, which shows a variation of 50 per cent in its sensitivity, may be constant to within 10 per cent, under constant conditions of operation, and, by following the proper procedure, it may be possible to obtain measurements with it with a high degree of precision. These transient effects practically disappear in vacuum tubes and are present, to any great extent, only in the highly red-sensitive tubes.

It is important to note that in a case such as this, where the overall response of the tube changes, it does not mean that there is a proportional change in all parts of the spectral-sensitivity curve. Some parts are affected more than others; it is even possible that a general decrease in overall sensitivity may be accompanied by an increase in sensitivity in some parts of the spectrum.

Photo E.M.F. Cell. Another type of photocell which is useful is the photo e.m.f.* type.[9] This type consists of a metallic surface covered with a thin film of a semiconductor, on top of which

* Also called "barrier layer cell" or photovoltaic cell.

is a transparent film of another metal.   When the cell is exposed
to radiant flux, an e.m.f. of the order of a few millivolts is generated which increases with increasing irradiation, although not in
direct proportion.   The internal resistance decreases with
increasing irradiation.   The result is that, when used with the
proper value of external resistance, the response is nearly propor-

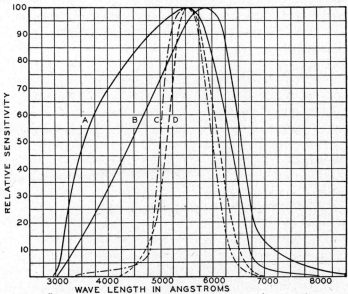

FIG. 153.—Spectral-energy distribution curve of a number of photo e.m.f. cells.
A, selenium; *B*, selenium; *C*, copper oxide; *D*, luminosity curve.   These curves
are plotted on relative scale as shown.   By measurements at the position of
maximum intensity, cell *A* gave 0.19 microamperes per microwatt falling upon
the total cell.   Cell *B* gave 0.16 microamperes per microwatt and cell *C* gave
0.11 microamperes per microwatt falling upon the cell.

tional to the incident energy.   As the external resistance is
increased, the current tends to saturate with increasing
irradiation.

Properly constructed cells of this type have been found to be
very constant in operation.   Their current sensitivity is approximately that of the best gas-filled phototubes.   Their great
advantage is in the fact that no external source of e.m.f. is
required.   They are well suited for any measurements where
the photocurrents are large enough not to require amplification.   At present there are no satisfactory methods for amplify-

ing low-voltage direct currents, and some form of light chopper and alternating-current amplifier must be resorted to. Figure 153*A* shows the spectral sensitivity of a selenium photo e.m.f. cell, and Fig. 153*C* that of a cuprous-oxide type. These types show considerable variation according to the manufacturing process used.

The liquid type of photovoltaic cell need hardly be considered in view of the other more satisfactory cells available.

Photocells for Measuring Infrared Radiation. *Thalofide Cell.* At best, the phototube is a very unsatisfactory device

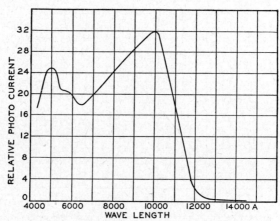

Fig. 154.—Spectral sensitivity of thalofide cell.

for the measurement of infrared radiation. Even the most red-sensitive of the modern caesium oxide tubes have a sensitivity barely extending to 11,000A, and their high response to light of shorter wavelengths makes very careful shielding from stray light necessary. The response curve of the thalofide cell extends somewhat further into the infrared, as is shown in Fig. 154, but its instability makes its use difficult. For work in this region, the nonselective detectors of radiation are more desirable.

Selenium Cell. The selenium cell[10] has not been used to any great extent in the study of spectral radiation. It functions by virtue of a change in resistance with irradiation. It requires an external source of e.m.f. like the photoemissive type of cell, but, unlike the latter, its response is proportional to the square root of the incident energy instead of directly proportional to it.

Its resistance is relatively low, so that its output cannot be amplified so readily by vacuum tubes. It also has the disadvantages of variability and dependence upon previous treatment, which make it unsuited for precision measurements. Its spectral-sensitivity curve lies in the red end of the spectrum, as can be seen from Fig. 155.

Measuring the Current Output of a Phototube.* Instruments for measuring photocurrents include practically all types. For the upper limit of currents, rarely more than a few microamperes, portable microammeters may be used. For currents too small

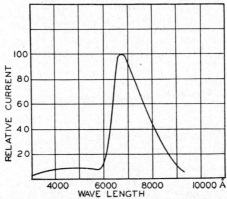

FIG. 155.—Spectral sensitivity of selenium cell.

for such instruments, galvanometers may be used down to currents of approximately 10^{-10} amp., and the current from a photoelectric tube may be measured by allowing it to flow through a known resistance, and measuring the drop of potential across the resistance with an electrometer. An enormous range of currents is measurable if there is available a series of resistors with resistances increasing in steps by a factor of at least three, at most ten. The lower limit of the measurable current is set by the leakage resistance of the portion of the circuit which acts as a shunt on the measuring resistor.

Thermionic Amplifiers. The most versatile measuring device, however, for currents of any order of magnitude is the thermionic amplifier.

* See Chap. X.

The simplest form is the resistance-coupled direct-current amplifier. For this purpose a high resistance R is included in the photocell circuit, and the drop across this resistance is applied between the amplifier grid and filament. Such a circuit is shown in Fig. 156. An increase in the photocurrent will result in an increase in the drop across the resistance R, which will make the grid more positive with respect to the filament. Thus the plate current will increase with increasing photocurrent. If the connections from R to the amplifier tube are reversed, the plate current will decrease with increasing photocurrent. In the former case, a common source of potential may be used for both the phototube and the amplifier. The latter case necessitates separate batteries. The size of the grid leak resistance depends upon the size of the current to be measured and upon the characteristics of the amplifier tube. This resistance is usually of the order of several megohms and rarely more than 10^9 ohms for very small currents. These values are small compared with the resistance of the phototube, so that R does not appreciably affect the photocurrent. By making the resistance high, a large voltage drop is obtained across it, and consequently the amplification is increased.

The change in plate current per volt change in the potential applied between grid and filament of a vacuum tube is a constant called its mutual conductance. The mutual conductance for vacuum tubes is in the neighborhood of 10^{-3} amp./volt. If we assume that we cannot detect a change in plate current of less than 10^{-6} amp., the change in grid voltage must be

$$\frac{10^{-6}}{\text{mutual conductance}}$$

which is of the order of millivolts. Accordingly, the grid resistance must be chosen so that the drop across it due to the photocurrent is at least of the order of millivolts. Thus, if the photocurrent is 10^{-9} amp., the grid leak should be at least 10^6 ohms. The maximum value of the resistance which can be used, however, is limited, since it is in multiple with the grid to filament resistance of the amplifier tube, so that it is useless to make it larger than the tube resistance. By special amplifier tube construction, however, it has been possible to increase the input resistance of the amplifier to the order of 10^{15} ohms and, with such tubes,[11] currents of the order of 10^{-14} amp. can be readily measured.

Phototube amplifier circuits may be divided into three general classifications.

1. Those which involve linearity of both the phototube and the amplifier.
2. Those which involve linearity of the phototube but not of the amplifier.
3. Those which involve linearity of neither the phototube nor the amplifier.

In the first classification, the procedure is simply to observe the amplifier current produced by a given amount of radiation falling on the phototube.

The second method is a null method in so far as the amplifier is concerned, but a deflection method with reference to the

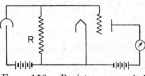

Fig. 156.—Resistance-coupled direct-current amplifier.

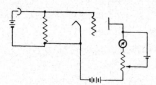

Fig. 157.—Resistance-coupled direct-current amplifier.

phototube. The circuit is the same as Fig. 156 or 157, but it is used in a slightly different manner. The amplifier current is observed with the phototube in the dark. The phototube is then irradiated, and the amplifier grid bias is adjusted until the amplifier current is restored to its original value. The change in grid bias necessary to do this is equal to the IR drop across the grid leak due to the photocurrent I. Since the grid resistance is known, the photocurrent I may be calculated. This is really the equivalent of measuring the photocurrent and, therefore, any lack of proportionality in the phototube is carried through into the final result.

In the third method the radiation source under investigation and a standard source irradiate the cell alternately, and the standard is varied by some form of intensity reducer, until the irradiation due to both is the same. Thus the characteristics of the phototube and of the amplifier do not enter into consideration, so long as they remain constant during the time of one cycle.

Bridge Circuits for Amplifying Photocurrents. The plate current of the amplifier, when the phototube is in the dark, may be large compared with the change in plate current observed when the phototube is irradiated. This difficulty is overcome by balancing out the steady value of the plate current by the circuit of Fig. 157, so that the meter indicates only *changes* in plate current.

The resistance in the plate circuit is adjusted so that, when

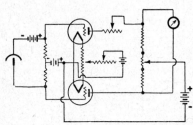

the phototube is in the dark, no current flows through the plate-circuit meter. When the tube is irradiated, the meter then indicates the change in plate current. The chief drawback to this and other direct-current amplifier circuits is their tendency to drift and, consequently, the necessity of

Fig. 158.—Bridge circuit for measuring photocurrents.

making frequent adjustments. These difficulties have been minimized to a great extent in bridge circuits in which two tubes are used, so that the various drifts tend to balance each other out. Figure 158 shows a bridge circuit. By means of a bridge circuit, DuBridge has measured photocurrents of the order of 10^{-18} amp. The amplification of small currents has been discussed in great detail by Nottingham[12] and by DuBridge.[13] Taylor and Kerr describe* an amplifier designed for use with phototubes.[14]

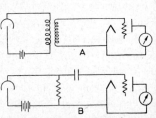

Some of the difficulties of direct-current amplification are overcome by the use of alternating-current amplifiers, but, on the other hand, this involves the use of the less desirable alternating-current measuring instruments. The amplifier may

Fig. 159.—*A*. Transformer-coupled amplifier for measuring photocurrents. *B*. Resistance-coupled amplifier for measuring photocurrents.

be transformer-coupled or resistance-coupled as in Fig. 159*A* and *B*, respectively. For this method the source must be intermittent. This is attained by "chopping" the beam at any convenient frequency by a sector disk or a wheel with an edge cut to give any desired wave form (*e.g.*, sine wave), or, in the case of discharges in gases, by modulating the supply

* See p. 322.

voltage. Modulation of the radiation and alternating-current amplification is often a very convenient means of separating two effects, one of which it is desired to study. For example, it makes it possible to study one source in the presence of a large amount of stray radiation. The alternating-current amplifier picks up only the modulated source, and does not respond to the steady component due to the stray radiation.

The Geiger-Müller Tube. For very feeble radiation, the Geiger-Müller tube has been used. This is a phototube of special construction in which each electron emitted gives rise to a pulse of current through the tube, which may be detected by sensitive instruments.[15] Using this type of tube, Rajewsky[16] detected radiant flux equivalent to 12 quanta/$(cm^2$ sec) *i.e.*,

$$(9.1 \times 10^{-11}) \text{ erg/}(cm^2 \text{ sec}).$$

Measuring of Radiant Energy of Short Duration. For the measurement of a pulse of radiant energy of very brief duration, steady deflection methods cannot be used. In such cases, the integrated current from the phototube may be measured directly with a ballistic galvanometer,[17] or it may be used to charge a condenser connected in series with the phototube circuit, the charge then being measured either by a ballistic galvanometer or by some type of electron-tube peak voltmeter.[18] Such apparatus may be calibrated by exposing the phototube to a source of known intensity for a known time interval which is comparable to the duration of the source to be measured, a convenient way of regulating the time of exposure being by means of a pendulum device with a calibrated opening and known period. Either of these methods measures the total quantity of electricity which has passed through the tube, and thus indicates the energy rather than the radiant flux falling on the phototube.

Measurement of the Maximum Intensity of Radiant Energy. The maximum intensity of a varying source, or the intensity of any source, may be determined by a modification of the above methods.[19] The current from the phototube is sent through a resistance R (Fig. 160) and the IR drop used to charge a condenser. An electric valve in series with the condenser permits the current to flow in only one direction. Thus the condenser is charged to a value corresponding to the maximum current flowing through the phototube. Since the condenser charges to $1/e$ th of the maximum charge in a time equal to the product of the capacity in farads and the resistance in ohms, for accurate results the values of capacity and resistance must be adjusted to give a proper time constant for the circuit.   If the time constant is small compared to the duration of the irradiation to be measured,

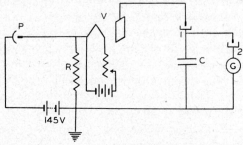

FIG. 160.—Circuit for measuring maximum intensity of light flash.

the apparatus may be calibrated with any source of known intensity.   In general, however, it is safer to calibrate with a source of short duration, such as the pendulum device already described.

Balanced Method of Measuring Output of a Phototube.   One method of measuring irradiation which avoids any assumption of proportionality in the phototube is the balance method shown in

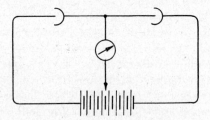

BALANCED PHOTOELECTRIC TUBE CIRCUIT
FIG. 161.—Balance method of measuring output of phototube.

Fig. 161.   The irradiation on each tube is adjusted initially so that both photocurrents are equal and no galvanometer current is observed.   Any change in irradiation on one of the tubes will upset the balance, which is then restored by means of a calibrated "intensity reducer."   While this method does not require any knowledge of the current-irradiation characteristic of the tubes, it does assume that both tubes will stay constant, or at least change in the same ratio, during the time of the experiment. This is not necessarily the case.   This method can be made very sensitive by using an electrometer or vacuum-tube amplifier for the indicating instrument.

If the radiation from the source under investigation and from a standard comparison source is alternately allowed to fall on the same phototube at a fairly high frequency, the errors due to any change in the phototube are avoided.   If the radiation from both sources is the same, the photocurrent will be constant.   If the two differ, the current will be a pulsating one.   The alternating-current component can then be measured by the usual methods, or, if a null method is preferable, the radiation from the comparison source is altered until the alternating component disappears.

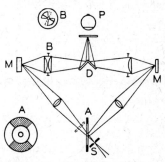

A Null Method Using a Vibration Galvanometer.   The spectral transmission or reflectance of different samples can be measured with a photoelectric tube as the detecting device by the following method which can be used with any monochromator.   Measurements in the

Fig. 162.—Arrangement of apparatus for measuring transmission or reflection factors by null method by using phototube as detector.

ultraviolet can be made if quartz optical parts are provided and a phototube sensitive in this region used.

Figure 162 shows schematically the arrangement[20] of the apparatus.   The radiant flux from the monochromator (not shown) slit strikes first the circular glass disk which has equal segments silvered and unsilvered.   The number of segments depends upon the speed of the synchronous motor used and upon the desired frequency of alternation of the beam.   The mirror-sector combination splits the beam into two parts at right angles to each other, and the lenses shown form images of the slit on the magnesia blocks.[21]

In conjunction with each of the collecting lenses is an adjustable quadrant sector, as shown in the upper left-hand portion of the diagram, which serves to cut down the light of that beam in a measurable manner.   A scale of 0 to 100 is attached to the left-hand sector, so that the amount of its opening may be read. It is not necessary that there should be a scale on the right-hand sector, since this serves for comparison purposes only in the usual use of the instrument.

The radiant flux is reflected by two mirrors nearly at right angles to each other on to a ground-glass screen placed immediately in front of the photoelectric cell. The purpose of the ground glass is to diffuse the radiation with some uniformity over the sensitive surface of the cell. Thus the phototube receives an alternating beam of radiant flux, which causes the tube to give an alternating current of the same period. This alternating current can be amplified and, since the condition of balance is that each half of the alternating beam of radiation is equal, a null method may be used.

A synchronous motor is used to drive the glass disk, so that the frequency of the beam alternations may be kept constant and that any difference in the two parts of the alternating current from the cell is amplified and detected with a properly tuned vibration galvanometer. If the intensities of the two beams falling on the cell are equal, the vibration galvanometer will not move; thus, as balance is approached by adjusting the sector, the beam of light from the mirror of the vibration galvanometer narrows down to its minimum width. The vibration galvanometer has very great advantages for use in this connection because of its high sensitivity, its freedom from static friction, and its relative insensitivity to frequencies other than the one to which it is tuned; also, with this method of detection neither the linearity of the cell nor that of the amplifying device used will enter the final results.

For ordinary spectrophotometric work, a gas-filled caesium cell which is sensitive over the entire visible spectrum is used. For work extending into the infrared, another gas-filled cell sensitive in this region replaces the first.

If this device is used, the reproducibility of the results depends upon the sector A. This can be made so that readings can be taken to within a small fraction of 1 per cent. The outstanding advantage of this method is that the readings do not depend upon the observer, and also readings of transmission or reflectance can be made in the ultraviolet and infrared, limited only by the range of the sensitivity of the photoelectric tube.

Neon-tube Indicators for Photocurrents.   Another method of measuring photocurrents makes use of a neon tube as an indicator.[22]   If a small condenser is connected in series with the phototube and a battery, its rate of charge will depend upon the resistance of the phototube, *i.e.*, the amount of radiation falling on the tube.   A small neon lamp in parallel with the condenser will light up when the voltage across the condenser rises to the breakdown voltage of the lamp, and will go out as soon as the voltage reaches the extinction voltage.   Thus the frequency of the flashing of the lamp is a measure of the resistance of, and therefore the amount of radiation on, the phototube.

Rentschler[23] has modified this method by employing a special-design glow-relay tube using argon in which the condenser discharge between one anode and the cathode ignites a discharge between the main anode and the cathode strong enough to operate a relay or other recording device.   The method is capable of good precision and can be used for measuring small currents, limited only by leakages in the circuit.

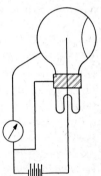

Fig. 163.—Method of using guard ring for phototube.

Leakage Currents.   In making measurements of small photocurrents, it must be kept in mind that the leakage currents may be comparable with the photocurrents.   The leakage currents are mainly of two kinds, true leakage over the glass surfaces and thermionic emission.   In well-designed phototubes which have been properly exhausted, the leakage over surfaces inside of the bulb is almost negligible.   The external leakage, however, may be quite appreciable.   This may be reduced to a minimum by carefully cleaning the glass surfaces with alcohol, and then keeping them dry by means of a drying agent such as P_2O_5. Covering the surface with an insulating wax, such as ceresin, helps reduce the leakage.   A guard ring, such as is shown in Fig. 163, will prevent leakage currents from passing through the galvanometer.   J. F. H. Custers[24] was able to measure currents of the order of 10^{-14} to 10^{-15} amp. by placing the entire amplifier system in an evacuated container.   While equally small currents have been measured with far less elaborate precautions, this set-up was noteworthy for the steadiness of the readings.   Whitford[25] and others have reported similar results. Selenyi has pointed out that the effect of imperfect insulation in tubes without a guard ring may be diminished by operating the cell on alternating potential. Since the leakage currents are alternating, they would not be indicated by the galvanometer, which would record only the true photoelectric current. This method applies, of course, only where the leakage is true resistance.

The surface leakage, however, is not the only limitation to the size of currents measurable. The thermionic current may be an even greater factor, particularly in some of the newer types of red-sensitive tubes. It is relatively unimportant in the case of pure metal surfaces. The Cs-CsO-Ag surfaces are excellent thermionic emitters and, since the cathode of a tube may have an area of as much as 100 cm², the emission can become quite large at elevated temperatures. In some tubes of this type, this thermionic current is of the order of 10^{-10} amp. at room temperature, so that at 100 volts the tube has a resistance of $10^{12}\,\Omega$. Accordingly, such a tube is not suitable for measuring photocurrents smaller than this. There is no simple electrical method of eliminating this leakage except the use of alternating-current amplifiers. Thermionic emission varies exponentially with temperature. For a Cs-CsO-Ag surface, an increase in temperature from 20 to 30°C would increase the emission 100 per cent. Accordingly, it is important to keep the temperature of the tubes as low as possible, not only by keeping the ambient temperature low, but by filtering out infrared radiation from the source which might otherwise raise the temperature of the cathode. Some tubes have been specially designed to be kept cool by liquid air. This leakage due to thermionic currents is relatively unimportant, except in the case of the red-sensitive tubes with their consequent low values of work function.

References

1. Ives and Kingsbury, *Jour. Optical Soc. Am.*, **21**, 541 (1931).
2. Ives, Dushman, and Karrer, *Astrophys. Jour.*, **43**, 9 (1916).
3. A. R. Olpin, *Phys. Rev.*, **36**, 251 (1930).
4. Adams, Barnes, and Forsythe, *Jour. Optical Soc. Am.*, **21**, 207 (1931).
5. Dorcas and Forbes, *Jour. Am. Chem. Soc.*, **49**, 308 (1927).
6. L. R. Koller and A. H. Taylor, *Jour. Optical Soc. Am.*, **25**, 184 (1935).
7. G. Dejardin, *Rev. gén. élec.*, **34**, 629 (1933).
8. W. Leo and C. Müller, *Phys. Zeitschr.*, **36**, 113 (1935).

9. L. R. KOLLER, "Physics of Electron Tubes"; Zworykin and Wilson, "Photo Cells and Their Application"; E. D. Wilson, *The Elec. Jour.*, **32,** 270 (1935); G. P. Barnard, *Proc. Phys. Soc.* (London), **47,** 477 (1935); L. A. Wood, *Rev. Sci. Inst.*, **6,** 196 (1935).

10. G. P. BARNARD, "The Selenium Cell," Richard R. Smith, Inc., New York, 1930.

11. G. F. METCALF and B. J. THOMPSON, *Phys. Rev.*, **36,** 1489 (1930).

12. W. B. NOTTINGHAM, *Jour. Franklin Inst.*, **209,** 287 (1930).

13. L. A. DuBRIDGE, *Phys. Rev.*, **37,** 392 (1931).

14. TAYLOR and KERR, *Rev. Sci. Inst.*, **4,** 28 (1933).

15. G. L. LOCHER, *Phys. Rev.*, **42,** 525 (1932).

16. B. RAJEWSKY, *Phys. Zeitschr.*, **32,** 121 (1931).

17. FORSYTHE and EASLEY, *Jour. Optical Soc. Am.*, **21,** 685 (1931).

18. L. R. KOLLER, *Rev. Sci. Inst.*, **2,** 551 (1931).

19. FORSYTHE and EASLEY, *Rev. Sci. Inst.*, **3,** 488 (1932).

20. SHARP and ECKWEILER, *Jour. Optical Soc. Am.*, **23,** 245 (1933).

21. TAYLOR, *Jour. Optical Soc. Am.*, **4,** 9 (1920); *Bur. Standards Jour.*, **391,** 405; *I.E.S.*, **15,** 811 (1920).

22. J. H. J. POOLE and H. H. POOLE, "Photoelectric Cells and Their Applications"—Edited by J. S. Anderson.

23. H. C. RENTSCHLER, *Trans. A.I.E.E.*, **49,** 113 (1930).

24. J. F. H. CUSTERS, *Zeitschr. tech. Physik*, **14,** 154 (1933).

25. A. E. WHITFORD, *Astrophys. Jour.*, **76,** 213 (1932).

CHAPTER VIII

MEASUREMENTS OF RADIANT ENERGY WITH PHOTOGRAPHIC MATERIALS*

L. A. Jones†

The magnitude of the response of a photographic material which has been exposed to radiant energy depends upon the wavelength of the radiant energy used in making the exposure. Photographic materials, therefore, are sensitive receivers of the selective type and can be used for the measurement of radiant energy in absolute terms only after having been calibrated by some form of nonselective receiver, such as a thermopile, a bolometer, or a vane radiometer. While in general the direct method of measuring radiant energy by use of a nonselective receiver may seem to be preferable to the use of a selective receiver requiring calibration, there are in fact many cases where the disadvantages arising from necessity of calibration are more than overbalanced by the advantages which arise from the inherent characteristics of the selective receiver. In the case of the photographic material, we may enumerate among the points of superiority the following:

1. It may be used for recording simultaneously the relative intensities of a large number of different samples of radiant energy and, moreover, it gives a permanent record of these intensities.
2. It is a receiver of the integrating type, and hence in the case of very low intensities the response can be increased up to easily measurable magnitudes by making the exposure times long. Furthermore, as a consequence of its integrating action, average values, for definite time intervals, of variable intensities may be obtained.
3. As a result of its integrating characteristic, its effective sensitivity is appreciably greater for very low radiation intensities than that of the nonselective radiation-sensitive elements.

---

* Photographic nomenclature and symbols used. May differ from nomenclature and symbols used in other parts of the book.

† *Physicist, Kodak Research Laboratories.*

The photographic method for the measurement of radiation has been looked upon by many workers in the field as satisfactory only for approximate determinations and we find the rather general impression that results of high precision cannot be obtained by the photographic method. This impression, we feel sure, is the result of attempts to make quantitative measurements by the photographic method without sufficient knowledge of the characteristics of the photographic material. It is perfectly true that the magnitude of the response given by a photographic material to a specified quantity of radiant energy

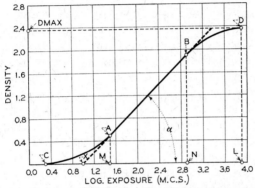

Fig. 164.—Typical *D*-log *E* curve of a photographic material.

depends upon many factors and it is only by the careful control of all of these factors which determine the magnitude of response that results of a high precision can be obtained. A complete understanding of the characteristics of the photographic emulsion is a necessary requirement to the use of this medium for work of high precision. A rather complete discussion of the reactions of the photographic material to radiant energy, therefore, seems in order.

THE CHARACTERISTIC CURVE

The general relation between the *stimulus* (exposure) and the resultant *response* (the amount of developed silver, usually expressed as *density*) may be shown graphically as illustrated in Fig. 164, where values of the logarithm of the exposure (log *E*) are plotted as abscissa and the corresponding values of response (density *D*) are plotted as ordinates. Since the photographic material is a sensitive receiver of the integrating type, the magnitude of the effect resulting from the action of radiant energy depends upon two factors: one which expresses the rate at which the radiant energy falls upon the sensitive surface, and the other denoting the time during which the action continues.

Exposure.   Exposure E may be defined by the expression,

$$E = \text{rate} \times \text{time} \qquad (57)$$

Since photographic materials are intended primarily for the making of pictures, *i.e.*, for the reproduction of light and shade, it is customary in this field to express exposure in terms of *light* units.   The unit that has been adopted for this purpose is the meter candle which is an evaluation of the *intensity* aspect of radiant energy in terms of the spectral sensitivity of the human eye.   For this purpose, therefore, exposure is defined as follows:

$$E = I \cdot t \text{ (meter candle seconds, mcs.)} \qquad (58)$$

where I = illumination, meter candles, mc.
$\quad$ t = times, sec.

In applying the photographic material to the measurement of energy, it is frequently necessary to deal with wavelengths to which the human eye is totally insensitive and for these wavelengths of radiant energy it is impossible to express exposure in terms of visual units.   It seems desirable, therefore, to abandon completely the use of the meter candle and to adopt for this discussion an energy unit applicable to the entire wavelength range.   For this purpose we shall use the erg and express exposure in terms of energy units, as indicated by the following expression:

$$E = I \cdot t \text{ (ergs/cm}^2) \qquad (59)$$

where I = radiant-flux density, (ergs/(sec cm^2.))
$\quad$ t = times, sec.

Density.   The amount of silver resulting from the development of the exposed photographic material is usually measured in terms of its light-absorbing power, and it is customary to express this as *density* (D), which is defined by the following relationships:

F_0 = luminous flux incident on the silver deposit.
F_1 = luminous flux transmitted by the silver deposit.
T = transmission factor.
O = opacity.
D = density.
$T = F_1/F_0$.
$1/T = O = F_0/F_1$.
$D = \log_{10} O$.

The graphic form of representing the relation between density and log exposure (Fig. 164) was proposed first by Hurter and Driffield[1-4] and is therefore quite commonly referred to as the *H and D* curve, although the terms *D-log E curve* and *characteristic curve* are frequently used in reference thereto. It has been found experimentally that in the case of many photographic materials a considerable portion of the D-log E curve is represented satisfactorily, within the limits of experimental errors, by a straight line. The limits of the straight-line region are designated by the points A and B. The exposure region covered by the straight-line portion of the characteristic curve is usually designated as the *region of correct exposure* since throughout this exposure range density is directly proportional to log E.

Gradient and Gamma. The gradient G at any point on the characteristic curve may be represented by the derivative $dD/(d \log E)$. For the straight-line portion, G is constant and may be conveniently expressed in terms of the angle α subtended by the line AB and the log E axis. The tangent of this angle is called gamma, γ.

$$\text{Gamma } (\gamma) = \tan \alpha \qquad (60)$$

It must be remembered that this expression can be applied only to the portion of the characteristic curve which is a straight line and has no significance for parts of the curve for which the gradient is not constant.

The value of gamma depends upon the extent to which development is carried and, in fact, was referred to by Hurter and Driffield (*loc. cit.*) as the *development constant*. It is frequently used as defining the *contrast* of the photographic material. The logic of its use in this connection is apparent when it is realized that the greater the value of gamma, the greater will be the *density difference* by which a photographic material reproduces a given *exposure difference*.

Latitude. Projection of the straight-line portion of the D-log E curve on the log E axis determines the exposure range over which direct proportionality between D and log E exists. By dropping perpendiculars from the points A and B, the points M and N are established. These fix the limits of this exposure range. The distance between M and N is called *latitude*, L, and may be expressed either in log E units or in exposure units. Thus,

$$L = \log E_n - \log E_m \text{ (log } E \text{ units)}$$

or

$$L = \frac{E_n}{E_m} \text{ (exposure units)} \tag{61}$$

Latitude is not constant for a given photographic material since its value depends directly upon the *extent* to which development is carried and to a lesser extent on other processing factors. It depends also upon certain exposure conditions, such as quality (spectral composition) of the exposing radiation.

Inertia, Sensitivity, and Speed. The straight line AB extended cuts the log E axis at the point x and the value of E at this point is called the inertia, i. Since a material of low sensitivity has a high inertia value, and vice versa, it is necessary to take the reciprocal of the inertia in order to obtain a value which is directly proportional to sensitivity. Hence

$$\text{Sensitivity} \propto \frac{1}{i} \tag{62}$$

The absolute values obtained by taking the reciprocal of the inertia (when expressed in the conventional manner, *i.e.*, in terms of *light* units, meter candle seconds) may be inconvenient for practical purposes since they may be less than unity and hence expressible only as decimals or fractions. It is customary, therefore, in setting up practical sensitivity or *speed* scales, to multiply this reciprocal by a constant, k, chosen more or less arbitrarily so as to give a series of convenient numbers. In general, therefore, speed is defined by the equation:

$$\text{Speed, } S = \frac{1}{i} \cdot k \tag{63}$$

Under- and Overexposure Regions. From the point A, Fig. 164, the D-log E curve continues to the left into the region of decreasing exposure with constantly decreasing gradient until at the point C this gradient becomes zero, *i.e.*, the curve becomes parallel to—or, if proper correction for fog has been made, coincident with—the log E axis.   This region, C to A, is generally referred to as the region of *underexposure*, or sometimes the *toe* of the characteristic curve.   Thus the density difference by which a given exposure difference is rendered decreases continuously from some finite value at the point A to zero.   As will be shown later, it is usually necessary where the highest precision is required, to use the photographic material as a null indicator.   Since there is always a certain probable error in determining where two densities are equal,* it follows that the greatest sensitivity is attained when the two densities being compared lie at a point on the curve where the gradient is relatively high, since a given error in density equality at such a point corresponds to a minimum uncertainty in the equality of the energy values.

From the point B the curve continues to the right into the region of increasing exposure with a constantly decreasing gradient until at the point D the gradient becomes zero, *i.e.*, the curve becomes parallel to the log E axis.   The value of density corresponding to the point D is the *maximum density*, D_{max}, obtainable with the existing processing conditions, development time, developer constitution, temperature, etc.   The value of D_{max} is not fixed entirely by these processing factors but depends to some extent on the quality of the exposing radiation.   This region, B to D, is called the *region of overexposure*, or sometimes the *shoulder* of the characteristic curve.   In this region also the density difference, ΔD, corresponding to some exposure difference, Δ log E, decreases progressively with increasing exposure and becomes zero at the point D.

Extent of Development. The shape and position of the characteristic curve depend upon the character of development, particularly upon the extent to which development is carried. The curves in Fig. 165 illustrate a rather idealized case in which identically exposed materials have been developed for different lengths of time in the same developing solution.   Curve **1** is

* See Chap. IX.

that obtained for a development time of 2 min. By increasing
the development time by successive steps of 2 min., curves 2 to 6
are obtained.   It will be noted that curve 1 has a relatively low
slope (γ), and as the development time is increased, this slope
increases rapidly at first and then more slowly as it approaches
curve 7 which represents the limiting slope to which this particular material can be developed.   This limiting value of gamma is
usually referred to as *gamma infinity* (γ_∞).

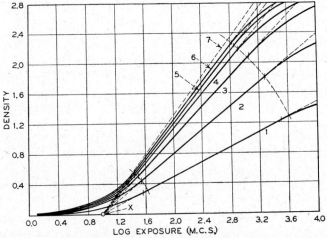

Fig. 165.—Family of *D*-log *E* curves illustrating the approach to gamma infinity
(curve 7) for increasing development time.

The figure also illustrates the way in which *latitude* decreases
as the time of development is increased.   The small vertical
lines drawn through each of the curves mark the beginning and
termination of the straight-line portion.   A somewhat more
graphic picture of the way γ increases with time of development
is illustrated in Fig. 166.   The horizontal dotted line marked
γ_∞ represents the limiting value of gamma which can be obtained
with this material when processed in this particular developer.
For any particular photographic material the rate at which
gamma increases depends upon the constitution, concentration,
and temperature of the developing solution, and upon the rate
of agitation during development.   Curve *B* in Fig. 166 illustrates
a lower rate of growth of gamma resulting from the use of a
less concentrated developer than is used in obtaining curve *A*.

Fog and Fog Correction. When a sample of photographic material is developed without exposure to radiant energy other than that which may be present in the darkroom in which the work is being done, a certain amount of density is in general produced. This is referred to as *fog*. Fog may be considered as falling into two general categories:

 a. Inherent fog.
 b. Development fog.

The former may be subdivided into: (1) fog arising from grains made developable by the chemical processes involved in the manufacture of the emulsion, and (2) fog from those grains

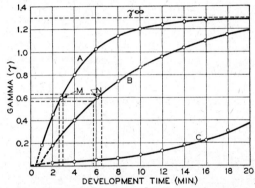

Fig. 166.—Time of development-gamma curves. *A*, for high rate of development; *B*, for low rate of development. Curve *C* is the corresponding time of development-fog curve.

made amenable to development by the exposure of the emulsion to light either during manufacture, inspection, packing or during handling of the material in the darkroom prior to development.

 Development fog may arise from various causes, such as the action of fogging agents or reaction products in the developer, aerial oxidation, etc. The amount of fog density generally increases with the extent to which development is carried, as illustrated by curve *C*, Fig. 166. If it is desired to know exactly how much density is attributable to the exposure which has been intentionally given to the photographic material, it is necessary to make a correction for fog. While Hurter and Driffield (*loc. cit.*) realized that the amount of fog present in any density is dependent upon the magnitude of that density, they nevertheless considered it satisfactory for sensitometric purposes to make the fog correction by subtracting a constant value from all densities, this value being determined by measuring the density formed on a sample of the photographic material which had not been exposed but had been subjected to the same development treatment. This custom has usually been followed since that time in sensitometric work.

Where photographic materials are used for the measurement of radiant-energy intensities by techniques which involve precise determination of the shape and position of the characteristic curve, more refined fog correction must be applied. This subject has been studied at considerable length by various investigators.[5-9] The modification of Meidinger's formula, as proposed by Wilsey[7] is probably the most reliable method for making this fog correction. This formula is

$$D_f = \frac{D_m - D_\infty}{D_m} \cdot F \qquad (64)$$

in which D_f is the fog to be deducted, D_m the maximum developable density, D_∞ is the limiting image density which can be obtained on extended development of the particular exposure under consideration, and F is the fog density on an unexposed area of the materials.

Deviations from Typical Behavior. The characteristic curves shown in Figs. 164, 165, and 166 represent what may be referred to as a typical or idealized case. Some photographic materials behave in the manner shown, all of the straight-line portions intersecting at a point on the log E axis. Many photographic materials, however, do not conform to this type. Some may show a common intersection point lying either below or above the log E axis and the position of this point may depend markedly upon the character of development. Moreover, in the case of many photographic materials, a single intersection point does not exist. Sometimes the characteristic curve shows very little if any straight-line portion, this being contracted to a mere inflection point with a typical S-shaped curve. Still other materials may show double or even triple straight-line regions with the accompanying double or triple gamma values. The subject of variation in the shape of the D-log E relationships for various photographic materials has been treated at considerable length by Sheppard.[10]

While attempts have been made to formulate analytically the
relationships between density and exposure, no generally successful formula has been evolved.   While formulas have been proposed which fit quite well a particular set of conditions, it is
impossible to rely on any of these formulas without first proving
that they fit the particular material and conditions under which
it is to be used.   We are forced, then, to the conclusion that
the only satisfactory way of establishing the relationship between
density and exposure is by experimental determinations on a
particular photographic material processed according to a definite
technique.

FAILURE OF THE RECIPROCITY LAW

Thus far, in this discussion, it has been implied that for a given
photographic material developed under fixed conditions the
magnitude of the response (density) is a function of exposure E,
regardless of the absolute values of I and t which determine the
value of exposure.   This is not true and the failure of photographic materials to obey the Bunsen-Roscoe[11] reciprocity
law is commonly referred to as the *failure of the reciprocity
law*.   In using photographic materials for the measurement of
radiant energy, the departure from the reciprocity relationship must be recognized and possible errors resulting from this
cause eliminated, either by using a correctly designed experimental technique or by the precise measurement of the magnitude of the departure from the reciprocity-law relationship
together with the application of a correction based upon such
determinations.

Because of the failure of the reciprocal relation between the
I and t factors of exposure, it is necessary to discriminate carefully between *intensity-scale*-characteristic curves and *time-scale*-
characteristic curves.   The former are based upon an exposure
scale in which the intensity factor is variable and the time factor
constant, while the latter are derived from an exposure scale in
which the time factor is variable and the intensity constant.
In the field of photographic sensitometry it is predominant
practice to use time-scale exposures, although this practice is by
no means universal.   Frequently incorrect conclusions have
been drawn from sensitometric data because of failure to recog-

nize differences which may exist between time- and intensity-scale results.

The subject of reciprocity-law failure has been studied at great length by workers[12-28] in the field of photographic sensitometry, and various so-called laws have been enunciated from time to time as defining the relationship between the magnitude of response and the magnitudes of the time and intensity factors of exposure. One of these deserves particular mention since it has received rather widespread acceptance. This is the so-called Schwarzschild law which states that the magnitude of the response is proportional to the expression

$$I \cdot t^p$$

in which p is a constant. It has been definitely proved that the value of p is far from constant, hence serious errors in photographic radiometry may result from use of the Schwarzschild expression.

The most recent work on the subject indicates that the relationship between the intensity and time factors can be most satisfactorily expressed by an equation of the catenary form as proposed by Kron[19] and by Halm[20]

$$It = \frac{I_0 t_0}{2}\left[\left(\frac{I}{I_0}\right)^a + \left(\frac{I}{I_0}\right)^{-a} \right] \qquad (65)$$

In Fig. 167 the solid curve A represents the relationship as indicated by the catenary equation given above, the ordinates being values of log It for *constant density*. These are plotted against the corresponding values of the logarithm of the intensity factor (log I). Curve B represents the condition which would exist in case there were no failure of the reciprocity law. It will be seen that there is an intensity value to which there corresponds a minimum value of exposure to produce a specified density. This value of intensity is known as *optimal intensity* being represented in the equation by I_0, while t_0 appearing in the equation, denotes the exposure time corresponding to the optimal intensity for the fixed value of density to which the relationship applies. It is evident that for the intensities either above or below *optimal* a greater exposure $(I \cdot t)$ is required to produce the fixed density.

The catenary equation fits the experimentally observed values, in the case of most photographic materials, over a relatively wide intensity range extending usually from 0.001 of optimal intensity to 1,000 times optimal intensity, a total range of approximately 1 to 1,000,000. Outside of this range, however, the catenary fails to agree with the experimental observations. To mention one case, it was found that at an intensity of 0.00001 of optimal the variation between the value called for by the catenary and that actually observed is of the order of 200 or 300 per cent. No analytical expression has been found which fits the observed values over the entire experimental range. It should be remarked, however, that the low intensities where the

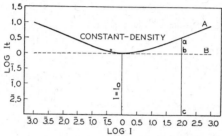

Fig. 167.—The catenary curve of reciprocity-law failure.

catenary fails to agree with observations are indeed very low, being so low that exposure times usually in excess of 24 hr. are required to give measurable densities.

The reciprocity data for a photographic material are usually expressed graphically as a family of curves as shown in Fig. 168. The four curves, which throughout the intensity range covered fit quite closely the catenary equation, are for fixed densities of 0.5, 1.0, 1.5, and 2.0, respectively. This family of curves contains complete information as to the character and magnitude of the reciprocity failure. From such a family of curves, characteristic *D*-log *E* curves may be plotted either on the basis of a *time scale* or on that of an *intensity scale*.[28] The constant-intensity lines on this diagram correspond to time-scale-characteristic curves, while the constant-time lines correspond to the intensity-scale-characteristic curves. It is obvious that any vertical line in Fig. 168 is a constant-intensity line. These are illustrated in the figure by the dotted vertical lines. The lines drawn at 45 deg. (Fig. 168) are lines of constant time, the times (in seconds) being shown along the top of the diagram.   Hence by using the log It values read at the intersections of the vertical lines, the time-scale D-log E curves may be plotted, while by using the log It values read at the intersections of the 45-deg.

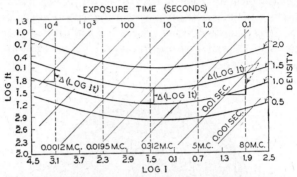

Fig. 168.—Family of experimentally measured reciprocity-failure curves.

line, the intensity-scale curves may be plotted.   In general the reciprocity curves (log It vs. log I) for different values of density tend to be parallel to each other.   Hence a family of time-scale D-log E curves all have the same contrast (gamma) and show that sensitivity is a function of I.   A family of *intensity-*

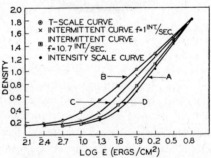

Fig. 169.—Curves showing the effect of mode of exposure on the D-log E relationship.

scale D-log E curves, on the other hand, yield variable values for both sensitivity (S) and contrast (γ).

The shape of the reciprocity relationship may depend to some extent upon the character of development and the extent to which development is carried, values of I_0, t_0, and a being dependent

upon these conditions.   The values of the constants I_0 and t_0 in
the catenary equation also depend upon the wavelength of the
exposing radiation.

In order to illustrate the magnitude of errors which may arise
from the failure of the reciprocity law, reference may be made
to the characteristic D-log E curves shown in Fig. 169.   Curve
B represents the relationship between density and log exposure
obtained for a specified set of processing conditions when variations in value of exposure are produced by a variation of the
time factor of exposure.

Fig. 170.—Sector wheel with logarithmic apertures commonly used in time-scale
sensitometers.

It is quite easy to devise exposing mechanisms which will
impose on a sample of photographic material a series of exposures
differing in time but of constant intensity.   One method of
doing this which is in very common use in the field of photographic sensitometry is the use of a rotating sector wheel such
as is illustrated in Fig. 170.   If this is mounted between the
standard light source and the photographic material, various
adjacent areas on the photographic material can be subjected to
a series of exposures differing in time, and if the mechanism is so
arranged that the exposure is made by only one revolution of the
sector, the exposure is continuous and not intermittent, as would
be the case were the sector wheel rotated at a relatively high
angular velocity.   Such exposure scales are commonly referred

to as *continuous time scales* to distinguish from the conditions resulting when the sector is rotated at a relatively high velocity, thus resulting in *intermittent time scales*.

Curve *A*, of Fig. 169, shows the *D*-log *E* relationship when all of the conditions are the same, except that the variation in exposure is obtained by a variation in the intensity factor. For this particular set of conditions it will be noted that the use of a time scale results in appreciably greater density values, particularly in the region of lower exposure values.

INTERMITTENCY EFFECT

Photographic materials in general do not integrate correctly an intermittent exposure.[29-41] The response (density) arising from the action of a specified exposure ($I \cdot t$) given in a series of intermittent flashes may be either greater than, equal to, or less than the same exposure given continuously. This fact is also illustrated in Fig. 169. Curve *C* shows the *D*-log *E* relationship obtained by exposing a photographic material under exactly the same conditions as those used in obtaining curve *B*, but with the sector wheel rotating at the rate of 1 r.p.s. This may be compared directly with curve *B* in which the exposure was continuous. It will be noted that breaking up the exposure into intermittent flashes in this case results in lower density values. By increasing the speed of rotation to 10 r.p.s., curve *D* is obtained, and by still further increase to 50 r.p.s., the resultant curve becomes coincident with curve *A*, the intensity-scale curve. Consideration of these facts indicates definitely that in using the photographic material for quantitative measurement of radiant energy, great care must be exercised in planning exposure techniques.

VARIATION OF CONTRAST (γ) WITH WAVELENGTH

Attention has already been called to the fact that sensitivity of photographic materials is a function of the wavelength of the exposing radiation. Superposed on this variation of sensitivity we find also a variation in contrast. For instance, if one sample of a given photographic material is subjected to a series of exposures using radiation of one wavelength, and another sample of the material is subjected to an identical series of exposures using radiation of a different wavelength, the resultant *D*-log *E*

characteristic obtained by plotting the density values after
development for the same time in the same developing solution
will in general give different values of gamma. This is illustrated in Fig. 171 which shows a series of characteristic curves

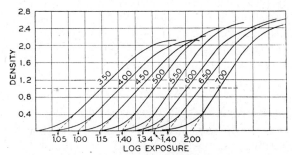

Fig. 171.—*D*-log *E* curves for the various wavelengths as indicated; development
time, 5 minutes.

obtained by exposing the same material to radiations of the
wavelengths as indicated. The dependence of contrast upon
wavelength may then be shown in the form of gamma-wavelength
curves similar to those shown in Fig. 172. These curves show

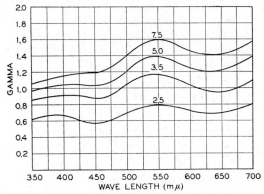

Fig. 172.—Gamma-wavelength curves for various time of development as
indicated.

the relation between gamma and the wavelength of the exposing
radiation as obtained by developing the photographic material to
different extents. As would be expected, when the development
is for a relatively short time, the magnitude of variation in gamma

value is considerably less than when development is carried to the point approaching gamma infinity.

One of the earliest observations of the dependency of gamma upon wavelength was that of Abney in 1901. Most observers since that time have agreed with Abney's findings, although T. Thorne-Baker, in 1923, reported that he found no change in gamma with wavelength in the region between 240 mμ and the visible. G. R. Harrison has published results which indicate conclusively that for the materials with which he worked there is a marked variation of gamma with wavelength in the near ultraviolet region. It should be emphasized, however, that this variation cannot be predicted but must be determined for the particular material being used and under the conditions of use. In the case of dye-sensitized material, the relationship between gamma and wavelength is not predictable. Thus, in the case of materials which have been rendered sensitive to green and red by dye sensitizing, the contrast (gamma) in these regions may be either greater or less than that in the blue and violet region, to which the silver halide is itself sensitive. Therefore, no general relationship between gamma and wavelength can be formulated which will be useful when using photographic materials for precise measurement of radiant energy. We find ourselves in this case in the same position as with respect to many other factors of the photographic material, *viz.*, that the relationship must be determined for the particular material being used and under the exact conditions of usage.[42-47]

GROWTH OR DECAY OF THE LATENT IMAGE

When radiant energy is incident on the photographic material, some change is produced within the sensitive silver-halide grains. The precise nature of this change is not known, although certain theories as to what occurs are strongly supported by experimental evidence. It is known, however, that, whatever the nature of this change may be, it is such that the grain in which this change has occurred is made developable; *i.e.*, it can be reduced to metallic silver by the action of a suitable developing agent which previously was not capable of reducing that grain to metallic silver, except perhaps by very prolonged action of the developing solution. The direct response of the photosensitive material to the radiant-energy stimulus is therefore a *latent image* which can only be converted into a *real image* (silver) by the process of development. This latent image may be subject to a certain amount of growth or decay[48–50] subsequent to the termination of exposure and hence the amount of silver which can be produced by a specified development treatment may depend to some extent upon the time which elapses between the termination of exposure and the development process. The magnitude of growth or decay is known to depend on many factors, such as the character of the emulsion itself, the condition of the material (temperature, moisture content, etc.) at the time of exposure, the conditions under which the exposed material is stored subsequent to exposure and prior to development, the development treatment to which the exposed material is subjected, etc.

It seems almost hopeless to attempt to predetermine with high precision the magnitude of these growth and decay effects. We are forced, therefore, either to determine them for a particular set of conditions or to require that the exposure of a material to an unknown sample of radiant energy and to the known sample of radiant energy with which it is to be compared, shall be simultaneous. In case it is impossible to make the exposure to the unknown sample of radiant energy simultaneous with the calibrating exposure, the possibility of errors arising owing to growth and decay effects may be minimized by making the ratio of the time elapsing between exposure to the calibrating radiant energy and the development of the material to the time elapsing between exposure of the material to the unknown sample of radiant energy and its development as nearly unity as possible.

TEMPERATURE AND MOISTURE CONTENT

The magnitude of the response of a photographic material depends to some extent at least upon the temperature of the material and its moisture content at the time the exposure is made. These two effects are referred to under the same heading since they frequently have been studied together, or one of the two factors has been studied without careful control of the other so that the resulting effects have frequently been confused. The literature references[51–61] to the various contributions on this subject are given without an attempt to separate out definitely those dealing with temperature effects from those dealing with moisture-content effects.

For the most part workers have reported that an increase in temperature is accompanied by an increase in sensitivity, although there are many exceptions to this finding. The work of Webb[61] shows definitely that the direction and magnitude of the temperature effect depend very much upon the intensity level at which the exposures are made. Thus it is quite possible to find the sensitivity either decreasing or increasing with increasing temperature, depending upon whether the work is being done above or below the optimal intensity value for the particular material being used. Likewise, the reverse may be true. It seems fairly reasonable to conclude, however, that the magnitude of the sensitivity change with temperature, with temperatures between $+40$ and $-40°C$, is relatively small when working at the intensity levels usually encountered in practical work. At temperatures between -40 and $-200°C$ the sensitivity change may be very great.

The literature relating directly to the dependence of sensitivity on moisture content (relative humidity of the atmosphere with which the material is in equilibrium at the time of exposure) is rather meager.[62–64] From the reported results it is apparent that different photographic materials behave very differently with respect to the magnitude of sensitivity changes which depend upon moisture content of the emulsion at the time of exposure. In some cases a change of from 0 to 80 per cent relative humidity produced a loss of effective speed amounting to as much as 25 per cent.

We must conclude that it is not possible at present to formulate any general relations between magnitude of response and temperature and humidity for all photographic materials. We must depend for the complete elimination of possible errors due to these causes upon a technique which provides for the exposure of the material to the unknown sample of radiation and to the calibrating exposures at identical temperatures and relative humidities. If this condition cannot be attained, then steps must be taken to prove that differences in temperature and moisture content on the two occasions are not sufficiently different to cause intolerable errors with the particular material being used.

NONUNIFORMITY OF EFFECTIVE SENSITIVITY

The most carefully made photographic materials may show measurable differences in sensitivity from point to point, even when the area used is relatively small.   These variations may be due to such factors as inequality in thickness of coating, variation in the specific sensitivity of the emulsion, or slight differences in the rate at which development takes place at different points on the plate owing, perhaps, to differential permeability to the developing solution.   While these inequalities are in general too small to be of consequence in the practical work to which these materials are usually applied, they may become of great importance and of sufficient magnitude to introduce serious errors when an attempt is made to use these materials for the purposes of precise quantitative measurement.

It is difficult to develop two separate samples of photographic materials to exactly the same extent.   This is particularly true if the attempt is made to obtain identical developments at different times and in different mixings of developer.   Moreover, it is quite difficult to obtain absolutely uniform development over a large area.   One of the chief causes for this difficulty, aside from variations in the concentration, constitution, and temperature of the developing solution, is the variation in the rate of the circulation of the developing solution at the surface of the photographic material.

In order to minimize errors arising from nonuniformity of effective sensitivity and nonuniformity of development, it is advisable to use areas which lie immediately adjacent to each other on the same sample of photographic material.

From a consideration of the foregoing discussion which is intended to emphasize that the relationship between an exposure and the resultant density depends on a multitude of factors, it seems reasonable to conclude that it is practically hopeless to determine all of the various relationships for a given sample of photographic material which will permit the direct computation of energy magnitudes in terms of a measured density.   It is quite possible, however, to plan the technique of photographic radiometry so that practically all of these disturbing variables may be eliminated and the photographic material employed according to a truly null method.

We can now set forth the conditions which must be fulfilled in order that the photographic result may show that two samples of radiant energy are of equal intensities.   First of all, let us require that the two samples of radiant energy, I_1 and I_2, which it is desired to compare, be used to expose two relatively small areas, A and B, on the photographic material, and, furthermore, that these areas be *immediately* juxtaposed.   This condition minimizes any possibility of error due to variation in sensitivity from point to point and also makes it possible to subject the two exposed areas to identical processing (development, fixing, washing, drying, etc.) treatment.

Now we shall designate the various factors involved as follows:

	A	B
Area	A	B
Intensity of incident radiation	I_1	I_2
Wavelength of incident radiation	λ_1	λ_2
Exposure time	t_1	t_2
Density	D_1	D_2

In general $I_1 = I_2$ only when:

  a. Both exposures are made nonintermittently.
  b. Exposures made simultaneously.
  c. $t_1 = t_2$
  d. $\lambda_1 = \lambda_2$
  e. $D_1 = D_2$

The above conditions are written on the assumption that we are dealing with homogeneous radiant energy, *i.e.*, radiant energy consisting of a single or at least an extremely narrow band of wavelengths.   The condition $\lambda_1 = \lambda_2$ may be replaced without any danger of the introduction of error by requiring, in case the energy is not homogeneous, that the two samples which are being compared shall have *identical spectral compositions*.

It may appear that the fulfillment of all of these requirements is difficult or impossible, but this is not the case and several methods of photographic radiometry have been devised which actually do meet all of these requirements.   When these requirements have been met, it is quite possible to obtain results subject to a probable error of not more than 1 or 2 per cent, and this in the case of a single determination.   When it is considered that it is very easy to make a large number of independent observations by a photographic method, it is evident that the probable error can be reduced with little difficulty to well under ± 1 per cent.

When it is necessary to compare the relative intensities of two samples of radiant energy which are not of identical spectral composition, the above rigid specifications for equality obviously cannot be met, and instead of a truly null method, we are forced to determine the wavelength sensitivity function for the photographic material and this, of course, can only be done by using some nonselective radiation-sensitive receiver, such as a thermopile or vane radiometer, or by using samples of radiant energy differing in wavelength but of known relative intensities.   For instance, by using a source of radiation, for which the relation between, let us say, temperature and spectral emission is determined by a known relationship, and a radiation-dispersing instrument of known characteristics, samples of radiant energy bearing to each other a definite intensity relationship may be obtained.   In this way the spectral sensitivity of the photographic material may be established, and further direct comparisons with unknown samples of radiant energy differing in wavelength may be made by a method conforming rigidly to our requirements earlier set forth.   The precision obtainable in each of these comparisons is of the order already mentioned, but it is, of course, obvious that we are depending for the precise relationship of one wavelength to that of another on elements other than the photographic material itself.

In Fig. 173 one method is illustrated by which the rigid requirements for the comparison of two homogeneous or spectrally identical samples of radiant energy may be compared by a method meeting all of the requirements set forth for the elimination of all possible errors due to the peculiarities of the photographic material.   In the upper part of the figure the two rectangular areas, A and B, show the appearance of the photographic material after development.   The area A was subjected to the exposure $E = I_x \cdot t_1$, this exposure being the same at all points on the area A, I_x being the unknown radiation intensity. The area B was subjected at the extreme left end to an exposure $E = I_a \cdot t_2$, the value of both factors being known.   The exposure given area B was increased in a known manner (without any modification of spectral distribution) reaching a maximum value at the extreme right end of $E = I_b \cdot t_2$. I_a was less than I_x, while I_b was greater than I_x. The time factor of exposure at all points on the area B was the same, t_2, the increase in exposure being due to an increase in the intensity factor of exposure.

In the case illustrated, the increase in I_a from left to right was logarithmic, as indicated by the log E scale at the bottom of the figure.   It is not essential that the increase be logarithmic

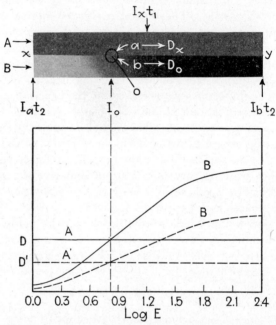

Fig. 173.—Illustration of a method of photographic radiometry using a continuously wedged calibrated exposure.

but only that the function relating intensity and distance along the strip be precisely known.   The two exposed areas lie immediately adjacent to each other, being separated by the line xy. It is quite possible to carry out the exposing in such a manner that when the density on the strip A is equal to that on the strip B, the line xy practically disappears. After exposure the photographic material is developed, reasonable care being taken to obtain uniform development over the entire surface, although as will be seen, the requirement for a high degree of uniformity is not essential. After development, the position of the point O

lying on the line xy, at which $D_a = D_b$, is determined. This can be done in a number of different ways,* either by direct inspection or by the aid of a suitable illuminating and magnifying optical device.

The curves in the lower part of the figure illustrate the distribution of density in the two areas. Curve B shows the density distribution for area B, and curve A that for area A. It is obvious that the balance point O must lie at the intersection of these two curves. The dotted curves B' and A' illustrate the condition that would have existed had the exposed material been developed for a much shorter time or to a less contrast. The position of density equality would have been exactly the same. This emphasizes the fact that when using such a method, it is of little importance to what extent the exposed material is developed except insofar as the slope of the characteristic curve B determines the angle at which the two curves intersect and therefore the precision with which the location of the balance point can be determined. For the case illustrated in the figure, the balance point O corresponds to an intensity, I_0, which, as indicated by the log E scale, is 6.61 (Δ log $E = 0.82$) $\times I_a$ and hence $I_x = 6.61 \times I_a$.

Let us review now the conditions which must be met in carrying out this technique in order that the various errors which might arise due to the characteristic of the photographic material may be eliminated.

a. Both exposures are given nonintermittently, thus eliminating any error which might possibly arise due to the failure of the photographic material to integrate correctly an intermittent exposure.

b. Exposures are simultaneous, thus eliminating any possible error due to growth or decay of the latent image which might occur during the time elapsing between the termination of the exposure and the development of the exposure.

c. The criterion that $I_x = I_0$ is that equal densities are produced ($D_x = D_0$) when the exposure times are the same ($t_1 = t_2$), thus eliminating any possibility of error due to failure of the reciprocity law.

d. Spectral composition of the radiant energy I_x is identical with that of the radiant energy I_a.

e. The two areas A and B which are actually used in the determination of the balance point O are small and lie immediately adjacent to each other, being separated by a line which practically disappears when the densities D_x and D_0 are equal. The total area involved may be reduced to very small

---

* See Chapter IX.

dimensions since a circle 1 or 2 mm in diameter bisected by the line xy is usually of ample size.   The fact that the two areas, of importance in establishing the position of the point O, lie so close together on the plate, practically eliminates any errors which might arise from nonuniformity of the photographic material or from nonuniformity in development.   It will be seen that the use of this technique reduces very greatly the requirements for uniformity of development, since the area concerned is so small.

f. Any possible errors due to differences of temperature or moisture content of the photographic material at the time of exposure are practically eliminated by the fact that the exposures are made simultaneously on small areas of photographic material immediately adjacent to each other.

To illustrate the repeatability of readings which can be obtained in a method of this type, the values shown in Table 22 are given.   These are taken from a discussion of a method for measuring the photographic reflecting powers of colored surfaces,[65] a problem directly analogous to the photographic measurement of radiation intensities.

TABLE 22.—REPEATABILITY OF RESULTS

No.	I_x	Δ
1	42.0	0.25
2	41.0	0.75
3	42.0	0.25
4	42.0	0.25
Mean	41.75	0.37
		0.88%

The values given are four separate determinations, each of which is based on a single determination of the position of the balance point O, as illustrated in Fig. 173.   The mean deviation from the average of the four readings is 0.37, or 0.88 per cent of the average intensity value.   Since, as mentioned previously, the number of individual determinations can be increased without undue additional labor, it is apparent that the probable error can be reduced to a very low value.   Thus, insofar as errors due to the photographic material are concerned, values of high precision can be obtained by such a method.   It must be remembered, of course, that the precision of the final result depends also upon the experimental errors involved in the establishment of the absolute value of the comparison intensity.   In the case illustrated in

Fig. 173, this involves the evaluation of the known intensity I_a and the establishment of the relationship between I_a and I_0.

The technique which we have been discussing calls for a variation in the intensity of the comparison beam which is continuous between the maximum and minimum values. Such exposures are usually referred to as "continuously wedged exposures."

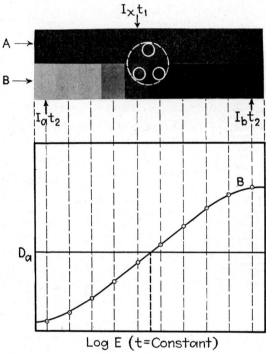

FIG. 174.—Illustrating a method of photographic radiometry using a stepped-wedge calibrating exposure.

In some cases it is difficult to control the exposure in this manner, and it is more convenient to use an exposure variation which is discontinuous or of the "stepped-wedge" type.

This is illustrated in Fig. 174, where, again, area *A* represents the part of a photographic material which is exposed to the radiation sample of unknown intensity and the area *B* is broken up into a series of 10 steps increasing from a minimum at the left to a maximum at the right. The relation between exposure given to each step must, of course, be known and in the particular case illustrated the increase is logarithmic, the exposure doubling from step to step, as indicated by the log E scale at the bottom of the figure. In general, the density in the area A will not be identical with that of any one of the steps. It is necessary, therefore, to read the densities and make a graphic interpolation. Curve B in the lower part of the figure represents the D-log E relationship as obtained by plotting the densities read from the various steps while D_a is the density for the area A. When using a technique of this kind, it is very much more important to obtain the highest possible uniformity of development at all points on the exposed area. Moreover, the possibility of variation in the effective sensitivity from point to point on the material is more serious since the criterion of equality is based upon density readings which must necessarily be made at points more widely distributed than in the case illustrated in Fig. 173. However, by exercising care in obtaining uniformity of development and by repeating determinations several times, errors arising from these sources may be reduced to a very satisfactorily low value.

It is, of course, obvious that in either of the methods illustrated, the intensity of the comparison beam may be held constant, while that of the unknown constant is varied in some known manner. In some cases it is also possible and advantageous to vary the intensity of both the comparison and the unknown sample, the two being "wedged" in opposite directions. Such a method has been proposed by Jones for absorption spectrophotometry.[66]

The precise control of the intensity of radiation incident on the photographic material is frequently one of the most difficult phases of photographic radiometry and, not only must one be able to control the intensity in a precisely known manner, but also in the case of nonhomogeneous radiation, this must be done in such a way that the spectral composition of the radiation is not altered. Many devices and methods have been developed for accomplishing this desired modulation of intensity. It does not seem feasible at this time to discuss in detail all of these various methods, but brief mention of some of them with references to the literature may be of value.

The utilization of the inverse-square law as a rule is not very practicable since an extremely long optical path is required to obtain intensity variation over a sufficiently wide range. The method, however, is of great use for checking the validity of other methods since intensity relations are subject to direct computation from a measurement of distance. Moreover, the variation of intensity accomplished in this manner is perfectly nonselective, being independent of wavelength. Continuously variable-wedged exposures may be made by using wedges of nonselectively absorbing material. Unfortunately no material is available which is nonselective over very great wavelength ranges, and hence such devices must be calibrated wavelength by wavelength where results of high precision are desired.

Probably the most suitable nonselectively absorbing material for making either continuous or stepped wedges is a deposit of platinum on quartz, as proposed by Merton.[67] The platinum may be applied either by sputtering[68] or by evaporation. Films made by these methods, however, differ somewhat with regard to selectivity.

In some cases "optical" wedges, as described by Miller,[69] can be used to advantage, since optical glass can be obtained which has practically no selective absorption within the visible and near ultraviolet regions.

Adjustable diaphragms or sets of fixed diaphragms may be used in some optical systems. In general, the iris type of diaphragm should be avoided since it is not possible to compute precisely the relation between intensity and aperture, this being due largely to the presence of zonal aberrations in the majority of lens systems. Diaphragms of the radial-sector type are free from this objection, but are somewhat inefficient in that their maximum opening is limited. However, carefully constructed and used, radial-sector diaphragms are capable of giving results of high precision.

Perforated plates and wire screens, singly and in combination, have been used by some workers with considerable success. For a more complete discussion of the subject, reference should be made to the very excellent papers by Harrison,[70] also to the general treatments of photographic photometry by Ornstein,[71] Dorgelo,[72] and Dobson, Griffith, and Harrison.[73]

Thus far it has been assumed that the modulation of exposure must be accompanied by variation in the intensity factor in order to avoid errors arising from possible failure of the reciprocity law. In many cases it is much easier to modulate exposure by con-

trolling the time factor.   For instance, with a sector wheel as
illustrated in Fig. 170, so arranged that the required exposure is
given by a single revolution of the sector, it is very easy to obtain
a nonintermittent stepped time scale; or by using a logarithmic
spiral sector, as shown in Fig. 175, it is equally simple to obtain a
nonintermittent continuously variable time scale.   By rotating
such sectors at a relatively high angular velocity (as compared
with the total duration of exposure) intermittent time-scale

exposures of either the stepped or
continuously variable variety may
be obtained.   In the latter case
there is a possibility of errors arising from two sources, the failure of
the reciprocity law and the failure
of the material to integrate correctly an intermittent exposure.
This method has in fact been used
very extensively in photographic
radiometry, but there has been
much controversy as to the validity
of the results obtained in this
way.

FIG. 175.—Sector wheel giving
a continuously modulated logarithmic time-scale exposure.

The rather recent investigations of O'Brien,[40] Twyman,[74] and
Webb,[41] have shown that under certain conditions an intermittent
time-scale method of modulating the exposure is entirely satisfactory.   Webb's contribution (*loc. cit.*) to this field is especially
valuable since he has shown conclusively that if the frequency of
interruption is sufficiently high, an intermittent time-scale exposure becomes identical with an intensity-scale exposure.   He has
shown that the frequency of flash or interruption is the critical
variable and the one which in the past has caused so much lack
of agreement between workers who have used intermittent
methods.   His results indicate that for a particular photographic
material, and for radiation of a particular wavelength and intensity, there is a critical frequency of interruption above which
it is perfectly safe to use intermittent exposures as equivalent to
continuous.   This equivalence occurs when the rate of interruption becomes sufficiently great so that each individual silver-
halide grain receives, *on the average*, approximately one quantum
per flash.[75]

The magnitude of the reciprocity and intermittency effects becomes greater as the intensity factor of the exposure becomes increasingly different, either greater or less, from the optimal intensity for the particular material. But even when conditions are such as to give rise to very large effects, results free from error due to these causes may be obtained, as has been shown by O'Brien and Parks[40] by using sufficiently high frequencies in making the intermittent exposure. It is impossible, of course, to make a general statement as to how fast sectors should be run to eliminate reciprocity-intermittency errors, but under the majority of conditions 30 interruptions per second are adequate. However, in order to insure the elimination of such errors, the critical frequency should be determined for the particular set of conditions.

Of apparatus commercially available for photographic spectroradiometry, probably the Hilger sector photometer combined with a suitable spectrograph is the oldest. Radiation intensities are modulated by a rotating sector and for many years the validity of results was subject to some suspicion because of intermittency effects. Recent work, however, by O'Brien and Webb seems to have settled this controversy and shown that results are valid provided the sector speeds are sufficiently high.

The firm of Adam Hilger, Ltd., has developed several very useful pieces of apparatus particularly adapted for absorption spectroradiometry and that have had wide usage. The theories underlying the principles of these instruments have been treated in detail by Twyman and others.[76] Quite recently the same firm has placed on the market the Spekker ultraviolet spectrophotometer[77] and a "notched-echelon-cell" spectrophotometric attachment.[78] In the case of the Spekker instrument the control of intensity is by a variable aperture actuated by a micrometer screw. The "notched-echelon-cell" provides a means whereby radiation may be made to pass through layers of the absorbing liquid varying in thickness so that by a single operation exposures may be made through 10 known thicknesses of absorbing material. The cell is of such a size that it requires a very small volume of liquid and the method has the great advantage that absorption curves can be obtained with materials which are changing rapidly in absorbing characteristics.

There seems to be no point in including in this discussion voluminous tables showing the numerical constants of various photographic materials which are available commercially.   Such numbers serve to show only approximately speed, contrast, etc. For precise work it is necessary to run calibration curves in each sample of photographic material being used, or to use a null method.   Information on characteristics of photographic materials is therefore only of value as a guide to the choosing of materials which have satisfactory characteristics for a particular problem. For this purpose it seems sufficient to give a few illustrative D-log E curves which represent rather broad classes of photographic materials.   These are shown in Fig. 176 in which curve A shows the general shape of this relation for high speed, relatively

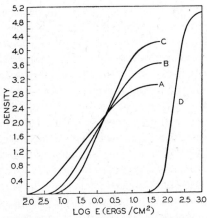

Fig. 176.—D-log E characteristic curves for four typical groups of photographic materials.

coarse-grained, low-contrast negative materials.   This class is characterized in general by relatively low gamma infinity and great latitude and exposure scale.   Curve B represents the relationship for a medium-speed negative material.   This group has in general a somewhat higher value of gamma infinity than the negative materials of extremely high speed.   The grain size is intermediate and latitude and exposure scale are also intermediate.   Curve C represents the general characteristics of low-speed high-contrast material, such as lantern-slide plates, process materials, and positive film.   This class has a high gamma infinity, fine grain, and a low latitude and exposure scale.   The abscissa values are expressed in terms of ergs/cm² for radiation of wavelength 435.86 mμ (blue mercury line).   Curve D represents a class of materials which has extremely high contrast (high gamma infinity) and resolving power.   The size of grain is very small, the speed very low, the latitude and exposure scale both being very low.

It is, of course, obvious that if a photographic material is to be used for the measurement of radiation, it must be sensitive to that radiation.   It seems quite useless to attempt to give quantitative information as to the spectral distribution of sensitivity for various commercially available photographic materials. Here, again, such information is of use only as a guide in choosing the material since it is necessary for precise work to determine the relative wavelength sensitivity on the particular sample of material that is being used.   All photographic materials are sensitive throughout the ultraviolet and to wavelengths in the visible less than approximately 500 mμ.   Sensitivity for longer wavelengths must be obtained by special dye sensitizing.   The effective sensitivity of materials in the ultraviolet decreases very rapidly for wavelengths less than about 250 mμ owing to the rapid increase in the absorption of energy in this region by the gelatin. It is frequently necessary, where energy levels are relatively low, to resort to methods of increasing the effective sensitivity in this region.   Schumann plates, which contain very little gelatin, are available commercially.   Special plates coated with fine crystals of fluorescent material are also available commercially.   Moreover, the effective sensitivity here may be increased very much by coating the surface of the plate with a thin film of fluorescent oil.[79]   This method has been discussed at considerable length by Lyman,[80] Harrison,[44] and Harrison and Leighton.[81]   Below about 200 mμ air becomes very absorptive and it is necessary here to use vacuum methods and plates specially sensitized as just noted.

For wavelengths longer than about 500 mμ resort is had to dye sensitizing.   Orthochromatic materials extend the sensitivity to about 600 mμ, while panchromatic materials extend the sensitivity still farther to about 700 mμ.

Photographic materials sensitive in the infrared region out to approximately 1,200 mμ are now available.   In general no one of these materials is most satisfactory for all spectral regions, and it is usually necessary—certainly where energy levels are relatively low—to choose the material which has the highest sen-

sitivity for a particular region.   Mees[32] has recently published
information on a series of special photographic materials suitable
for various spectral regions.   The chart from his paper on this
subject is shown in Fig. 177.   The black areas show the spectral
region in which the material has the highest sensitivity, while the
shaded areas indicate the spectral regions in which the material
has some sensitivity.

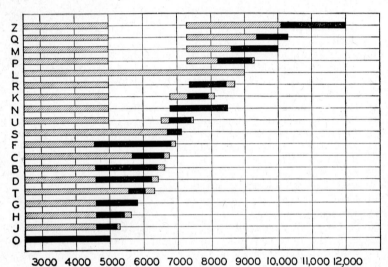

FIG. 177.—Chart showing spectral sensitivity of various commercially available
photographic materials.

References

1. *Chem. News*, **36**, 103 (1877); *Jour. Gas Lighting*, **30**, 337 (1877); *Electri-cian*, **11**, 188 (1883).
2. *Elektrotech. Zeitschr.*, **5**, 20 (1884).
3. F. HURTER, and V. C. DRIFFIELD, Photo-chemical Investigations and a New Method of Determination of the Sensitiveness of Photographic Plates, *Jour. Soc. Chem. Ind.*, **9**, 455 (1890).
4. "The Photographic Researches of Ferdinand Hurter and Vero C. Driffield," W. B. Ferguson, Editor, Royal Phot. Soc., 1920.
5. A. H. NIETZ, "Theory of Development," Monograph No. 2 from the Kodak Research Laboratories, Eastman Kodak Co., p. 141, 1922.
6. W. MEIDINGER, Untersuchungen über die photographische Schwär-zungskurve, *Zeitschr. physik. Chem.*, **114**, 89 (1924).
7. R. B. WILSEY, Fog Corrections in Photographic Densities, *Phot. Jour.*, **65** (n.s. **49**), 454 (1925).

8. A. P. H. TRIVELLI, E. P. WIGHTMAN, and S. E. SHEPPARD, Note on the Relationship of Photographic Emulsion Fog to Grain Size, *Phot. Jour.*, **65** (n.s. **49**), 134 (1925).

9. H. A. PRITCHARD, The Fog Correction of Photographic Densities: A Sensitometric Study, *Phot. Jour.*, **67** (n.s. **51**), 447 (1927).

10. S. E. SHEPPARD, Characteristic and Anomalies of Emulsions on Development, *Phot. Jour.*, **50**, 190 (1926).

11. BUNSEN and ROSCOE, *Pogg. Ann.*, **96**, 96; **100**, 43; **101**, 255; **108**, 193 (1876).

12. J. SCHEINER, Application de la Photographie à la Détermination des Grandeurs Stellaires, *Bull. Comité*, **1**, 227 (1889); *Astron. Nach.*, Nr. 2889.

13. W. DE W. ABNEY, The Failure in a Photographic Law with very Intense Light, *Phot. Jour.*, **18**, 302 (1893–1894).

14. A. SCHELLEN, Gültigkeit des Bunsen-Roscoe-Gesetzes für Bromsilbergelatine, *Inaug. Dissert.*, Rostock, 1898.

15. EDER, "Handbuch," v. 2, Jahrbuch, p. 457, 1899.

16. K. SCHWARZSCHILD, On the Deviations from the Law of Reciprocity for Bromide of Silver Gelatine, *Astrophys. Jour.*, **11**, 89 (1900).

17. E. ENGLISCH, "Das Schwarzungsgesetz für Bromsilber Gelatine," W. Knapp, Halle, 1901.

18. S. E. SHEPPARD, and C. E. K. MEES, On the Development Factor, *Phot. Jour.*, **43** (n.s. **28**), 48 (1903).

19. KRON, Ueber das Schwärzungsgesetz photographischer Platten, "Eder's Jahrbuch," p. 6, 1914.

20. J. HALM, *Roy. Astron. Soc. Mon. Not.*, p. 473, June, 1922.

21. P. S. HELMICK, The Variation in the Blackening of a Photographic Plate with Time of Exposure, Total Energy Remaining Constant, *Phys. Rev.*, **11**, 372 (1918); The Blackening of a Photographic Plate as a Function of Intensity of Light and Time of Exposure, *Phys. Rev.*, **17**, 135 (1921); The Blackening of a Photographic Plate as a Function of Intensity of Monochromatic Light and Time of Exposure, on the Basis of Hurter and Driffield's and Ross' Formulae. *Jour. Optical Soc. Am.*, **5**, 336 (1921).

22. LOYD A. JONES, and EMERY HUSE, On the Relation between Time and Intensity in Photographic Exposure, *J. Optical Soc. Am.*, **7**, 1079 (1923); **11**, 319 (1925).

23. LOYD A. JONES, EMERY HUSE, and V. C. HALL, On the Relation between Time and Intensity in Photographic Exposure, *Jour. Optical Soc. Am.*, **12**, 321 (1926).

24. LOYD A. JONES, and V. C. HALL, On the Relation between Time and Intensity in Photographic Exposure, *Jour. Optical Soc. Am.*, **13**, 443 (1926).

25. L. A. JONES, V. C. HALL, and R. M. BRIGGS, On the Relation between Time and Intensity in Photographic Exposure, *Jour. Optical Soc. Am.*, **14**, 223 (1927).

26. H. ARENS, and J. EGGERT, Über die Schwärzungsfläche photographischer Schichten, *Zeitschr. physik. Chem.*, **131**, 297 (1927–1928).

27. J. H. Webb, The Photographic Reciprocity Law Failure for Radiation of Different Wave Length, *Jour. Optical Soc. Am.*, **23**, 316 (1933).

28. L. A. Jones, and J. H. Webb, Reciprocity Law Failure in Photographic Exposures, *Jour. Soc. Mot. Pict. Eng.*, **23**, 142 (1934).

29. W. de W. Abney, Chemical Action and Exposure, *Phot. Jour.*, **18**, 56 (1893).

30. R. Englisch, Über die Wirkung intermittierender Belichtungen auf Bromsilbergelatine, *Arch. wissensch. Phot.*, **1**, 117 (1899).

31. K. Schwarzschild, On the Effect of Intermittent Exposure on Bromide of Silver Gelatine, *Astrophys. Jour.*, **11**, 92 (1900); *Phot. Corr.*, **36**, 171 (1899).

32. A. E. Weber, Über die Anwendung des rotierenden Sektors zur photographischen Photometrie, *Ann. Physik*, **45**, 801 (1914).

33. F. Eckert and R. Plummerer, Photographische Spektralphotometrie der Absorptionspektren von Farbstoffen, *Zeitschr. physik. Chem.*, **87**, 605 (1914).

34. H. E. Howe, On a Modification of the Hilger Sector Photometer Method for Measuring Ultraviolet Absorption and Its Application in the Case of Certain Derivatives of Fluoran, *Phys. Rev.*, **8**, 674 (1916).

35. R. Davis, Experimental Study of the Relation between Intermittent and Non-intermittent Sector Wheel Photographic Exposures, *Bur. Standards Sci. Papers*, **528**, 95 (1926).

36. L. A. Jones, A New Non-intermittent Sensitometer, *Jour. Franklin Inst.*, **189**, 303 (1920).

37. E. A. Baker, On the Validity of Talbot's Law for the Photographic Plate, *Proc. Optical Soc. Conv.*, **238**, Part I (1926).

38. B. O'Brien, Photographic Spectral Energy Measurement with a Spiral Aperture Disc, *Phys. Rev.*, **33**, 640 (1929).

39. B. O'Brien, and E. Dickerman, Intermittent Exposure in Photographic Spectrophotometry over Wide Intensity Ranges, *Phys. Rev.*, **37**, 471 (1931).

40. B. O'Brien and V. L. Parks, Photographic Reciprocity and Intermittency Defects Near the Long Wave-length Limit of Plate Sensitivity, *Phys. Rev.*, **41**, 387 (1932).

41. J. H. Webb, The Relationship between Reciprocity Law Failure and the Intermittency Effect in Photographic Exposure, *Jour. Optical Soc. Am.*, **23**, 157 (1933).

42. W. de W. Abney, On the Variation in Gradation of a Developed Photographic Image when Impressed by Monochromatic Light of Different Wave-lengths, *Proc. Roy. Soc.*, **68**, 300 (1901).

43. T. Thorne-Baker, The Behavior of Silver Bromide to Rays of Short-Wave-length, *Trans. Farad. Soc.*, **19**, 335 (1923).

44. G. R. Harrison, Photographic Sensitometry with Fluorescent Oils, *Jour. Optical Soc. Am.*, **11**, 113 (1925).

45. G. R. Harrison, Characteristics of Photographic Materials in the Ultraviolet, *Jour. Optical Soc. Am.*, **11**, 341 (1925).

46. L. A. Jones, Photographic Spectrophotometry in the Ultraviolet Region, *Bull. Nat. Res. Council*, No. 61, 109 (1927).

47. L. A. JONES and O. SANDVIK, Spectral Distribution of Sensitivity of Photographic Materials, *Jour. Optical Soc. Am.*, **12**, 401 (1926).

48. C. F. BRUSH, Photographic Photometry and Some Interesting Photographic Phenomena, *Brit. Jour. Phot.*, **57**, 781 (1910); *Phys. Rev.*, **31**, 241 (1910).

49. F. H. SEARS, Photographic Photometry with the 60-inch Reflector of the Mount Wilson Solar Observatory, *Astrophys. Jour.*, **39**, 307 (1914).

50. E. R. BULLOCK, On the Question of a Spontaneous Growth of the Latent Image between Exposure and Development, I, II, III, IV, *Sci. Ind. Phot.* Series II, **1**, 124, 169, 321, 366 (1930).

51. W. DE W. ABNEY, Molecular Physics and Photographic Action, *Phot. News*, **28**, 315 (1884).

52. A. and L. LUMIERE, Sur les actions de la Lumière aux tres Basses Températures, *Compt. rend.*, **128**, 359 (1899).

53. J. PRECHT, Neuere Untersuchungen über die Gültigkeit des Bunsen-Roscoe'schen Gesetzes bei Bromsilbergelatine, *Arch. wiss. Phot.*, **1**, 57 (1899).

54. E. S. KING, Photographic Photometry, *Photo-Beacon*, **17**, 267 (1905).

55. R. J. WALLACE, On the Sensitiveness of Photographic Plates at Different Temperatures, *Astrophys. Jour.*, **28**, 39 (1908).

56. J. BAILLAUD, La Méthode de l'Échelle de Teintes en Photométrie photographique, *Ann. de phys.*, **5**, 131 (1916).

57. G. DALEZKI, Über den Temperatureinfluss auf die photographischen Platten, *Zeitschr. wiss. Phot.*, **18**, 233 (1919).

58. A. ZIMMERN, Influence de la température sur la sensibilité des emulsions en radiographie, *Compt. rend.*, **174**, 453 (1922).

59. J. EGGERT and F. LUFT, Die Temperaturabhängigkeit des Photographischen Prozesses, *Veröffent. wiss. Zentral-Lab. Phot. Agfa*, **2**, 9 (1921).

60. S. E. SHEPPARD, E. P. WIGHTMAN, and R. F. QUIRK, The Temperature Coefficient of Photographic Sensitivity, *Jour. Phys. Chem.*, **38**, 817 (1934).

61. J. H. WEBB, The Effect of Temperature upon Reciprocity Law Failure in Photographic Exposure, *Jour. Optical Soc. Am.*, **25**, 4 (1935).

62. C. E. K. MEES, The Effect of Humidity on the Sensitiveness of Photographic Plates, *Astrophys. Jour.*, **40**, 236 (1914).

63. F. F. RENWICK, Effect of Humidity upon Photographic Speed, *Trans. Soc. Mot. Pict. Eng.*, No. 18, 69 (1924).

64. E. R. BULLOCK, "On the Question of a Spontaneous Growth of the Latent Image between Exposure and Development," I. Sci. ind. phot. Series II, **1**, 124, 1930.

65. L. A. JONES and J. W. MCFARLANE, The Precise Measurement of Filter Factors and Photographic Reflecting Powers, *Jour. Soc. Mot. Pict. Eng.*, **19**, 361 (1932).

66. L. A. JONES, A New Method for Photographic Spectrophotometry, *Jour. Optical Soc. Am.*, **10**, 561 (1925).

67. T. T. MERTON, On Ultraviolet Spectro-photometers, *Proc. Roy. Soc.* (London), **A106**, 378 (1924).

68. B. O'BRIEN, and T. A. RUSSELL, Preparation and Optical Properties of Evaporated Metal Wedge Films, *Jour. Optical Soc. Am.*, **24**, 54 (1934).

69. ORAN E. MILLER, Wedge Spectrograms without an Absorbing Wedge, *Rev. Sci. Inst.*, **3**, 30 (1932).

70. G. R. HARRISON, Instruments and Methods used for Measuring Spectral Light Intensities by Photography, *Jour. Optical Soc. Am.*, **19**, 267 (1929); Current Advances in Photographic Photometry, *Jour. Optical Soc. Am.*, **24**, 59 (1934).

71. L. S. ORNSTEIN, Intensity of Multiple Spectral Lines: Experiment and Theory, *Proc. Phys. Soc.*, London, **37**, 334 (1925); Methoden und Resultate der Intensitätsmessung, *Phys. Zeitschr.*, **28**, 688 (1927).

72. H. B. DORGELO, Die photographische Spektralphotometrie, *Phys. Zeitschr.*, **26**, 756 (1925).

73. G. M. B. DOBSON, I. O. GRIFFITH, and D. N. HARRISON, "Photographic Photometry," Oxford University Press, 1926.

74. F. TWYMAN, Various Publications of Adam Hilger, Ltd.; F. TWYMAN, and G. F. LOTHIAN, Conditions for Securing Accuracy in Spectrophotometry, *Proc. Phys. Soc.*, London, **45**, 643 (1933).

75. L. SILBERSTEIN, and J. H. WEBB, Photographic Intermittency Effect and the Discrete Structure of Light, *Phil. Mag.*, Ser. 7, **18**, 1 (1934).

76. F. TWYMAN and F. SIMEON, The Logarithmic Wedge Sector and Its Use in Quantitative Spectrum Analysis, *Trans. Optical Soc.* (London), **31**, 169 (1928–1930); and Hilger publications.

77. F. TWYMAN, The "Spekker" Photometer for Ultra-violet Spectrophotometry, *Trans. Optical Soc.* (London), **33**, 9 (1931–1932).   Also Hilger publication No. 184.

78. F. TWYMAN, L. J. SPENCER and A. HARVEY, Rapid Spectophotometry with Bi-multiple Spectra and a New Type of Wedge Cell, *Trans. Optical Soc.* (London), **33**, 37 (1931–1932); and Hilger publication No. 178.
    F. TWYMAN, A New Apparatus for Rapid Spectrophotometry of liquids in the Ultra-violet Region, *Proc. Phys. Soc.*, London, **45**, 1 (1933).

79. R. LADENBURG and C. C. VAN VOORHIS, The Continuous Absorption of Oxygen between 1750 and 1300 A and Its Bearings upon the Dispersion, *Phys. Rev.*, **43**, 315 (1933).

80. T. LYMAN, "Spectroscopy of the Extreme Ultraviolet," Longmans Green and Co., New York, 1928.
    P. R. GLEASON, The Reflecting Power of Some Substances in the Extreme Ultra-violet, *Proc. Nat. Acad. Soc.*, **15**, 551 (1929).

81. G. R. HARRISON and P. A. LEIGHTON, Homochromatic Spectrophotometry in the Extreme Ultraviolet, *Jour. Optical Soc. Am.*, **20**, 313 (1930).

82. C. E. K. MEES, Photographic Plates for Use in Spectroscopy and Astronomy, *Jour. Optical Soc. Am.*, **25**, 80 (1935).

CHAPTER IX

DENSITOMETERS AND MICROPHOTOMETERS

G. R. Harrison*

When a photographic emulsion is used to measure the intensity of a beam of radiation, some means must be provided to determine the density of the photographic deposit produced. This can be done most readily with a special form of photometer, designed to determine the amount of light transmitted by the deposit. Such an instrument is called a densitometer, or, if the area being measured can be limited to that covered by a small slit or pinhole, a microphotometer or microdensitometer.

All densitometers contain as fundamental features a source of light to provide the measuring beam traversing the plate, a means of limiting this beam to a desired area of the emulsion, and a means of comparing the brightness of this beam with that of another (or a part of the same) which has passed through a clear portion of the plate. The comparison can be made by visual observation, but accurate and reproducible results can be obtained in this way only when the two light beams being compared can be placed in optical juxtaposition, with provision for diminishing the intensity of the stronger beam by known amounts until it matches the intensity of the weaker. Such an instrument is of the subjective type because it depends on the judgment of the observer as to when a match has been obtained. Objective instruments, which are in more common use at present, use some type of physical photometer which gives a deflection definitely related to the amount of light falling on it. These are in general more convenient to use than eye-match instruments, and are capable of giving more accurate results. In some cases they are almost indispensable, since they can be arranged for automatic recording.

The measured value of the density of a photographic deposit varies somewhat with the quality of light used to measure it, since

* *Professor of Physics, Massachusetts Institute of Technology.*

the reduction in intensity of the measuring beam by the emulsion grains depends on both scattering and absorption, each of which varies with wavelength. In general the density as measured with blue light is greater than that measured with red or infrared. For this reason the temperature of an incandescent source used to produce the measuring beam should not be allowed to vary greatly during the course of measurement of a single plate (except with instruments using approximately monochromatic radiation), since the wavelength-energy distribution of the beam varies with the temperature of the source.

The value of the density of a deposit obtained depends also on the mode of illumination and the optical system used to measure it, and we must distinguish between diffuse and specular densities. Defining density as $d = log_{10} \dfrac{I_0}{I}$, where I_0 is the intensity of the incident-measuring beam and I is the intensity of the radiation after it has traversed the plate, we note that the value of I, and hence of d, will depend on whether we measure only the radiation in collimated emergent beam (specular density), or include all the radiation which has passed through the plate, no matter in what direction it may be traveling (diffuse density). Specular density is always greater than diffuse density, since so much of the scattered radiation is lost from the collimated beam used. Most microdensitometers measure specular densities; where diffuse densities are required, an integrating sphere attachment must be used with them, or else a means of diffuse illumination must be provided. Either type of density will serve, of course, for photographic photometry, and when the type of density is not specified, specular density is usually meant.

In selecting a densitometer, one of the most important criteria should be convenience of operation, since almost any standard type of instrument will give accurate and reproducible results. In recording microdensitometers the exact method of holding the plate, or its position, is of relatively small importance, but in many cases, in both astronomical and spectroscopic work, it is desired to measure only selected spots on the plate. Under such conditions it is most useful to have the plate rest on a horizontal table, unless the instrument is of the projection type, when its image can be observed on a screen and it can be moved by hand controls. All shutter and focusing adjustments and scales to be read should be placed so as to be readily accessible, for long-continued operation of a microphotometer is apt to be fatiguing under the best conditions.   This is especially true of the eye-match or subjective instruments.

An insidious source of error to which many densitometers are subject is the Schwarzschild-Villiger effect,[1] which is apt to appear with any instrument in which more of the plate is irradiated than the actual area being measured.   It arises from the introduction of radiation, scattered by parts of the optical system, into the measured beam.   With instruments of the projection type its effect is to make high density values appear to be somewhat less than they really are, and it is therefore most productive of error when dense areas surrounded by lightly exposed ones are being measured, as in the case of heavy spectrum lines. The effect can be eliminated by covering all of the plate, except the part being measured, by a diaphragm.   This is often objectionable, however, since one may wish to be able to view the surrounding parts of the plate.   In projection-type instruments this has frequently been taken care of by making the viewing light of a different color than the measuring radiation, and of such a color that the measuring instrument is insensitive to it. The Schwarzschild-Villiger effect can also be minimized by using a very small shutter, to simulate a small area of infinite opacity, and by taking a zero reading with this over every area measured.

In designing means of eliminating errors of this sort it should be borne in mind that one must take into account not only the deflection due to scattered radiation, but also the variation in this due to the variation in transmission and scattering of the surroundings, as one point or another on the plate is being measured.

SUBJECTIVE MICROPHOTOMETERS

Eye-match density-measuring devices are usually simple modifications of some well-known type of photometer.   The Lummer-Brodhun cube is most often used as photometer head on account of the simple optical means it provides for matching two beams of light.   In order to eliminate errors due to variation in lamp brightness it is common practice to use a beam-splitting device which produces two optical beams from a single lamp, the two varying together if fluctuations occur.   The principal variations of design occur in the means used to diminish the intensity of the stronger beam, the methods most commonly employed being absorbing filters or wedges, polarizers, rotating sectors, variable diaphragms, and the inverse-square law.

The prototype of all microphotometers was that designed by Hartmann,[2] in which two beams of light were produced by means of mirror-lens systems from one source of light, one of these being sent by means of a microscope projection system through a small area of the plate being measured, while the other was sent through an absorbing layer of photographic emulsion whose density could be varied by known steps. The two beams were then reunited in a Lummer-Brodhun cube, which was observed visually. By using the eye to match the brightness of the two parts of the field while varying the intensity of one beam by varying the density of its absorbing screen, the operator can match densities of known and unknown.

Most of the subjective microphotometers now in use are modifications of the Hartmann type, which in its original form was not very accurate. Its chief difficulties arose from the fact that enlarged images of the grains of the photographic emulsion were produced in the field, and since these are irregular in distribution they render it difficult to make a density match. The Schwarzschild-Villiger effect was also apt to produce errors in the original Hartmann model.

Instruments designed to overcome the difficulties of the Hartmann-type microphotometer have been described by a number of workers,[3] of which those discussed by Martin[4] and by Fabry and Buisson[5] are typical. The optical system of Martin's instrument is illustrated in Fig. 178. A beam of light from the source L is made to pass through the plate being measured at P, while a second beam passes through the absorbing wedge W and illuminates one field of the Lummer-Brodhun cube C, the other field of this having been illuminated by the plate-measuring beam. The observer moves the wedge until a match is observed at E, the resulting density being read off from a calibrated scale attached to the wedge. The photometric field is perfectly uniform since the photographic grains are not in focus at the eye. Small apertures are utilized at strategic points to reduce stray light and hence errors resulting from the Schwarzschild-Villiger effect.

The optical system of the instrument designed by Fabry and Buisson is illustrated in Fig. 179. Light from a mercury arc A coming through a small opening O, is split into two beams, and an image of the surface of the plate is formed, not on the retina of the observer as in the Hartmann instrument, but on the pupil of his eye, which causes the graininess of the plate to be invisible. A Lummer-Brodhun cube is used, viewed at E.

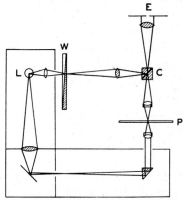

Jones[6] has designed an instrument for measuring extremely high densities, a field in which visual instruments are superior

FIG. 178.—Optical system of Martin's microphotometer.

to objective ones on account of the great sensitivity of the eye. Jones uses a rotating sector disk, to decrease the intensity of the comparison beam, in combination with iris diaphragms and diffusing screens. In this way specular densities up to 8 and diffuse densities up to 10 can be matched. High density values of this sort seldom occur except in xray photographs. The success of

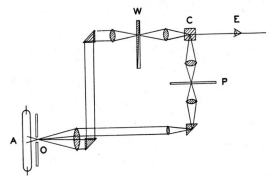

FIG. 179.—Optical system of Fabry and Buisson photometer.

the instrument is due to the reduction of scattered light to a minimum.

A somewhat different type of subjective densitometer is that described by Meggers and Foote,[7] which is based on the principle of the optical pyrometer. The light passing through the plate is compared in brightness with that entering the eye from the filament of an incandescent lamp, the current through this being varied until a brightness match is obtained. By calibrating filament current in terms of density match for a lamp running under given conditions, densities can be read off directly.

An ingenious densitometer, which, while it has not come into wide usage, appears to be the most accurate of the subjective instruments, is that designed by Danjon.[8] This is of the differential type, in which the intensity match is determined by the disappearance of interference fringes between two plane-polarized beams of light, one of which has traversed the plate being measured and the other the comparison wedge or other density standard. The two beams are polarized at right angles to each other by means of a Wollaston prism and form two images which are observed with a Savart polariscope, producing interference fringes whenever the beams are of unequal intensity. By introducing an absorbing screen into the stronger beam the fringes can be made to disappear, indicating equality of illumination. Differences of blackening of about 1 part in 1,000 can be observed with this instrument.

Wedges of neutral-tinted glass suitable for comparison microphotometers can be obtained commercially, or the wedges can be made by exposing photographic emulsions, preferably of a similar type to those being measured. Since the developed emulsion is not entirely neutral in color, changes in the quality of the viewing light may cause changes in apparent density when a truly neutral comparison wedge is used.

An important consideration in design is to keep the optical properties of the measuring beam and of the comparison beam as similar as possible, so that mechanical and thermal disturbances will produce only unimportant variations.

OBJECTIVE OR PHYSICAL MICROPHOTOMETERS

In an effort to increase the accuracy of densitometry, recourse has been had to a type of apparatus consisting of a sensitive element which, when connected to a deflecting instrument, such as a galvanometer or an electrometer, will give an objective indication of the radiation intensity falling on it. Such instruments are of two main types, deflecting and null, according to

whether the intensity of the radiation passing through the plate
is measured directly, or whether the density of the plate is balanced against a variable and known density, the sensitive instrument being used merely to indicate balance as the eye does in an
eye-match instrument.   Deflecting instruments are usually
quicker acting and simpler to use than others, while the null type
can often be made more accurate.   Deflecting instruments,
in turn, can be either direct-reading or automatic recording or
both.   Small-deflection quick-acting instruments are usually
made to record automatically, and this type is of great value
when complicated band or line contours are to be studied or
where thousands of readings are needed in a short space.   For
measuring multiplet intensities, or in other cases where a single
reading at the peak of a flat-topped line is sufficient to obtain its
intensity, a direct-reading instrument is more useful, especially
if of the projection type, since the desired lines can be selected
readily for measurement, and it is less trouble to read the scale
directly than to measure the record afterward.   Also a more
extended scale can be used, with greater resulting accuracy.

Most commercial microdensitometers are of the deflection type
with automatic recording, since they must be self-contained and
must fit themselves to a wide variety of needs.   Numerous
workers have constructed their own instruments in the laboratory, as when this is done special features can be included which
increase the usefulness of the instrument in particular directions.
An instrument equipped for both direct-reading and automatic
recording, and combining also the functions of the comparator,
can be built quite readily.   A number of general discussions of
the design and use of objective microdensitometers can be found
in the literature.[9]

Null Instruments.   Because of their similarity in principle to
the eye-match instruments, we consider first those objective
microdensitometers in which two beams, the measuring and
comparison beams, are made to balance by some objective means.
The photoelectric tube used with a quick-acting electrical device
has been found most suitable for this because of its immediate
response and freedom from external disturbances.   Such a null
instrument probably forms the most accurate type of densitometer yet devised, since almost every factor producing irregularities can be readily balanced out.   As in all null instruments,

however, two operations are necessary: the two beams must first be balanced, and then the comparison-wedge scale must be read. With the development of self-adjusting servomechanisms, however, it seems likely that this type of instrument offers the best design on which to base future developments. An especial advantage is that the accuracy is about the same for high as for low densities.

Dobson[10] has designed a balanced photoelectric instrument whose optical and electrical systems are illustrated in Fig. 180.

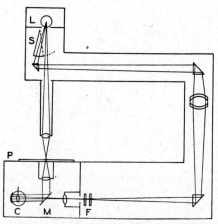

Fig. 180.—Balanced photoelectric system for microdensitometer.

It will be noted that the device uses a phototube as a balancing instrument instead of the photometer head used in similar eye-match densitometers, while instead of the eye an electrometer serves to determine balance. A shutter allows one or the other beam to fall on the sensitive phototube surface as desired, and balance is indicated by equality of electrometer deflection, this being used to measure the potential drop across a high resistance. This resistance, of about 10^{10} ohms, is made by sealing a mixture of very pure alcohol and xylene in a glass capillary tube with platinum electrodes. A quick-acting and sensitive string electrometer gave the desired prompt and uniform response.

With the Dobson instrument densities can be measured to 0.0005, or with about 10 times the accuracy of the ordinary visual instrument; this is typical of photoelectric null instruments. Similar devices have been designed using selenium cells as sensitive detector,[11] but such tubes are apt to be slower and less reliable in response than photoelectric tubes.

A modification of the Dobson densitometer would involve a rotating sector disk, allowing first one beam and then the other to fall on the tube, say 60 times per second. The output of the tube could then be fed into an alternating-current amplifier, and the amplified current rectified and fed to a quick-acting galvanometer, or directly to a pair of telephones, when the minimum hum would indicate balance as in an acoustically balanced flicker

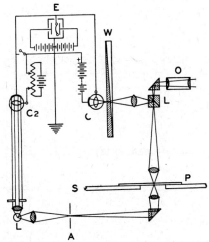

FIG. 181.—Rosenberg's photoelectric null instrument.

radiometer. Changes in tube sensitivity, in radiation intensity, and in amplifier sensitivity would produce no disturbance of balance, and instruments of this type are relatively free from thermal and other disturbances.

Rosenberg[12] has constructed a photoelectric null instrument which is illustrated in Fig. 181. One beam of light formed by a microscope objective projects a diminished image of the aperture A on the plate being measured, which is held on the stage S. The light is then focused on the Lummer-Brodhun cube L, which reflects it into the phototube C after passing through the absorbing wedge W. The function of the Lummer cube is merely to enable the operator to observe the focusing and lining up of the image through the ocular O. The comparison beam passes through a system which renders it parallel and causes it to fall on a second phototube C_2, which is connected to the same string electrometer as C. By placing absorbing screens and diaphragms of suitable diameter in the parallel beam striking C_2, one can adjust the sensitivity of the electrometer to any desired value, tube C_2 acting as a compensating leak in the manner first devised by Koch.[13] The intensities of the two beams are adjusted to give a definite reading of the electrometer for a medium density of the plate being measured; when this density is changed, the change is compensated for by suitable movement of the comparison wedge W, the sums of the two densities being kept constant. The scale connected to the comparison wedge is so arranged that the density of the plate can be read directly from it. Various other forms of null densitometer have been described in the literature, and obvious modifications of those tried suggest themselves.

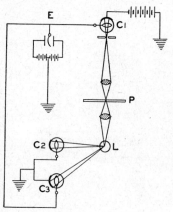

Fig. 182.—Koch deflection microdensitometer.

Deflection Microdensitometers. For many types of density measurement, as, for example, where automatic recording is useful, a direct-deflection method is desirable, in which the reduction of intensity in the measuring beam produced by its absorption in the emulsion is determined by the change in deflection of a physical photometer.

The original instrument of this kind was designed by Koch,[13] and its principle is indicated in Fig. 182. Light from the Nernst lamp L (which in later models has been replaced by an incandescent filament source such as an automobile-headlight lamp) passes through the plate to be measured in the usual way, and is focused on the phototube C_1. The voltage across this tube is read with the string electrometer E and is modified not only by the amount of light passing through P, but by that falling on tubes C_2 and C_3. These are connected so as to form a variable compensating leak across C_1, the two being used in parallel so that the electrometer can work on either side of ground potential.

In this original form of registering microdensitometer a second projection system was used to throw an image of the electrometer thread on a recording plate, which was moved by clockwork in exact relation to the motion of the plate being measured.

Koch's instrument has been improved by Goos,[14] and the Koch-Goos microdensitometer is manufactured commercially by Krüss of Hamburg. A viewing projection system has been added, with a red filter in the viewing beam so that the Schwarzschild-Villiger effect will be eliminated, and very rapid and accurate records

FIG. 183.—Zeiss microdensitometer.

can be made. Various degrees of magnification of the wavelength scale are provided, and it is claimed that wavelength measurements corresponding to 0.0001 mm accuracy on the original plate can be made. A somewhat similar instrument is manufactured by Zeiss and is depicted in Fig. 183.

Just as Koch's instrument was the prototype of photoelectric deflection microdensitometers, so that of Moll,[15] illustrated in Fig. 184, fathered a succession of thermoelectric microdensitometers. There has been much controversy regarding the relative merits of the two types; for some years the fatigue effects and other uncertainties of photoelectric tubes acted against their general acceptance, but with the great improvement resulting from their introduction into commercial use, and their advantages of quick response and freedom from thermal effects, they appear to be winning in popularity. The Moll instrument is manufactured commercially by Kipp & Zonen of Delft.

In considering the general design and use of a deflecting device of this sort, it should be borne in mind that each density determination fundamentally requires the determination of four qualities, of which one or more can usually be suppressed. Suppose the deflecting instrument to be a galvanometer. Then the density $d = \log \dfrac{I_0}{I} = \log \dfrac{g - g_0}{g' - g_0}$, where I_0 is the incident radiation which is being used to measure the plate, I is that transmitted

Fig. 184.—Moll microdensitometer.

by the portion of the plate being measured, and g, g', and g_0 are the readings of the galvanometer corresponding to intensities I_0, I, and *zero*. It cannot be taken for granted that g_0 will remain constant from one reading to the next, since drifts may be present. We shall call the difference in deflection $g - g_0$ the clear reading, since it is usually made by making measurements on a clear or unexposed portion of the plate. It is, of course, necessary to assume that the intensity remains constant while g' and g are being read, and this condition should be carefully fulfilled, at least for each pair of values of g and g'.

Ordinarily, by using an incandescent lamp run on storage batteries for a source, the incident intensity can be kept constant throughout a whole series of readings, so that g need be determined only a few times for each plate.   It should be remembered, however, that g depends not only on the intensity but also on the transmission of the unexposed portion of the plate.   This necessitates that for accuracy chemical and other controllable fog shall be kept to a minimum, and as uniform over the plate surface as possible.   For the same reason it is desirable to keep the zero drift of the deflecting instrument low so that a small number of determinations of g_0 will serve for a given plate. When these two conditions are fulfilled g' is the only quantity which must be determined for all the points on the plate which are to be measured, and it is the continuous curve of g' values, which is given by the continuous record of a recording microdensitometer.   In such an instrument radiation from a constant source is focused by a lens on a slit, which usually is either placed almost in contact with the emulsion being measured, or imaged on the emulsion by another lens.   The radiant energy then passes through the small area of the emulsion being measured, and another lens focuses the beam on to the receiver of the sensitive element which is to measure it.   This may be a photoelectric tube, a thermocouple or thermopile, a photo e.m.f. cell, a Nichols radiometer, a radiomicrometer, or a selenium cell, these devices being listed roughly in the order of the frequency with which they have been used in densitometers.

The advantages of the photoelectric tube are high sensitivity and quick response, freedom from thermal disturbances, limited spectral sensitivity so that less complete achromatization of focusing lenses is required, and the fact that they can readily be used to operate amplifiers and other instruments which require fairly great voltage variations.   Either vacuum or gas-filled tubes can be used, the former being more stable but less sensitive. Gas-filled tubes are often subject to fatigue effects when run on full voltage or subjected to intense radiation, but usually this can be eliminated by using a lower tube voltage.   The phototube is frequently used directly connected to a string electrometer, which makes a quick-acting system for automatic recording and is thus used in several instruments based on the Koch microdensitometer.[16]   Or, if used in connection with an amplifier with a galvanometer as output measurer, one of the balanced bridge amplifiers is very suitable.[17]   These are arranged so as to automatically compensate for battery-voltage variations. Single-tube amplifier circuits are somewhat more sensitive than the bridge circuits, and can be made almost as stable.[18]   All amplifier outfits usually drift somewhat when first turned on, necessitating a preliminary warming-up period.   Also they must be carefully shielded from high-frequency disturbances.

As to the choice of tube, much depends on the optical characteristics of the microdensitometer used, but the potassium hydride tube sensitive in the blue is quite suitable.   Red-sensitive tubes may show greater deflections when used with incandescent lamps, but in this case use of a color filter is desirable unless carefully achromatized lenses are used.

The advantages of thermoelectric devices lie in the simplicity of their attendant circuits and in the fact that they can be made very free from drift.   They are slightly less sensitive than photoelectric devices can be made and somewhat slower in response.   They must be carefully shielded from thermal disturbances and, since they are sensitive to all wavelengths, from stray radiation.   This last factor also requires careful achromatization of all focusing lenses used in the optical system, since most of the radiation received from the incandescent lamp is in the infrared.   Neglect of this may greatly reduce the resolving power of the instrument where an image of the slit is thrown on the plate by an incompletely achromatized lens.   Also the density of an exposed emulsion varies with the wavelength of the light used to measure it, so here it is especially necessary that the color temperature of the light used be kept constant during a run.

Perhaps the cheapest type of densitometer which can be built in the laboratory is one using a radiomicrometer;[19] this can be readily constructed by the designer and requires no galvanometer or other deflecting instrument, since it embodies this in itself. The selenium cell has been used in a number of densitometers,[20] but this is considerably slower in response than most other detectors and may suffer from fatigue and other disturbing effects.   It has been almost entirely supplanted by photoelectric and thermoelectric devices.

A very stable and sensitive instrument has been constructed by Smith and Wilson,[21] using a modified Nichols radiometer. This has an unusually great freedom from drift, high sensitivity, and a period of only 0.2 sec, features making it especially valuable for recording purposes. It can be readily constructed in the laboratory and is not affected by electrical disturbances. The system must be free from leaks because it must be filled with helium at 1 mm pressure and slight changes in pressure would change the sensitivity and produce drift.

The newer types of photo e.m.f. cell have been used to a limited extent for the purpose under discussion, instruments incorporating them having been described by Lange[22] and Milligan.[23]

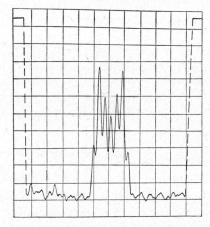

FIG. 185.—Typical record taken with Moll microdensitometer.

The Bausch and Lomb Optical Company of Rochester now manufacture a very compact direct-reading instrument using a photronic cell, which is in a lower price class than most commercial densitometers.

Automatic Recording. In making an automatic record of the deflections of a microdensitometer one usually obtains a plot of the deflection against distance along the plate. Often wavelengths are to be measured from the record rather than from the original plate, and it is desirable to have a known ratio of speeds between the two. This can be done by gearing with various stages of reduction,[24] by driving with a wedge,[25] or by connection with a metal band moving around templates.[26] Synchronous motors running both plate and record have also been used;[27] this can be done especially conveniently now since electric-clock drives are so readily obtainable.

For the highest accuracy a nonshrinking record is needed, so some instruments have been constructed to record on glass plates up to 1 m in length.[28]   This is expensive, and only necessary if a low degree of magnification is used.   Double-width moving-picture film has been found suitable,[29] but more commonly a bromide or other fast paper in widths up to 6 or 8 in. is used.[30]

The magnification ratio between plate movement and record movement as ordinarily used ranges from 1:1 to 1:100, depending

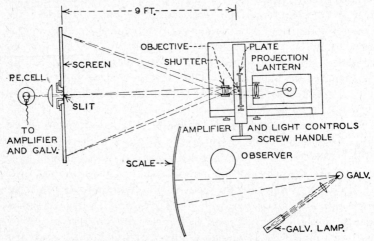

FIG. 186.—Diagram of a direct-reading instrument.

on the type of curve being reproduced.   The complexity and cost of several of the commercial instruments are largely due to the elaborate arrangements made for obtaining various exact degrees of magnification of plate translation.   A typical record taken with a Moll microdensitometer is shown in Fig. 185.

Direct Reading.   When one wishes to obtain density values for a number of selected spots on a plate or film, a direct-reading instrument is convenient, especially if a large area surrounding the point being measured can be directly observed, as in the projection-type microphotometers.   A typical instrument of this sort is that designed by Harrison and Hesthal,[31] the principle of which is depicted in Fig. 186.   An ordinary projection lantern is used to throw a 10 times enlarged image of a large area of the plate being measured on to a 6-ft. projection screen, in the center of which is a slit over 5 cm long and of adjustable width, length, and inclination. Radiation which has passed through that portion of the plate being measured enters this slit and is condensed on the surface of a phototube. This is connected to a balanced amplifier system, the output of which is fed to a short-period galvanometer whose deflections can be readily observed by the operator on a 1,000-mm scale directly in front of him.

The advantages of an instrument of this type for direct reading are: direct control of the plate, so that any desired line or spot can be measured immediately; high accuracy, due to the long and open scale; great flexibility, due to the wide range of sensitivity available; and the use of large lenses and slits instead of micro-projection. A wavelength scale printed on rubber can be stretched along the screen when desired and adjusted to the dispersion of the plate used. The instrument is not very suitable for automatic recording since it is difficult to eliminate all drift from the amplifier system.

Several modifications of this type of microdensitometer have been described in the literature.[32] While the Schwarzschild-Villiger effect can be eliminated by using a narrow shutter, a special type of dichromatic microphotometer has been described by Harrison,[33] which while slightly more complicated than the original model, has the advantages of greater sensitivity, smaller steady voltages required, and entire freedom from errors due to scattered light. It is in effect a combination of an ordinary microphotometer using blue light with a projection lantern using red light.

While almost any deflecting microdensitometer can be arranged for direct reading, the important features of such an instrument should be direct control of the plate, and length and visibility of the scale.

Since it is not possible in the space available to discuss in detail all the microphotometers and densitometers which have been recorded in the literature, for further information the original articles should be referred to.

CONTRAST MICRODENSITOMETERS

Under certain conditions, as with xray-diffraction photographs and in sensitometry, the direct measurement of the variation of density of the emulsion from point to point is important. Often a point of maximum or minimum density must be accurately located, as in setting on a spectrum line, and a plot of density against position does not give such a definite indication as one of the rate of change of density with position.   To give such an indication of density gradient directly, several investigators have designed contrast microdensitometers.

Sears[34] has described a contrast microdensitometer which, in its basic features, is a photoelectric densitometer of the common type.   He superposes on the steady motion of the plate across the microdensitometer slit, however, a small oscillatory motion parallel to its direction of travel and perpendicular to the slit. The intensity of the radiation transmitted by the plate then varies in accordance with the variation in density over the range covered by the oscillation.   The transmitted radiation falls on a phototube which feeds an alternating-current amplifier, and the amplified output current is a measure of the density gradient on the plate. Sears also discusses a modification of this method using the principle of the Hardy color analyzer,[35] which eliminates the necessity of vibrating the plate but is somewhat more complicated.

Harrison[36] has described a high-speed contrast microdensitometer in connection with his automatic comparator, which gives a density curve and a density-gradient curve simultaneously.   An image of the plate being measured is thrown on a screen by means of radiation interrupted at 4,800 cycles, and the radiation in that portion of the image being measured passes through a slit, to be divided laterally into three beams.   The two outer beams fall on two phototubes connected in opposition, their difference current being amplified and demodulated to give an oscillograph record of the density differences between the two edges of the part of the image passing through the slit.   These two outer phototubes are balanced to 0.3 per cent at all intensities.   The central beam falls on a single phototube and is amplified, demodulated, and sent through a second oscillograph which records the density trace. With this device an ordinary spectrum plate can be measured in less than a minute.

Jones and Russell[37] have described a split-beam contrast densitometer for sensitometric work which uses eye-match methods. Different portions of the sensitometric strip are viewed through two slits.   Light coming through the slit covered with the less opaque portion of the emulsion is reduced in intensity by means of a calibrated neutral wedge until the eye decides that the two beams are equal.

SPECIAL TOPICS

The accuracy available in almost any well-designed microdensitometer is far greater than that required for most forms of photographic photometry. Instrumental errors can very readily be kept below 0.5 per cent for the objective type and 2 per cent for the subjective type, and failure to reproduce readings to this accuracy is usually due to the difficulty of setting on the same portion of the plate. Occasionally, where very short and narrow slits are used, variation is encountered owing to graininess of the emulsion, and several methods of reducing or eliminating this effect have been proposed.[38]

After the readings of a densitometer have been recorded they must be interpreted in terms of the intensity of the radiation which has produced them by means of the calibration and standardization curves of the photographic emulsion.[39] This procedure is often more lengthy than the actual measurement of the plate, and naturally it would be desirable to have it done automatically. While means for carrying this out completely suggest themselves, no such apparatus appears to have been built as yet, though at least one model is under construction. Wouda[40] has, however, described an instrument for the rapid reduction of data from a calibration curve. An image of a long straight-filament lamp is moved across a plot of the calibration curve by the deflection of a galvanometer mirror which moves in accord with density values. Thus the line intensities can be read off directly from the intersection of the filament image and this curve. An even more nearly automatic device is that of Thompson,[41] who sends a long line of light from the galvanometer mirror of the microdensitometer through a template slit cut to the predetermined shape of the calibration curve for a portion of the plate, that section of this line which is transmitted through the slit being in a position which indicates the intensity of the line directly.

A limitation of both these devices is that the calibration curve for each portion of the plate must be determined by the operator and set into the machine, and as from 2 to 20 calibration curves may be required for reduction of a single plate, depending on its dispersion, the region which can be reduced from a single curve is

very limited.   A great advantage is that intensity curves obtained
from continuous recording can be integrated directly by means of
a planimeter, to obtain total intensities of lines which are not
flat-topped.

References

1. K. Schwarzschild and W. Villiger, *Astrophys. Jour.*, **23**, 287 (1906).
2. J. Hartmann, *Zeitschr. Instrumentenk.*, **19**, 97 (1899).
3. *Subjective Type:*
   E. Lehmann, *Ver. deut. physik. Ges.*, **13**, 335 (1911); P. P. Koch,
   Ann. Physik, **38**, 507 (1912); *Compt. rend.*, **156**, 113 (1913); J. Baillaud,
   Astr. France, 527, (1913); *ibid.*, 27 (1914); H. Chretien, *ibid.*, 59, (1913).
   Photoelectric Type:
   P. P. Koch and A. S. King, *Astrophys. Jour.*, **39**, 213 (1914); J. O.
   Perrine, *Jour. Optical Soc. Am. and Rev. Sci. Inst.*, **8**, 381 (1924); E. A.
   Baker, *Jour. Sci. Inst.*, **1**, 345 (1924); *Proc. Roy. Soc.* (Edinburgh), **45**,
   166 (1925); P. P. Koch, *Zeitschr. Instrumentenk.*, **45**, 494 (1925); Zeiss
   (Commercial) Cat. Sheet 460; G. Hansen, *Ann. Physik*, **78**, 570 (1925);
   P. Lambert and D. Chalonge, *Rev. d'Opt.*, **5**, 404 (1926); F. A. Linde-
   mann and G. M. B. Dobson, *Engineering*, **122**, 402 (1926); E. Banty,
   Rev. d'Opt., **5**, 404 (1926); Goldschmidt, *Meteorolog. Zeitschr.*,
   241 (1926); F. C. Toy, *Jour. Sci. Inst.*, **4**, 369 (1927); C. Müller,
   Zeitschr. tech. Physik, **9**, 154 (1926); J. A. Carroll and E. B. Moss,
   Mo. Not. Roy. Ast. Soc., **91**, 191 (1930); F. C. Toy, *Jour. Sci. Inst.*, **7**, 253
   (1930); J. and J. F. Thouvert, *Jour. phys.*, **7**, 475 (1930); *ibid.*, **7**, 245
   (1932); *ibid.*, **3**, 1235 (1932); H. C. Heil, *Phil. Mag.*, **11**, 736 (1931);
   D. Chalonge and P. Lambert, *Rev. d'Opt.*, **10**, 405 (1931); J. K. Lees,
   Jour. Sci. Inst., **8**, 273 (1931); E. Gambetta, *Compt. rend.*, **196**, 906
   (1933); A. G. Winn, *Trans. Faraday Soc.*, **29**, 689 (1933); W. Schutz,
   Phys. Zeitschr., **34**, 566 (1933); G. Todesco, *N. cimento*, **9**, 138 (1932);
   G. A. Boutr, *Compt. rend.*, **196**, 1101 and 1344 (1933); J. Weigle, *Rev.
   Sci. Inst.*, **4**, 595 (1933).
   Thermoelectric Type:
   M. Siegbahn, *Phil. Mag.*, **27**, 910 (1914); *Ann. Physik*, **42**, 689
   (1913); H. T. Stetson, *Astrophys. Jour.*, **43**, 253 and 325 (1916);
   A. E. Lindh, *Zeitschr. Physik*, **6**, 303 (1921); Schilt, *Bull. Astron. Inst.*,
   Nederland, **1**, 10 (1922); II, No. 60 (1924); Stetson and Carpenter,
   Astrophys. Jour., **58**, 36 (1923); E. Pettit and S. B. Nicholson, *Jour.
   Optical Soc. Am. and Rev. Sci. Inst.*, **7**, 187 (1923); M. Siegbahn, *Phil.
   Mag.*, **48**, 217 (1924); G. R. Harrison, *Jour. Optical Soc. Am., and Rev.
   Sci. Inst.*, **10**, 157 (1925); E. Albrecht and M. Dorneich, *Phys. Zeitschr.*,
   26, 514 (1925); W. J. H. Moll and H. C. Burger, *Phil. Mag.*, **50**, 618
   (1925); E. Backlin, *Zeitschr. Instrumentenk.*, **47**, 373 (1927); E. Spiller,
   ibid., **47**, 493 (1927); E. A. Harrington, *Jour. Optical Soc. Am. and
   Rev. Sci. Inst.*, **16**, 211 (1928).
4. L. C. Martin, *Trans. Optical Soc.*, **26**, 109 (1925).

5. C. Fabry and H. Buisson, *Compt. rend.*, **156**, 389 (1913); *Jour. phys.*, **9**, 37 (1919); *Rev. d'Opt.*, **1**, 1 (1924).

6. L. A. Jones, *Jour. Optical Soc. Am.*, **7**, 231 (1923).

7. W. F. Meggers and P. D. Foote, *Jour. Optical Soc. Am.*, **4**, 24 (1920).

8. M. A. Danjon, *Rev. d'Opt.*, **5**, 55 (1926).

9. H. B. Dorgelo, *Phys. Zeitschr.*, **26**, 774 (1925); G. R. Harrison, *Jour. Optical Soc. Am. and Rev. Sci. Inst.*, **10**, 157 (1925); *ibid.*, **19**, 296 (1929); *Jour. Optical Soc. Am.*, **24**, 59 (1934); G. M. B. Dobson, I. O. Griffith, and D. N. Harrison, "Photographic Photometry," Oxford Univ. Press, p. 55, 1926; L. S. Ornstein, W. H. J. Moll, and H. C. Burger, "Objektive Spektralphotometrie," Vieweg, p. 56, 1932.

10. G. M. B. Dobson, *Proc. Roy. Soc.*, **104**, 248 (1923).

11. F. C. Toy, *Proc. Phys. Soc. London*, **36**, 432 (1924); Toy and Rawling, *Jour. Sci. Inst.*, **1**, 362 (1924).

12. H. Rosenburg, *Zeitschr. Instrumentenk.*, **45**, 313 (1925).

13. P. P. Koch, *Ann. Physik*, **39**, 705 (1912); *ibid.*, **41**, 115 (1913).

14. F. Goos, *Phys. Zeitschr.*, **22**, 648 (1921); *Zeitschr. Instrumentenk.*, **41**, 313 (1921); F. Goos and P. P. Koch, *Phys. Zeitschr.*, **27**, 41 (1926); *Zeitschr. Physik*, **44**, 855 (1927).

15. W. J. H. Moll, *Proc. Phys. Soc. London*, **33**, 207 (1921).

16. See list of "Photoelectric Type" under ref. 3.

17. J. Brentano, *Nature*, **108**, 532 (1921); *Phil. Mag.*, **7**, 685 (1929); H. Rosenberg, *Zeitschr. Physik*, **7**, 18 (1921);C . E. Wynn-Williams, *Proc. Camb. Phil. Soc.*, **23**, 811 (1927); *Phil. Mag.*, **6**, 324 (1928); A. Marcus, *Phys. Rev.*, **31**, 302 (1928); J. Razek and P. J. Mulder, *Phys. Rev.*, **33**, 284 (1929); J. M. Eglin, *Jour. Optical Soc. Am. and Rev. Sci. Inst.*, **18**, 393 (1929). W. B. Nottingham, *Jour. Franklin Inst.*, **209**, 287 (1930); L. A. DuBridge, *Phys. Rev.*, **37**, 392 (1931).

18. L. A. Turner, *Rev. Sci. Inst.*, **4**, 665 (1933); L. A. Turner and C. O. Siegelin, *ibid.*, **4**, 429 (1933).

19. G. R. Harrison, *ibid.*, **7**, 999 (1923).

20. A. L. Schoen, *Jour. Optical Soc. Am. and Rev. Sci. Inst.*, **7**, 483 (1923); C. B. Bazzoni, R. W. Duncan, and W. S. Mathews, *ibid.*, **7**, 1003 (1923); F. C. Toy, *Proc. Phys. Soc. London*, **36**, 432 (1924); Toy and Rawling, *Jour. Sci. Inst.*, **1**, 362 (1924).

21. S. Smith and O. C. Wilson, Jr., *Astrophys. Jour.*, **76**, 117 (1932).

22. B. Lange, *Zeitschr. tech. Physik*, **13**, 600 (1932).

23. W. O. Milligan, *Rev. Sci. Inst.*, **4**, 493 (1933).

24. See Kipp & Zonen catalog, or ref. 15.

25. M. Siegbahn, *Phil. Mag.*, **48**, 217 (1924).

26. A. E. Lindh, *Zeitschr. Physik*, **6**, 303 (1921).

27. S. Smith and D. C. Wilson, Jr., *Astrophys. Jour.*, **76**, 117 (1932).

28. E. Pettit and S. B. Nicholson, *Jour. Optical Soc. Am. and Rev. Sci Inst.*, **7**, 187 (1932).

29. See Ref. 27.

30. W. H. J. Moll, *Proc. Phys. Soc. London*, **33**, 207 (1921).

31. C. E. Hesthal and G. R. Harrison, *Phys. Rev.*, **34**, 543 (1929); G. R. Harrison, *Rev. Sci. Inst.*, **19**, 302 (1929); *ibid.*, **3**, 572 (1932).

32. E. GWYNNE-JONES and H. L. BROSE, *Jour. Sci. Inst.*, **8**, 145 (1931); C. S. BEALS, *Mo. Not. Roy. Astron. Soc.*, January, 1932; W. DUANE, *Phys. Rev.*, **40**, 132 (1932).

33. G. R. HARRISON, *Rev. Sci. Inst.*, **3**, 572 (1932).

34. F. W. SEARS, *Jour. Optical Soc. Am.*, **25**, 162 (1935).

35. A. C. HARDY, *Jour. Optical Soc. Am.*, **25**, 305 (1935).

36. G. R. HARRISON, *Jour. Optical Soc. Am.*, **25**, 169 (1935).

37. L. A. JONES and M. E. RUSSELL, *Jour. Optical Soc. Am.*, **25**, 396 (1925).

38. F. E. WRIGHT, *Jour. Optical Soc. Am.*, **21**, 485 (1931); W. LINNIK, *Zeitschr. Physik*, **61**, 700 (1930); G. KELLSTROM, *Roy. Soc. Sci.*, Upsala, 38, May, 1932; F. K. RICHTMYER and F. R. HIRSH, JR., *Rev. Sci. Inst.*, **4**, 353 (1933); S. HARRIS, *ibid.* **4**, 598 (1933).

39. See Chap. VIII.

40. J. WOUDA, *Zeitschr. Physik*, **79**, 511 (1932).

41. N. THOMPSON, *Proc. Phys. Soc. London*, **45**, 441 (1933).

CHAPTER X

GALVANOMETERS FOR USE IN MEASUREMENT OF SPECTRAL RADIATION

P. H. Dike*

In the measurement of spectral radiation by electrical instruments such as the bolometer, the thermopile, and the photoelectric cell, the galvanometer often sets a very definite limit to the sensitivity and accuracy that can be attained, and the whole scheme of measurement must be planned with a view to the limitations thus imposed. A knowledge of the characteristics of available galvanometers is a requisite in planning an attack on a problem in spectral analysis, as is also an understanding of the difficulties to be encountered in their use, and the precautions to be observed in securing dependable results. It is not our purpose to present the theory on which the galvanometer design is based, but rather to summarize the results that have been attained, and to offer some hints as to the points to be considered in the choice of a galvanometer for a particular problem, and the precautions to be observed in its use.

Types of Galvanometers. Sensitive galvanometers are of either the moving-coil (d'Arsonval)[1] type or the moving-magnet (Thomson)[2] type. The former is in much more common use and the statements to be made in this paper, except where otherwise specified, will apply to it.

Type of Measuring Circuit. The first point to be considered in choosing a galvanometer for any problem is the nature of the circuit into which it is to be connected. Two main types of circuit are to be considered, that in which the external resistance connected across the galvanometer terminals is low, and that in which it is high, with, of course, many intermediate cases. Under the former fall the thermopile and the bolometer applications, while the photoelectric tube is representative of the high-resistance applications.

* Physicist, Leeds & Northrup Company.

In any case the galvanometer chosen should give the required sensitivity in its critically damped[3] condition when connected to the circuit in which it is to be used; *i.e.*, the external resistance across the galvanometer terminals must be equal to, or slightly more than, the rated external critical damping resistance of the galvanometer. If possible, the measuring circuit proper should be so designed as to meet this requirement. It is true that it is always possible to secure critical damping by the use of series or parallel resistors, or both, but in most cases only at the expense of a loss of sensitivity, which may be serious if the characteristics depart widely from those best suited to the circuit in which it is used.

When a galvanometer system approaches its final position at the greatest possible rate without overshooting, it is critically damped. The advantage of the critically damped condition rests chiefly in the fact that it aids in rapid work, since a galvanometer system when critically damped returns more promptly to rest than when in an underdamped or overdamped condition. Practically, it is best to work with the galvanometer very slightly underdamped so that the coil overshoots the rest position a trifle and drops back to it. This removes uncertainty as to whether the galvanometer is swinging absolutely freely.

A high-resistance circuit, such as that of a photoelectric tube, calls for a galvanometer of high critical-damping resistance, to avoid the necessity of cutting down the current sensitivity by means of a low shunt, in order to secure the proper damping. Precautions must be taken against overdamping when using galvanometers of high current sensitivity, since they usually require a high critical-damping resistance and, if used in an ordinary bridge or potentiometer circuit, are almost sure to be overdamped.

A very common statement in textbooks is that for maximum sensitivity the galvanometer resistance should be equal to the external resistance, and this has often been made the basis of choice of a galvanometer for a particular purpose. It has been shown[4] that the galvanometer resistance may be as much as five times, or as little as one-fifth, that of the external circuit without reducing the sensitivity more than 25 per cent. Consequently, much leeway can be allowed in making use of this criterion in the choice of a galvanometer or the design of a circuit.

While, in general, the current sensitivity increases with an increase of galvanometer coil resistance, the fact that the coil resistance of a certain galvanometer is greater than that of another of a different type does not signify that its current sensitivity is greater. By changes in design, particularly in the form and size of the coil, and in the length and thickness of the suspension, it is possible to increase the current sensitivity while decreasing the coil resistance.

In general, a sensitive galvanometer cannot be equally suitable for all types of measurements (see Table 23). As an example, let us compare the characteristics of two galvanometers: A, with a 16-ohm coil and an external damping resistance of 10 ohms, having a sensitivity of 0.05 μv; B, with a coil resistance of 800 ohms and an external damping resistance of 70,000 ohms, with a sensitivity of 0.00004 μa. (See section on "sensitivity" below, for definitions of microvolt and microampere sensitivity.) The microvolt sensitivity of B is 0.00004 $\times$ 70,800 or approximately 3 μv, *i.e.*, only one-sixtieth as sensitive as A for balancing a low-resistance bridge. A has a current sensitivity of 0.05/(10 + 16), or approximately 0.002 μa, and when provided with the requisite damping shunt, this would be effectively reduced to about 0.004 μa, or a hundredth as sensitive as B in a high-resistance circuit.

It is not safe to assume that the most sensitive galvanometer is the one best adapted to a particular piece of work, even though precision measurements are involved. High sensitivity can be attained only by some sacrifice of other desirable characteristics, such as speed of operation, ruggedness, stability, and reproducibility of readings, and ease of mounting and adjustment. Consequently, it is inadvisable to purchase the most sensitive type of galvanometer on the chance that this high sensitivity, while not immediately needed, may be required at some future time, or with the idea that a more sensitive galvanometer will lead to more precise results.

It is true that by the use of shunts and series resistance the sensitivity of the galvanometer can be reduced to what is requisite for the problem in hand, but this does not add strength to the suspension, shorten the period, or improve the stability of the zero reading, and a less sensitive and sturdier instrument would yield more accurate results with far less exertion and annoyance.

Sensitivity. A galvanometer is essentially a device for measuring or detecting electric currents, and its sensitivity is fundamentally expressed in terms of its deflection for a given current passing through it. Usually the current sensitivity of a galvanometer is stated as the current in microamperes required to produce a deflection of 1 milliradian, *i.e.* 1 mm on a scale placed 1 m from the galvanometer mirror. Other expressions for galvanometer sensitivity are derived from its current sensitivity. For our present purposes the microvolt sensitivity, used in measuring the e.m.f. of a thermopile, is also of interest. This is defined as the e.m.f. in microvolts which, applied across the galvanometer and its critical-damping resistance, in series, will produce the standard deflection of 1 milliradian. The relationship between the microvolt and the microampere sensitivities is expressed as follows:

$$\mu v \text{ sens.} = \mu a \text{ sens.} \times (R_i + R_e) \tag{66}$$

where R_i is the internal resistance of the galvanometer, and R_e is the series external critical-damping resistance.

It should be noted that there is another meaning given to the term "microvolt sensitivity," formerly much used by European instrument makers, according to which it is the difference of potential between the binding posts of the galvanometer which will give the standard deflection. Since this form of statement leaves out of account entirely the necessary critical-damping resistance, it does not represent an actual possible working condition of the galvanometer and gives an exaggerated idea of the sensitivity practically attainable. The purchaser of a galvanometer should ascertain which system is used by the maker in specifying its sensitivity in order to avoid misapprehension.

It is obvious that for high voltage sensitivity the internal resistance of the galvanometer should be kept as low as is consistent with the requisite current sensitivity, and that the external critical-damping resistance should not be greater than the resistance of the circuit into which the galvanometer is to work.

Moving-magnet Galvanometers. So far we have considered only the moving-coil type of galvanometer, but in some cases it may be necessary to go farther, than is possible at present with this type, in the search for higher sensitivity. The moving-magnet galvanometer is capable of a higher sensitivity than is at present attainable with moving-coil galvanometers. Coblentz describes in a paper not yet published a 5,300-ohm iron-clad Thomson galvanometer in which the easily obtainable current sensitivity is of the order of 1×10^{-12} amp. The voltage sensitivity of this galvanometer at its terminals is therefore 0.005 μv, or with an external circuit having a resistance equal to the coil resistance 0.01 μv.

These galvanometers require extremely complete shielding[5] against variations in external magnetic fields, due to fluctuations of the earth's magnetic field, and to electric circuits and magnetic materials in the vicinity of the galvanometer, and require a considerable acquired skill to adjust them to their best working condition. They are to be recommended for use where the utmost attainable sensitivity is required, and where the surrounding conditions are such as to make it possible to take full advantage of their inherent sensitivity. It is possible that as high a sensitivity can be obtained more easily with moving-coil galvanometers by the use of some of the methods of amplification described in this chapter.

Since the damping of the Thomson type of galvanometer is mainly due to air friction and to eddy currents resulting from the motion of the suspended-magnet system, the remarks above concerning external critical-damping resistance do not apply to it.

Galvanometer Mounting. The utmost care must be taken in mounting a sensitive galvanometer, to free it as far as possible from the effects of mechanical vibration, from whatever source, such as machinery in operation, traffic, or earth tremors. In quiet regions the effect of such vibrations can be avoided by mounting the galvanometer on a heavy pier of concrete, brick, or stone, entirely free from the laboratory floor, and resting on rubber blocks and sand, supported by the earth. Galvanometers of somewhat less than the maximum sensitivity can be used quite satisfactorily when mounted on a bracket on a heavy wall or supporting pier of the building. This is not satisfactory if a railway or a highway carrying heavy traffic passes close to the building or in a region where heavy machinery is in operation; in such cases the pier mounting is inadequate to eliminate disturbing vibrations. The first of these "vibration-free" supports was the well-known Julius[6] suspension. Following this were suspensions designed by Johnsrud,[7] Müller,[8] and others. While a rigid shelf, attached to a vibration-free wall is much the most satisfactory support for a galvanometer, experience has demonstrated that the Müller support, when carefully protected from air drafts, is very satisfactory. When well-designed and carefully mounted, such a suspension has made it possible to use a high-sensitivity galvanometer in a power plant.

A sensitive galvanometer should be very carefully leveled since the coil must swing freely in the narrow space between core and pole pieces. An effect resembling that of faulty leveling may be produced by dust collecting between the galvanometer coil and the pole faces or core. The galvanometer system should be exposed and handled as little as possible, and only in a room free from dust. Magnetic dust is particularly to be avoided, as magnetic particles collecting on the coil will seriously affect the period and sensitivity of the galvanometer.

Zero Shift. The usual significance of the term "zero shift" is the failure of the coil to return to its original zero position after a deflection. This may be due to a hysteresis effect in magnetic impurities, in or on the coil, or to a set in the suspending filament, or to both. When the galvanometer is used as a deflection instrument, the deflection should be reckoned from the zero reading after the deflection rather than that before it. When used as a null-type instrument, if precautions are taken never to produce a large deflection, there should be no zero drift due to these causes.

A sensitive galvanometer left undisturbed on open circuit will often change slightly in zero reading over a period of hours or days. These changes are probably to be ascribed to a lack of homogeneity in the suspension strip, and a very gradual readjustment of the mechanical strains produced in it in the process of rolling and by the weight of the suspended coil.

Erratic Momentary Shifts. It may often be observed, when using a sensitive galvanometer, that the coil takes a momentary short excursion from its equilibrium position, returning to it almost immediately. The causes are various. At the extreme limit of galvanometer sensitivity Brownian movements may introduce such fluctuations, but in general they are caused by either electrostatic or electromagnetic pick-up in the galvanometer circuit or by mechanical jars. A sudden movement of an electrostatic charge in the neighborhood of one of the leads, such as might be caused by brushing a coat sleeve over a table top, may induce sufficient flow of electricity through the galvanometer to produce a deflection of a centimeter or more. If the metal parts surrounding the moving system are not electrically connected to one of the galvanometer terminals, there is a possibility of a more or less steady deflection due to electrostatic attraction between the suspended coil and the pole pieces. These sources of disturbance can be eliminated by careful electrostatic shielding of galvanometer and leads, and by attention to the provision of ground connections where they will prevent electrometer action without forming a shunt on the galvanometer system.

Another possible cause of momentary fluctuations is electromagnetic pick-up. A sudden change in magnetic field causing a change of flux through some loop in the galvanometer circuit may cause such a disturbance. The starting or stopping of a large direct-current motor or the operation of a relay may be sufficient to produce the effect. The remedy is to keep all loops in the wiring as small as possible, and in particular the leads to the galvanometer should be very close together, and preferably twisted.

Temperature Effects. In most moving-coil galvanometers the combined effect of changes in rigidity of suspension and strength of magnetic field with change of temperature is to increase the sensitivity by less than 0.05 per cent per degree centigrade rise in temperature. This is of little importance in most galvanometer work and no attempt is made to reduce it, but in some cases it may be necessary to determine the correction for the particular instrument used, and to correct for it.

A more important temperature effect is that of thermal e.m.fs. arising from lack of uniformity in temperature of the galvanometer system. It causes a deflection of the galvanometers when the circuit is closed with no apparent source of e.m.f. in it. If the galvanometer is placed where it is exposed to drafts or to radiation, the effect is particularly pronounced, especially in galvanometers of high voltage sensitivity. It is almost completely eliminated by using copper binding posts, copper leads, copper suspensions, and a copper coil in the galvanometer. This is a standard construction for high-voltage-sensitivity galvanometers. The effect can be reduced in galvanometers lacking this refinement by careful heat insulation of the instrument by the liberal use of loose cotton in a metal or pasteboard tube surrounding the galvanometer. The all-copper-circuit galvanometer, or, where corrosive gases may be present in the atmosphere, one with a 24-carat gold suspension, is to be recommended for all precise high-voltage-sensitivity measurements.

Deflection vs. Null Measurements. Precision measurements are always more satisfactorily made by the use of a method which involves the use of the galvanometer as a means of determining absence of current rather than using its deflection as a measure of the current present in the circuit. The deflection method may be more simple and direct, and lends itself to photographic recording, but it requires very frequent calibration to avoid errors due to changing sensitivity and zero drift due to large deflections.

Consequently, when using a bolometer it is preferable to use the galvanometer as a means of bringing the bridge to an exact balance rather than as a deflection instrument to indicate the amount of unbalance of the bridge.

The thermopile, to be operated by a null method, requires the use of a potentiometer, and for very low e.m.fs. the demands on the characteristics of the potentiometer are very severe. Parasitic thermal e.m.fs. in the potentiometer switches and dial contacts, and even in the soldered joints between copper leads and manganin resistors, are of an order of magnitude to introduce appreciable errors when reading very low e.m.fs. In the type K potentiometer these errors may amount to as much as 10 μv if precautions are not taken to maintain temperature conditions constant in the instrument. The Wenner potentiometer, a low-resistance instrument by the same makers, carefully designed to minimize the effects of thermal e.m.fs. is subject to errors not to exceed 0.1 μv from this source. Used in conjunction with a suitable high-sensitivity galvanometer, this should give excellent results with a thermopile.

A modification of the Lindeck and Rothe potentiometer circuit[9] has been used with success. This involves balancing the e.m.f. of the thermopile against the voltage drop through a standard resistor, for example, 0.1 ohm, by varying the current through the resistor. The current required can be measured by means of an ammeter, as was done by Lindeck and Rothe, or by measuring the voltage drop through a higher resistance, say 100 ohms, in the same circuit by means of a type K potentiometer or its equivalent, employing a galvanometer of moderate sensitivity in the potentiometer circuit. The 0.1- and 100-ohm resistors, rheostat, and battery are thermostated. In effect there is a voltage amplification of 1 to 1,000, a change of 1 μv in the e.m.f. of the thermopile resulting in a change of 1 mv in the reading of the potentiometer. The method is slow, since it requires two galvanometers and a double balance, but is capable of giving very satisfactory results.

Measurements involving small currents in high-resistance circuits, such as are encountered in vacuum-type photoelectric tubes exposed to radiation, may also be carried out by null-type methods employing galvanometers with high current sensitivity and large external damping resistance. In view, however, of the rather easy applicability of vacuum-tube amplification to direct currents in a high-resistance circuit, it is often better to use a vacuum-tube amplifier with a less sensitive galvanometer in making such measurements. If a deflection method is employed in a high-resistance circuit, it is very advantageous to use in conjunction with the galvanometer an Ayrton shunt with a resistance fairly close to the critical-damping resistance of the galvanometer employed, preferably higher, rather than lower than the rated value. For example, in choosing the Ayrton shunt for the galvanometer designated as B earlier in this paper, which requires a critical-damping resistance of 70,000 ohms, with the choice lying between a 40,000- and a 100,000-ohm shunt, the latter should be chosen. The galvanometer will then be slightly underdamped which, as has already been pointed out, is more desirable than overdamping. Further, the circuit in which the current is to be measured, connected across the shunt, reduces its effective value, and decreases somewhat the amount of underdamping.

Partial-deflection Methods. It is frequently possible to use a sensitive calibrated galvanometer as a means of measuring the residual unbalance of a potentiometer or of a Wheatstone bridge. If the galvanometer circuit resistance is kept constant for all settings of the measuring circuit, the galvanometer deflections may be interpreted to give readings between the steps of the lowest dial in the measuring circuit. This plan is carried out in the White potentiometer.[10] It has the advantage over the straight null method of reducing the number of dials to be operated, and by eliminating the lowest resistance dial avoids some of the contact resistances and parasitic e.m.fs. which enter into such measurements. It also gives greater speed of operation. It has the great advantage over the straight-deflection method that only the last one or two significant figures in the result are read from the galvanometer, so that it is unnecessary for the galvanometer to undergo large deflections, and a high percentage accuracy can be attained without extremely close readings of the deflection.

Galvanometer-reading Devices. The optical system of the galvanometer requires very careful attention. In order to keep the moment of inertia of the suspended system low, the mirror should be as narrow and as thin as possible. It must be attached to the system in such a way as to introduce no distortion in its reflecting surface, and the reflecting surface should be truly plane, or in the case of a concave mirror, truly spherical. Plane mirrors are to be preferred, the focusing being accomplished by means of lenses, if a lamp and scale device is to be used in reading deflections. A telescope-and-scale reading device in general demands a plane mirror.

The telescope-and-scale arrangement is capable of more precise readings than the spot-of-light method, at a given deflection distance, but it is somewhat more tiring to the observer. A 0.5-m deflection distance is commonly used with a telescope and scale with a magnification of about six diameters. An increased deflection distance multiplies the sensitivity *in scale divisions* by the ratio of increase in distance, but it also diminishes the apparent width of the scale divisions in the same ratio while the cross hair in the telescope remains constant in width. Therefore, actually to increase the sensitivity beyond what could be secured by subdividing the scale more finely rather than increasing the deflection distance, a telescope with a higher magnifying power must be used. The limitations on increase of sensitivity with increased scale distance are imposed by the imperfection and size[11] of the mirror, and by the magnifying power and quality of the telescope, as well as by the difficulty of freeing the whole system from vibration.

With the lamp-and-scale method of reading, if the lamp and scale are kept together, and focusing at a greater distance is accomplished by the use of a longer-focal-length lens in front of the galvanometer mirror, the sensitivity actually increases in the predicted ratio, but the intensity of the reflected light beam falls off, since a smaller portion of the light from the lamp is incident on the mirror, and a long deflection-distance requires either a very powerful light source or a well-darkened room. Imperfections of lens and mirror also become more troublesome. Accurate readings require very careful focusing of the spot of light or projected cross hair. An expedient sometimes used to increase the ease of reading at long scale-distance is to momentarily apply an overvoltage to the galvanometer lamp while the reading is being made, thus increasing the visibility of the image.

If the change of deflection distance is accomplished by moving the lamp closer to the galvanometer as the scale is removed from it, keeping the same lens in front of the galvanometer, the image of the spot of light or cross hair increases in size as the distance of the scale increases, with a consequent decrease in brightness and an apparent fuzziness, so that there is little actual increase in accuracy of reading with the increased scale distance. As good an accuracy could more easily be attained by the use of a magnifying glass between the eye and the scale at the original deflection distance.

Too little thought and care are usually given to the choice and adjustment of the optical system of a galvanometer. A good, amply lighted system adds greatly to the ease and accuracy of readings.

Vacuum-tube Amplification. It is not in the province of this paper to discuss vacuum-tube amplifier circuits, but the fact should not be ignored that it is possible in the measurement of small currents in high-resistance circuits to secure much higher sensitivity by the use of vacuum-tube amplification than has been attained with galvanometers alone. Sensitivities[12] of the order of 10^{-17} amp. are claimed, employing certain highly insulated vacuum tubes. Such sensitivities are attained only by the use of the utmost precaution in shielding, and under very favorable conditions. It is relatively easy to obtain current sensitivities of the order of 10^{-12} amp., with a rugged, short-period galvanometer using carefully evacuated and well-insulated vacuum tubes as amplifiers, and to set up a circuit which permits a null-type measurement (from the point of view of galvanometer deflection) in which this sensitivity is attained.

The difficulties of eliminating spurious effects in these circuits multiply as the sensitivity is increased, and the user if he designs his own apparatus should not hope to find in such a device a means of attaining the desired sensitivity without the expenditure of much care, patience, and ingenuity.

TABLE 23. Showing the Influence of Characteristics of External Circuit on Galvanometer Response

Gal- vanom- eter	Period, sec.	Resistance, ohms			Sensitivity (criti- cally damped)	
		Damping	Coil	Circuit (ext.)	Micro- volts	Micro- amperes
A	7	10	16	10	0.05	0.002
	7	10	16	100	0.4	0.004
	7	10	16	70,000	280.	0.004
B	20	70,000	800	70,000	3.	0.00004
	20	70,000	800	100	3.	0.00004
	20	70,000	800	1,000,000	43.	0.00004

The use of direct-current amplification by means of vacuum tubes in low-resistance circuits such as that of the thermopile offers more serious difficulties than in the high-resistance case. The excessively small fluctuations of grid potential due to change in e.m.f. of the thermopile are of the same order of magnitude as, or smaller than, the unavoidable accidental variations in grid voltage due to extraneous causes.

An industrial application[13] of amplification of small thermal e.m.fs. has been developed. In this device the unbalanced e.m.f. in the potentiometer used to measure the voltage of the thermopile is modulated with a definite frequency, and the modulated current passed through the primary of a step-up transformer. The alternating-current voltage thus generated in the secondary of the transformer is amplified by means of vacuum tubes, and detected by any suitable alternating-current device such as an alternating-current galvanometer or a telephone receiver. Up to the present this apparatus has been used only for the measurement of total radiation, but with some refinements

TABLE 24.   CHARACTERISTICS OF AVAILABLE GALVANOMETERS SUITABLE FOR USE IN MEASUREMENT OF SPECTRAL RADIATION

Maker	Designation	Sensitivity		Period, sec.	Resistance, ohms	
					Internal	Damping
K. & Z.	Za	0.4	μv	1.3	7	50
	Za	0.18	μv	1.3	7	0
	Zb	0.4	μv	3	10	200
	Zb	0.05	μv	3	10	0
	Zc	0.16	μv	7	15	400
	Zc	0.036	μv	7	15	15
	Zd	0.0005	μa	3	25	2,000
	Zd	0.0025	μa	3	25	80
	Ze	0.00015	μa	7	25	3,000
	Ze	0.0005	μa	7	25	200
	Moll	0.009	μa	2	50	120
L. & N.	2284-a	0.5	μv	1.5	20	40
	2284-b	0.05	μv	7	16	10
	2285-a	0.1	μv	7.5	16	25
	2285-b	0.2	μv	5.	12	40
	2285-f	0.00004	μa	20	800	70,000
	2290	0.00001	μa	40	800	100,000
	2270*	0.0002	μa	5	40	...... } Coblentz
	2270*	0.002	μv	5	2.5	......
Cam.	41142	0.009	μa	6	25	130
	41142	0.0018	μa	6	450	infinite
	41147	0.0055	μa	6	30	600
	41147	0.0012	μa	2	400	6,000
	41811	0.003	μa	15	15	300
	41811	0.0016	μa	22	15	400
	41811	0.00008	μa	22	2,800	3,600
	41214*	0.0008	μv	6	12	...... } Paschen
	41214*	0.0000075	μa	6	3,000	......
	41246*	0.017	μv	6	20	
	41246*	0.00018	μa	6	1,000	

* Moving-magnet galvanometers.

Notes on Table 24: K. & Z.—Kipp & Zonen; L. & N.—Leeds & Northrup Company; Cam.—Cambridge Scientific Company.

it may be applicable to the measurement and automatic recording of spectral radiation.

The Kipp & Zonen moving-coil galvanometers are provided with magnetic shunts for varying the effective field-strength of the magnets, thus varying the sensitivity and the critical-damping resistance through the ranges indicated in the table.

Sensitivities given are taken from the respective catalogs. The microvolt sensitivities are given for the instruments which are better suited for low-resistance work and the microampere sensitivity for the high-resistance-circuit instruments. The relationship between microvolt and microampere sensitivity is given by the equation μv sens. $= \mu a$ sens. $\times (R_i + R_e)$, where R_i is the internal resistance of the galvanometer, and R_e is the external critical-damping resistance, and either one can be computed when the other is given by substituting the values given in the last two columns of the table in the formula. In the case of the Cambridge Scientific Instrument Company galvanometers the figures thus obtained will not agree with those given in their catalog, as they do not take into account the external resistance in computing the voltage sensitivity.

The sensitivity of the moving-magnet galvanometers can be varied through rather wide limits by changing the resultant permanent magnetic field about the suspended magnets by means of the control magnets, thus changing the force tending to restore them to equilibrium. A considerably higher sensitivity than that given in the table can be attained by weakening the field and, as a result, increasing the period of the galvanometer. The quartz suspension contributes only a negligible portion of the force tending to restore the system to its equilibrium position.

The Leeds and Northrup No. 2290 galvanometer has been given its extra-high current sensitivity by making the pole pieces of the No. 2285 instrument adjustable by means of thumbscrews operated from outside the case. This makes it possible to control the configuration of the magnetic field between the pole pieces and the core so as to make the field stronger near the edges than near the center, so that the magnetic impurities present in the coil tend to move toward the edges of the field, thus in part annulling the restoring torque of the suspension. The result is practically the same as if a finer suspension with the same resistance and tensile strength had been substituted for the actual suspension. The period is lengthened, but the sensitivity is greatly increased. The desired sensitivity is attained by careful adjustment of the pole pieces, after the galvanometer is set up, ready for service.

THE AMPLIFICATION OF SMALL GALVANOMETER DEFLECTIONS

A. H. PFUND*

If the coil of a galvanometer were hung from a perfectly elastic suspension, any direct current of magnitude greater than zero would cause a definite deflection. Since amplification may be carried to almost any degree, the sensitivity of the galvanometer could be made to approach infinity. The fallacy of this argument was first pointed out by Ising[14] who showed that the irregular motion of coil and mirror, occasioned by Brownian motion, sets a limit to the attainable sensitivity. According to Ising, the limiting volt and ampere sensitivity of a galvanometer (single deflection) is:

$$V = 4.48 \times 10^{-10} \sqrt{\frac{R}{t}} \text{ volts} \qquad (67)$$

$$I = 4.48 \times 10^{-10} \frac{1}{\sqrt{Rt}} \text{ amp.} \qquad (68)$$

where R = resistance of total circuit, ohms
t = time required to reach a steady deflection, seconds.

This limit of sensitivity is difficult to realize by the usual mirror-and-scale method of observation, hence it has been found advantageous to resort to amplification. In the following, several representative types of amplifiers will be described.

The prototype of all deflection-amplifiers is the Moll[15] thermo-relay. This device, shown diagrammatically in Fig. 187, consists of a primary galvanometer I whose mirror focuses an image of the lamp filament L on the blackened center of a compensating thermocouple T. Since the heat conduction along the central element of the thermocouple to the two junctions R and S is the same, the second galvanometer II will indicate no deflection. However, a minute deflection from galvanometer I will displace the image nearer to one of the two junctions—in consequence of which a large deflection of galvanometer II will result.

* *Professor of Physics, Johns Hopkins University.*

Modifications, involving the use of photo e.m.f. cells in place of the thermocouple *T*, have been introduced by Barnes and Matossi[16] and, more recently, by the Leeds and Northrup Company.[17] The latter have mounted both galvanometers and the amplifying device as a single, portable unit. This is shown diagrammatically in Fig. 188, where I is the primary galvanometer

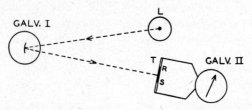

Fig. 187.—Schematic arrangement of Moll amplifier for galvanometer deflections.

whose concave mirror *M* forms an image of the lamp filament *L* on the center of a photo e.m.f. cell *P*. This consists of a strip, cut out of a regular photo e.m.f. cell whose thin upper metallic coating is filed away along a narrow line upon which the lamp filament is focused. Obviously, we now have two opposing photo e.m.f. cells whose surfaces, when illuminated successively, impart opposite deflections to the secondary galvanometer II. As in the case of the Moll amplifier, a small deflection resulting in a slight shift of the image will result in a large deflection of

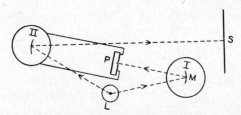

Fig. 188.—Amplifying system using two galvanometers.

galvanometer II, as indicated on the scale at *S*. With these devices the Brownian-motion limit of sensitivity may be reached.

It is clear that these amplifiers magnify all deflections—including those due to "drift." This defect has been overcome by Firestone[18] whose "drift-free" amplifier is admirably suited for photographic recording. While it will be necessary to refer

to the original article for details, the underlying principle may
be quoted briefly as follows:

. . . Theoretically, one can eliminate the drifts from any radiometer
system merely by periodically interrupting the radiation and connecting
a large condenser in series with the galvanometer.   Practically, however,
any ordinary size of condenser to be found in the laboratory will have
so much impedance at this low frequency that its presence in the
galvanometer circuit would seriously impair the sensitivity.   By using
a photoelectric tube and vacuum-tube amplifier, circuits of sufficiently
high resistance are encountered so that the impedances of the series
condensers at the working frequency are not of serious consequence,
while their presence effectually bars the drifts.

As in the case of the Moll amplifier, both galvanometers are
critically damped.

The "resonance radiometer" was originally designed for the
purpose of attaining high amplification and at the same time
minimizing drift, tremors, etc.   Here again the original articles[19]
must be consulted for details.   The underlying idea may be
stated briefly as follows: If primary and secondary galvanometers
are underdamped and adjusted to the same period, then, by
interrupting the radiation falling on the thermopile with a
periodicity corresponding to that of the galvanometers, a condition of resonance is set up.   As a class, resonating systems are
characterized by high sensitivity to "tuned" periodic disturbances and by indifference to random disturbances.

From Ising's formulas it is evident that, since the term t
denotes the time required by the galvanometer to reach, say,
95 per cent of its maximum deflection, the Brownian-motion limit
of sensitivity is proportional to $1/\sqrt{t}$.   While the normal
working period of a critically damped galvanometer is of the
order of 6 sec., the value of t in Hardy's experiments with a
resonance radiometer was 90 sec.   Whether or not a critically
damped galvanometer having this large value of t can be used
successfully is an open question.   Hardy concludes that " . . .
the resonance radiometer of 90 sec. response time is from five to
eight times as sensitive as the equivalent steady deflection
galvanometer, when in use with a thermocouple."   These
remarks are all matters of experimental efficiency and not
amenable to other proof than trial.

A PHOTOELECTRIC-TUBE GALVANOMETER AMPLIFIER

A. H. Taylor[*]

A galvanometer amplifier, which is a modification of the Moll thermorelay, that uses two photoelectric tubes in the place of a thermojunction to drive the second galvanometer has been found quite satisfactory when used to amplify the deflections of a thermopile galvanometer.

The thermopile galvanometer *G*-1, Fig. 189, is a Leeds and Northrup No. 2285A having a sensitivity rating of 0.09 μv/mm.

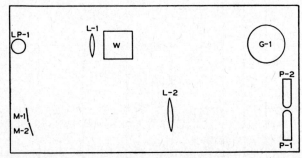

Fig. 189.—Arrangement of primary galvanometer and accessories. *LP*-1 lamp with straight-coiled filament; *L*-1 and *L*-2, lenses; *W*, water cell; *G*-1, primary galvanometer; *M*-1 and *M*-2, mirrors; *P*-1 and *P*-2, caesium phototubes.

By means of lens *L*-1, radiation from lamp *LP*-1, reflected from the mirror of the galvanometer *G*-1, is brought to a focus at a point about 8 in. in front of the galvanometer mirror (after reflection) and is next reflected by the split mirrors *M*-1 and *M*-2. Lens *L*-2 again focuses the two images a short distance in front of the two phototubes *P*-1 and *P*-2, spreading the radiation over a large part of the cathode areas of the phototubes (PJ-23 caesium). The water cell *W* is used to remove heat from the beam, and thus to reduce disturbances due to heated air currents in the galvanometer *G*-1. Lamp *LP*-1 has a straight-coiled filament normal to the lamp axis. Although the lamp used is a special lamp, a similar lamp is the one designated as Mazda 1321 spotlight.

Any deflection of *G*-1 increases the radiation on one phototube and decreases it on the other. This causes a deflection of an

[*] *Physicist, Lighting Research Laboratory, General Electric Company, Cleveland, Ohio.*

external galvanometer *G*-2, which is a Leeds and Northrup No. 2500b, having a sensitivity rating of 2,000 megohms.

Figure 190 shows a wiring diagram of the two galvanometers and accessory circuits. When the two phototube currents are equal, no current flows through galvanometer *G*-2. If a change in the relative amounts of radiation on the two phototubes

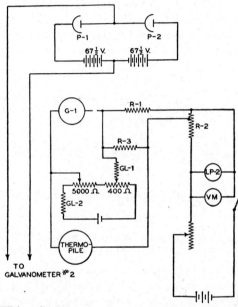

Fig. 190.—Wiring diagram of galvanometer amplifier with potentiometer system for controlling galvanometer zero and accessory system for calibration of deflection. *R*-1, ¼ Meg.; *R*-2, ¼ to 1 Meg. in series with low resistance; *R*-3, damping resistance, 40 ohms; *GL*-1 and *GL*-2, high-resistance grid leaks; *G*-1, primary galvanometer; *P*-1 and *P*-2, caesium phototubes.

occurs, a current proportional to the change in the radiation passes through *G*-2. If the zero of *G*-1 drifts, it can be restored by means of a parallel circuit consisting of two potentiometers, two high-resistance grid leaks and a single dry cell. An auxiliary circuit, consisting of a battery, lamp *LP*-2, voltmeter or potentiometer, rheostat, and high resistance *R*-2, can be used to calibrate the amplifier. Resistance *R*-3 is a damping resistance.

The primary galvanometer *G*-1, phototubes, lenses, mirrors, etc., may be mounted in a box approximately 15 by 30 by 12 in. high. By placing heavy weights in the bottom of the box and mounting it on four pyramids of four rubber handballs, the apparatus may be insulated fairly well from ordinary building vibrations.

Lamp *LP*-1 (Fig. 189) must be maintained at a constant current during use. The amount of amplification can be varied by varying the current in this lamp. The amplification obtainable with this apparatus may be further increased by use of a thermionic amplifier instead of galvanometer *G*-2, and apparently is limited only by the stability of the primary galvanometer. Connections which give spurious thermal e.m.fs. must, of course, be avoided.

This galvanometer amplifier is quite similar to one described by Moss[20] but differs in essential details, so that a higher amplification is possible.

References

1. W. Jaeger, Die Empfindlichkeit des Drehspulengalvanometers in aperiodischem Grenzfall, *Zeitschr. Instrumentenk.*, **23**, 353 (1903); Das Drehspulengalvanometer nach Deprez-d'Arsonval, in aperiodischem Grenzfall, *Zeitschr. Instrumentenk.*, **23**, 261 (1903); P. E. Klopsteg, On the "Current Deflection" Method for Determining Ballistic Constants of Moving Coil Galvanometers, with a Note on the Nonuniformity of Magnetic Fields in such Instruments, *Phys. Rev.*, **7**, 633 (1916); F. A. Laws, "Electrical Measurements," McGraw-Hill Book Company, Inc., p. 49; Leeds & Northrup Notes on Moving Coil Galvanometers, Note Book 2, 1930; W. P. White, Sensitive Moving Coil Galvanometers, *Phys. Rev.*, **19**, 309 (1904); Some Properties of the Moving Coil Galvanometer, *Phys. Rev.*, **22**, 371 (1906); Everyday Problems of the Moving Coil Galvanometer, *Phys. Rev.*, **23**, 382 (1906).

2. W. W. Coblentz, New Type of Ironclad Galvanometer, *Bur. Standards Bull.*, **4**, 391 (1908); **9**, 7 (1911); Sensitivity and Magnetic Shielding Tests, *Bur. Standards Bull.*, **13**, 423 (1916).

3. F. Wenner, General Design of Critically Damped Galvanometers, *Bur. Standards Bull.*, **13** (S.P. 273) (1916).

4. H. B. Brooks, Sensitivity of a galvanometer as a function of its resistance, *Bur. Standards Jour. Research*, **4**, 297 (1930).

5. E. F. Nichols and S. R. Williams, A Convenient Form of Galvanometer with Magnetic Shielding, *Phys. Rev.*, **27**, 250 (1908); B. J. Spence, A Form of Ironclad Thomson Astatic Galvanometer, *Jour. Optical Soc. Am. and Rev. Sci. Inst.*, **6**, 696 (1922); W. Weniger, Improved Absorption Spectra, *Phys. Rev.*, **31**, 393 (1910).

6. A. P. Carman, A Suspension to Eliminate Mechanical Disturbances, *Jour. Optical Soc. Am. and Rev. Sci. Inst.*, **6**, 694 (1922); W. H. Julius, *Ann. Physik*, **56**, 151 (1895).

7. A. L. Johnsrud, *Jour. Optical Soc. Am.*, **10**, 609 (1925).

8. R. Müller, *Ann. Physik*, **1**, 613 (1929).

9. Lindeck and Rothe, Prüfung von Thermoelementen, *Zeitschr. Instru-mentenk.*, **20**, 293 (1900).

10. W. P. White, Neue Doppelkompensatoren, *Zeitschr. Instrumentenk.*, **34**, 147 (1914).

11. A. C. Hardy and F. H. Perrin, "Principles of Optics," McGraw-Hill Book Company, Inc., p. 541, 1932.

12. W. B. Nottingham, Measurement of Small D.C. Potentials and Currents in High Resistance Circuits by Using Vacuum Tubes, *Jour. Franklin Inst.*, **209**, 287–348 (1930).

13. Leeds and Northrup, *Speedomax Instruments*, **6**, 211 (1933). A. W. Smith, "Electrical Measurements," McGraw-Hill Book Company, Inc., p. 146, 1914.

14. Ising, *Phil. Mag.*, **1**, 827 (1926); Barnes and Silverman, *Rev. Mod. Phys.*, **6**, 162 (1934).

15. S. Steele, Infrared Radiation from an Otto Cycle Engine, *Jour. Ind. Eng. Chem.*, **25**, 388 (1933); W. J. H. Moll, *Phil. Mag.*, **50**, 624, 626 (1925).

16. R. B. Barnes and R. Matossi, *Zeitschr. Physik*, **76**, 24 (1932).

17. Private communication from Dr. P. H. Dike from the Leeds & Northrup Company.

18. F. A. Firestone, *Rev. Sci. Inst.*, **3**, 163 (1932).

19. A. H. Pfund, *Science*, **2**, 69 (1929); J. D. Hardy, *Rev. Sci. Inst.*, **1**, 429 (1929); *Rev. Sci. Inst.*, **5**, 120 (1934).

20. E. B. Moss, *Jour. Sci. Inst.*, **12**, 141 (1935).

CHAPTER XI

SPECTROPHOTOMETRY

KASSON S. GIBSON*

The optical principles involved in spectrophotometers can be illustrated by describing in some detail certain of the instruments and equipment which are now manufactured or used in the measurement of spectral transmission or spectral apparent reflectance. It is not attempted to survey the field completely or to give an historical account of the development of spectrophotometric methods. Such an effort was made in the report of the Spectrophotometry Committee of the Optical Society of America, in 1925.[1] However, the various methods described herein are believed to include most of the new or improved designs effected in spectrophotometers since that date.

The instruments selected for discussion illustrate most of the devices that have been used to secure the necessary two-part photometric field and the methods employed to vary the brightness of one or both parts of the field in a measurable manner. These are essential conditions of all photometry† and arise from the well-known fact that the eye is totally incapable of any reliable judgment regarding absolute brightness, but that it is able to decide with considerable precision whether two properly juxtaposed photometric fields of the same chromaticity are equally bright. By combining these essential photometric conditions with means for dispersing the light and isolating a narrow spectral region of the desired wavelength one obtains the fundamental basis of all spectrophotometers.

After the instruments and methods are described, the various factors will be considered which are of importance in the elimination of errors, such as proper methods of illumination, reference

---

* *Chief, Colorimetry Section, National Bureau of Standards.*

† Excluding consideration of the well-known "flicker" method of heterochromatic photometry and other methods which have been rarely used in spectrophotometry.

standards for apparent reflectance measurements, wavelength calibration, elimination of stray light, slit-width corrections, and means of checking the reliability of the photometric scale and the overall accuracy of the instrument.

TYPICAL INSTRUMENTS AND METHODS

All the instruments described have photometric fields which will be classified as type I or type II, depending on their method of formation. These two types are illustrated in Fig. 191, which is taken from the Spectrophotometry Committee report to which reference has just been made.

Type I, known as the "juxtaposed-spectra" type, is so designated because the photometric field consists of a selected portion

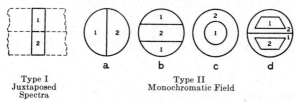

Type I
Juxtaposed
Spectra

Type II
Monochromatic Field

FIG. 191.—Illustration of various forms of two-part photometric field used in spectrophotometry.

of two juxtaposed spectra. These spectra are formed in the focal plane of the telescope lens of the spectrometer and are viewed by a magnifying eyepiece. The horizontal dividing line between the two spectra is produced by some optical device external to the spectrometer, either placed at the collimator slit or imaged upon that slit. The amount of spectrum viewed at one time may be varied by changing the width of the shutter indicated by the vertical lines in Fig. 191, type I. It is apparent that, in general, the color of both halves of the field will vary from left to right and that any sudden change in brightness with wavelength will be visible in the field.

In type II the dividing lines of the field are produced by some optical device either placed between the collimator and telescope lenses or imaged between them from some region outside of the spectrometer. The eye is placed at the exit slit of the instrument close to the focal plane of the telescope lens. In this position any object placed in the path of the beam between the collimator and telescope lenses or close to them will appear sharply defined. In particular a two-part photometric field may readily be formed by placing an appropriate optical device in this position or imaging such device in this location. Various means for doing so are illustrated in the several instruments. The photometric field thus obtained is called the "monochromatic-field" type because, regardless of the slit widths used, the whole field is of the same chromaticity. This method of securing the photometric field is also referred to as the "Maxwellian field of view."

Polarization Methods

Polarization methods perhaps have been more commonly used than any other as a means of varying the brightness of the photometric field. Three different types of polarization instruments are illustrated: (1) The König-Martens spectrophotometer made by Schmidt and Haensch, with auxiliary equipment designed at the National Bureau of Standards; (2) the Martens photometer combined with spectrometer and auxiliary equipment, made by (a) the Bausch and Lomb Optical Company, and (b) the Gaertner Scientific Corporation; and (3) the spectrophotometric equipment designed by Dowell and made by Adam Hilger, Ltd.

König-Martens Spectrophotometer,[2] with Auxiliary Equipment Designed at the National Bureau of Standards. This apparatus is outlined in Fig. 192, which is a reproduction of Fig. 3 of *Bureau of Standards Research Paper* No. 30.[3]

Light entering the collimator slits, A and B, forms beams 1 and 2. These beams follow the usual course through the collimator lens, dispersing prism, and telescope objective. Cemented to the latter lens is a combination of Wollaston prism, wedge,[*] and biprism. The combined action of the Wollaston prism and biprism is to form four spectral images of each of the slits A and B in the plane of the ocular slit. The angle of the biprism is chosen, with regard to the separation of slits A and B and the construction of the Wollaston prism, so that two of the eight images overlap at the ocular slit. The designations, A_1v and B_2h, indicate that one of these images is formed by light entering

---

[*] The purpose of wedges in the collimator and telescope is to prevent passage to the eye of certain multiply reflected rays from the optical surfaces.

slit *A* and passing through part 1 of the biprism.   It is plane-polarized with electrical vibrations in a vertical plane.   The other image is formed by light from slit *B* passing face 2 of the biprism and is polarized with vibrations in a horizontal plane.

Looking through the ocular slit one sees the surface of the biprism uniformly illuminated by a mixture of light of wave-length range determined by the widths of the collimator and

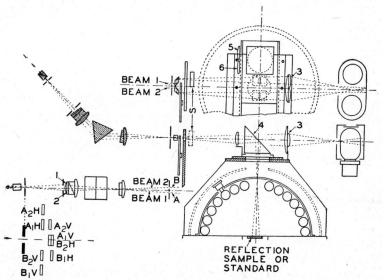

Fig. 192.—König-Martens spectrophotometer, with auxiliary equipment de-signed at the National Bureau of Standards.

ocular slits, the mean wavelength corresponding to the position of the ocular slit in the spectrum.   The biprism edge forms a vertical dividing line in this photometric field, which is of type II-a, with the lights in the two halves of the field plane-polar-ized in directions mutually perpendicular to each other.   By turning the nicol between the eye and the ocular slit, the two parts of the field may be matched in brightness.

For spectral-transmission measurements three different illumi-nants are used, *viz.*, the mercury arc in quartz, the helium lamp, and the incandescent lamp.   Only the last is shown in the diagram.   Each of the three illuminants is mounted in a small inclosure, the inside surface of which is coated with MgO.   In each case the light used for the transmission measurements is taken from the diffusing rear surface of the inclosure; this is collimated by the combination lenses (3) and enters the collimator slits *A* and *B*, as shown (prism (4) and lenses (5) and (6) removed).

The specimen whose transmission is to be measured is placed in beam 1 at *S* as shown and the angle of match θ_1 of the nicol is read; the specimen is then transferred to beam 2 and the angle of match θ_2 determined, after which the sample is returned to beam 1 and the determination of θ_1 repeated. The transmission τ of the sample is given by the relation

$$\tau = \cot \theta_1 \tan \theta_2 \qquad (69)$$

The transmission may also be measured by taking readings first with the sample placed in either beam and then with it removed from both beams. If θ_0 is the angle of match in this latter case, τ is given by the relations

$$\tau = \tan^2 \theta_0 \cot^2 \theta_1 \qquad (70)$$
$$= \cot^2 \theta_0 \tan^2 \theta_2 \qquad (71)$$

The interchange method of measurement, Eq. (69), is superior to the simple substitution method, Eqs. (70) and (71), because errors due to partial polarization of light by the sample are thereby largely eliminated, as noted below.

The mercury and helium illuminants afford ready means of checking the wavelength calibration of the spectrophotometer; they also enable measurements of transmission to be made at certain wavelengths free from slit width or wavelength error. These wavelengths are: Hg 578 (*i.e.*, 576.9 and 579.0), 546.1, 435.8, 404.7 mμ; and He 667.8, 587.6, 501.6, and 447.1 mμ.

The rotating sector, shown in the diagram between the collimator slit and the transmission sample, serves two purposes:

1. It enables a direct check to be made on the reliability of the photometric scale of the instrument.[4] A number of sectors were prepared having respective apertures such as to give transmissions of approximately 0.01 to 0.80. These apertures were accurately determined mechanically. Any desired sector may be placed in position, rotated rapidly enough to eliminate flicker, and its transmission determined photometrically in the same manner as for the usual transmission sample.

2. To measure low transmissions, the 0.10 or 0.01 sector is placed in the blank beam and the transmission of the sample is measured relative to that of the sector. This brings the angles of match away from the extinction

points into a more suitable region of the scale and greatly extends the range of the instrument for low-transmission measurements.

For measurements of spectral apparent reflectance, the sample and reference white standard* are placed as shown at the center of the base of a hemisphere whose interior surface is coated white with MgO and studded with 156 small lamps, so that in effect the sample and standard are in completely diffused illumination. The light reflected at right angles from the sample and standard, respectively, forms beams 1 and 2 and enters the spectrophotometer via the right-angled prism (4) and lenses (5) and (6). Sample and standard may be reversed in position by the observer and the apparent reflectance of the sample, ρ_s, relative to that of the standard, ρ_0, is given by the relation, analogous to Eq. (69),

$$\frac{\rho_s}{\rho_0} = \cot \theta_1 \tan \theta_2. \qquad (72)$$

The effect of polarization on the values of τ or ρ_s/ρ_0, obtained with this equipment, is discussed by McNicholas.[3] If X represents either of these quantities, the complete expression is

$$abX = \cot \theta_1 \tan \theta_2 \qquad (73)$$

where a and b represent the respective changes in the state of polarization of beams 1 and 2, due to the introduction of the sample into the beam. It is shown that any initial difference in the beam intensities or any degree of polarization of the light emitted by the source† along beams 1 and 2 does not affect the measurement of X; it is only the changes in polarization that may cause error. This error is usually negligible for the following reasons:

1. With this equipment the vast majority of samples do not affect the state of polarization of the light beams in either transmission or apparent-reflectance measurements.

---

* The choice of reference standard is considered later.

† It was found by McNicholas that the initial polarization of the light from the tungsten-incandescent, mercury-vapor, or helium illuminants (*i.e.*, from the MgO diffusing surfaces where beams 1 and 2 originate) is less than 1 per cent. Under the symmetrical illumination from the hemispherical source there is no appreciable polarization of the light reflected at right angles from a surface having no structural regularities.

2. In case the light reflected from a sample is partially polarized, owing to structural regularities such as those exhibited by silk and velvet, the method of interchanging sample and standard greatly minimizes the resulting error.

3. If the sample is placed so that the plane of polarization of the reflected light as it enters the spectrophotometer is inclined at 45 deg. to the principal planes of the instrument, the small residual error is completely eliminated.

The König-Martens spectrophotometer may also be used for measuring the spectral distribution of one illuminant relative to the other. A means of doing this, even for a fluctuating illuminant such as the carbon arc, has been described[5] by Priest.

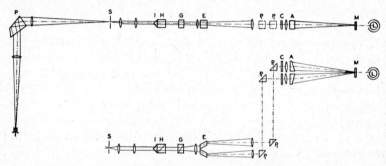

Fig. 193.—Optical parts of Bausch and Lomb spectrophotometric equipment.

Various other methods of illumination, designed for special purposes, particularly for transmission measurements, are illustrated in catalogues issued by Schmidt and Haensch[6] and by Akatos, Inc.[7]

Martens Photometer and Spectrometer Combinations. a. *Bausch and Lomb Spectrophotometric Equipment.* The Bausch and Lomb equipment consists of three units: (1) a spectrometer, (2) a Martens photometer, and (3) auxiliary attachments for holding the sample and furnishing the proper illumination. One arrangement of apparatus is shown in Fig. 193. (See Fig. III-b from the Bausch and Lomb catalogue.[8]) This arrangement facilitates the measurement of the transmittancy of liquids in varying thickness. The solution and solvent are placed in the cups located in the vertical part of the beam. By raising the cups about plungers the thicknesses of liquids measured may be varied from less than 1 to 65 mm.

The illuminant consists of light from the incandescent lamp, *L*, diffused by the double ground-glass window, *M*. The beams are collimated by the wedges A and lenses and follow the paths indicated, arriving at the respective entrances to the Martens photometer.

The action of the Martens photometer is similar to that already described for the König-Martens spectrophotometer. The Wollaston prism G transmits two beams to the nicol H, one from each entrance aperture, the beams being polarized in mutually perpendicular planes.* The intensities of the two beams may then be equalized by rotation of the nicol. The biprism I directs these two beams along the axis of the photometer, and auxiliary lenses focus an image of the horizontal biprism edge onto the vertical collimator slit S.

The spectrometer forms a spectral image of the collimator slit in the focal plane of the telescope objective. Viewing this image through the eyepiece, the observer sees a pair of juxtaposed spectra, the widths of which are controlled by a V slide at the collimator slit. The length of spectrum viewed is regulated by a shutter in the eyepiece holder. The photometric field is thus of type I. The two halves of this field may be equalized in brightness by turning the Nicol prism in the Martens photometer.

The transmission of a solution relative to that of the solvent may be determined at any wavelength by means of the same formulas as are used with the König-Martens spectrophotometer. The scale of the Martens photometer is calibrated not only in degrees, but also in terms of τ and $- \log_{10} \tau$, so that if θ_0 can be made exactly equal to 45 deg., the instrument is direct-reading. Other arrangements of apparatus for both transmission and apparent-reflectance measurements are illustrated in the Bausch and Lomb catalogue, Figs. I-b and II-b.

b. *Gaertner Polarizing Spectrophotometer.* This apparatus likewise consists of three units, a spectrometer, a Martens photometer, and auxiliary equipment for mounting and illuminating the samples. The arrangement is illustrated in Fig. 194, which is a reproduction of a diagram shown on page 13 of the Gaertner catalogue.[9]

---

* This arrangement of optical parts in the Martens photometer is considered superior because no optical part, with reference particularly to the biprism with its inclined refracting surfaces, is placed between the Wollaston and Nicol prisms.

The illumination unit consists of a white-lined diffusing sphere containing four 200-watt incandescent lamps.   For transmission measurements (upper part of diagram) a diffusing white surface is placed at the back of the sphere and serves as the illuminant; if desired, this may be replaced by an opal glass plate permitting illumination from an external source such as the mercury arc. Light from the diffusing surface is collimated by a lens and then separated by a pair of rhombs into two beams which pass through the tubes holding solution and solvent.   The beams are then

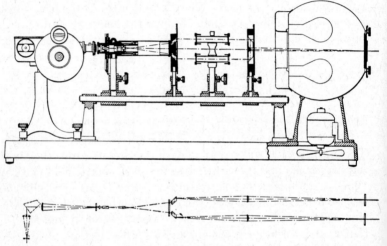

Fig. 194.—Gaertner polarizing spectrophotometer. The upper part of the picture shows the arrangement of the different parts of the apparatus together with the light path for measuring transmission.   The lower part of the picture shows the light path for measuring apparent reflectance.

directed by rhombs and lenses into the Martens photometer, as shown.

For apparent-reflectance measurements (lower part of diagram) the first pair of rhombs is removed, the two beams coming directly from the surfaces of sample and reference standard.   The sample and standard are carried on a holder and may be interchanged in position.

The photometric field is of type II-a, with dividing line horizontal.   To secure this, the photometric field of the Martens photometer is projected through the entrance slit to a position in the collimator objective where it is viewed from the ocular slit without eye lens. Transmission and apparent-reflectance are computed by the same formulas as are used with the two instruments already described. The instrument also is made direct-reading if the angle of match can be secured at exactly 45 deg.

Hilger Spectrophotometric Equipment. The most recent spectrophotometer made by Hilger is described in two papers by Dowell.[10] Figure 195 is a reproduction of Fig. 3 from the first paper, and illustrates the optical system employed.

Light from A is separated and collimated by rhombs and lenses as shown at B and C. The two beams pass through the respective fixed nicols D_1 and D_2, the rotatable nicol E, the fixed nicols F_1 and F_2, the deflectors G_1 and G_2, and the lenses H_1 and H_2, to a biprism K mounted on the collimator slit of the spectrometer.

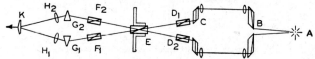

FIG. 195.—Photometer designed by Dowell and used on the Hilger industrial and research spectrophotometer.

The biprism edge is at right angles to the slit and forms the dividing line in the juxtaposed spectra, the photometric field being of type I. The planes of polarization of D_1 and D_2 are perpendicular to each other, as are also those of F_1 and F_2; the planes of polarization of D_1 and F_1 are parallel, as are also those of D_2 and F_2.

If d_1 and d_2 represent the amplitudes of the beams transmitted respectively by nicols D_1 and D_2, and if ϕ is the angle of rotation of nicol E required to equalize the intensities of the beams transmitted by nicols F_1 and F_2, then

$$\frac{d_1}{d_2} = \tan^2 \phi$$

and the ratio of intensities is given by the expression

$$\frac{I_1}{I_2} = \left(\frac{d_1}{d_2}\right)^2 = \tan^4 \phi$$

From this, it follows that

$$\begin{aligned} \tau &= \tan^4 \phi_1 \cot^4 \phi_0 \\ &= \cot^4 \phi_2 \tan^4 \phi_0 \\ &= \tan^2 \phi_1 \cot^2 \phi_2 \end{aligned} \tag{74}$$

where τ = transmission of a sample inserted in either beam.

  ϕ_1 = angle of match for the sample in beam 1.

  ϕ_2 = angle of match for the sample in beam 2.

  ϕ_0 = angle of match with the sample removed from both beams.*

The tan^4 arrangement gives a more open scale for low transmissions than does a tan^2 arrangement, and it is, therefore, considered especially suitable for absorption measurements. Other

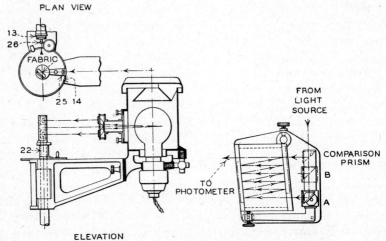

FIG. 196.—Details of sample holders designed by Dowell.

features of the arrangement stressed by Dowell are: (1) no optical parts are placed between the polarizing prisms, and (2) the nicols F_1 and F_2 are effective in removing scattered light transmitted by nicol E.

In the assembled apparatus provision is made for reflectance measurements as well as for transmission measurements. For this purpose, the lamp house carrying A and B, Fig. 195, is rotated 90 deg. about a vertical axis between B and C. The arrangement is indicated in Fig. 196, left, which is a reproduction of Fig. 4 of Dowell's second paper. The end of the photometer box C, in Fig. 195, is indicated at (13) in Fig. 196. The sample (fabric)

---

* Compare the formulas given above for the König-Martens spectrophotometer. The final form in either case depends, of course, on whether the beam extinguished when θ or ϕ equals zero is defined as beam 1 or 2.

and reference standard are mounted one above the other on a fitting (22) which is an extension of the spindle on which the lamp house rotates.   The angle at which the sample and standard are fixed for measurement is determined from the scale and index (25) and (14).   For apparent-reflectance measurements a 500-candlepower pointolite lamp is used.

At the right in Fig. 196 is outlined the attachment used to measure the reflectance of polished surfaces.   This consists of a platform carrying a prism and a mounting by means of which two plane-reflecting surfaces of the material being tested are placed accurately parallel and facing each other.   The light follows the course indicated, the comparison beam being reflected into the photometer by means of a right-angled prism underneath the platform.   The purpose of this arrangement is to secure increased sensitivity by multiple reflection.

Dowell's instrument is considered a development from the Hilger-Nutting spectrophotometer.   The most recent design of this latter instrument is described in Fig. H56a of the Hilger catalog.[11]

NONPOLARIZATION METHODS

Various means other than polarization of light have been used in spectrophotometers to vary the brightness in a continuous and known manner.   Such are rotating sectors variable while in motion, variable distance with the inverse-square law, absorption wedges, variable voltage on lamps, etc.   Some of these will now be illustrated.

Keuffel and Esser Color Analyzer.   The arrangement of this spectrophotometer[12] is shown in Fig. 197.   As in some of the polarization instruments, the apparatus is made up of three principal parts—in this case, (1) an illuminating device with sample holders for transmission and apparent-reflectance measurements, (2) a rotating-disk photometer, and (3) a spectrometer.

The rotating-disk photometer* consists of two sectored disks which revolve around the same axis at the same speed and in the same direction, the speed being great enough to eliminate flicker. One sector is larger in diameter than the other and transmits a constant amount of the incident light near its edge when in rotation.   The combined aperture of the two sectors near the edge of

* For additional details the article by Keuffel should be consulted.

the smaller one may be varied relative to that of the constant sector by an amount varying from 0 to 110 per cent; this variation is produced while the sectors are rotating by turning the knurled handle to which the photometer scale is attached.

The illuminating device consists of a white-lined sphere containing two 400-watt lamps. For apparent-reflectance measurements the sample and standard are placed at the rear of this sphere, the sample above and the standard below. Direct

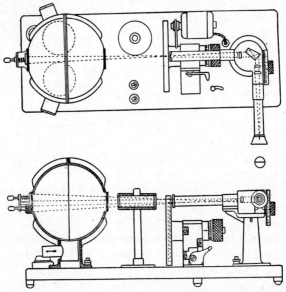

FIG. 197.—Two views of the Keuffel and Esser color analyzer.

illumination on sample and standard from the lamps is prevented by the use of shields. Light from the sample passes through the constant aperture of the rotating sector, that from the standard through the variable aperture. The directions of the axes of these beams are determined by the angle of the biprism, placed between the dispersing prism and the telescope lens. The edge of the biprism forms the dividing line of the circular photometric field and is viewed by the eye placed at the ocular slit. The instrument is thus of type II-a, with dividing line horizontal.

The instrument is designed to be direct-reading. Let R_x be the reading of the sector when a photometric match is obtained with sample in place, R_0 the reading for a match when the sample is replaced by a duplicate of the reference standard. The apparent-reflectance of the sample relative to that of the standard is given by the ratio R_x/R_0. The value of R_0 may be adjusted by varying the relative widths of the lower and upper halves of the entrance slit. If this value can be made 100.0 at all wavelengths, the instrument becomes direct-reading.

Transmissions are measured by replacing the sample by the standard and mounting the sample in the upper beam between the sphere and sector. Absorption tubes are shown in the lower part of the figure, the lower one being for the solvent. For low transmissions there is an adjustment which lowers the sectors, doubling the amount of the transmitted light and giving a more open scale, the sectors being so constructed that the scale then reads four times the actual value.

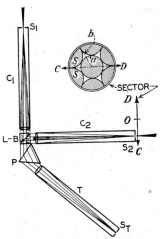

Fig. 198.—Lummer-Brodhun spectrophotometer with variable rotating sector designed by Hyde.

Lummer-Brodhun Spectrophotometer.[13] This instrument is outlined in Fig. 198. The illustration is a combination of Fig. 11 of the report[14] of the spectrophotometry committee of the Optical Society of America, and of Fig. 7 of a paper by Hyde[15]. The instrument is characterized by the separate collimators C_1 and C_2 and the Lummer-Brodhun cube L-B, by means of which the two beams are brought into proper juxtaposition. In the diagram as shown, the photometric field would be of type II-c. A more common type of field, known as the Lummer-Brodhun contrast field,* is that illustrated in Fig. 191 as type II-d. When the two parts of the photometric field are matched, the two trapezoids are approximately 8 per cent darker than the rest of the field, owing to the reflection from transparent nonabsorbing glass plates properly placed in each beam close to the L-B cube. At low brightnesses this contrast type of field has greater sensibility than the equality-of-brightness field.

* See p. 390.

The Lummer-Brodhun spectrophotometer is particularly suitable for measuring the relative spectral-energy distribution of two illuminants, because of the wide separation of the two entrant beams; it has been used considerably for such measurements both with incandescent illuminants and with fluorescent materials. No means for varying the brightness of either half of the photometric field in a continuous and accurately known manner was originally provided on the instrument itself. The width of one of the collimator slits has, therefore, often been used to vary the brightness of the field, the brightness being taken proportional to the slit width. This procedure is not to be recommended, however, as other more accurate methods are available.

To avoid this undesirable use of variable slits, any of the methods of varying brightness noted elsewhere in this chapter may be used with the Lummer-Brodhun spectrophotometer. Rotating sectors of fixed or variable aperture (*i.e.*, variable while in rotation) have often been used. Several have been designed that are similar to the Keuffel and Esser sector already described, in that they consist of two sectors in series, rotating at the same rate, whose relative orientation may be varied while in motion.

Preceding these designs were those by Brodhun and Hyde. The Brodhun sector[16] consists of a pair of rotating rhombs which carry the beam of light across a stationary sector whose aperture may be varied while the rhombs are rotated. This sector is quiet and convenient but transmits only 0.4 of the incident light at its maximum opening. The scale is linear.

The sector designed by Hyde is illustrated in Fig. 198.* The rotating sector is moved bodily along the direction C-D in front of slit S_2, its effective transmission depending on its position relative to the slit. In this particular sector, the transmission varies from 0.90 at radial distance a to zero at radial distance b, in this respect being superior to sectors which have radial openings limiting the maximum transmission to approximately 0.50. A second feature of this sector is the shape of the edges which are so designed that the transmission gradient $\Delta\tau/\tau$ changes but slightly for values of τ greater than 0.07. $\Delta\tau$

* Hyde's sector design has since been incorporated in the Lummer-Brodhun spectrophotometer assembly by Schmidt and Haensch. See Catalog II, p. 6.

is the change in transmission corresponding to a given linear motion (*e.g.*, 0.1 mm) along *C-D*.

A cylindrical sector has been recently designed[17] for use in a similar manner. This is illustrated in Fig. 199, which is a reproduction of Fig. 2 of Dunn's paper. The direction of motion is along *R-R'*. The actual transmission of the rotating sector varies from zero to 1.00, the beam being brought along the direction *L-P* and directed into the slit *S* by the prism *P*. In the design shown, the transmission is linearly proportional to distance along *R-R'*, and is given by the ratio I/I_0.

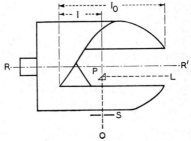

FIG. 199.—Variable rotating sector designed by Dunn.

Spectrophotometric Equipment at the National Physical Laboratory. Two designs of apparatus have been constructed at the National Physical Laboratory, both employing fixed rotating sectors of various apertures in combination with auxiliary devices for securing continuous variation of brightnesses.

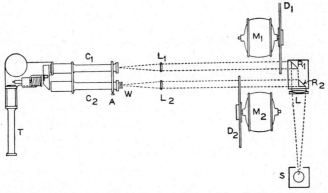

FIG. 200.—Spectrophotometric equipment designed by Guild at the National Physical Laboratory.

a. Design by Guild. This equipment is illustrated in Fig. 200, which is a reproduction of Fig. 2 of Guild's paper.[18] A constant-deviation spectrometer is provided with a second collimator C_2 and a combination prism, *P* so mounted that a

Lummer-Brodhun contrast field of type II-d, is secured, although not exactly of the same pattern as that shown in Fig. 191.

Light from an incandescent lamp S, with single vertical-coil filament, is formed into two beams by lenses and prisms and focused onto the two collimator slits, as shown. The diagram shows the apparatus arranged for spectral-transmission measurements, the sample being placed in beam 1. For spectral-energy measurements, the prism R_1 is removed and the standard and unknown illuminant alternately illuminate C_1, S serving as the comparison lamp.

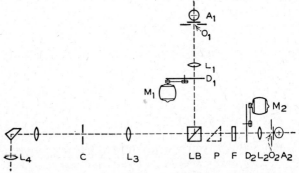

Fig. 201.—Spectrophotometric equipment designed by Buckley and Brookes at the National Physical Laboratory.

Fixed-aperture sectors D_1 and D_2, placed in the beams, provide the major part of the necessary variations in brightness. Thirteen sectors are used, with effective transmissions varying from 0.90 to 0.010. In addition, a pair of absorption wedges are mounted at W to provide the necessary continuous adjustment of brightness within the intervals afforded by the sectors. In these wedges the absorption is due to finely divided lampblack in gelatine. The wedge scale is calibrated in place by means of the rotating sectors, using (1) a series of sectors at some one wavelength, and (2) one chosen sector at the various wavelengths. Thicknesses are, of course, correlated with the linear scale readings on the wedge unit, so that the wedges may be completely calibrated by following this procedure.

This design of instrument gives high light efficiency and the combination of sectors and wedge unit makes possible the measurement of very low transmissions.

b. Design by Buckley and Brookes. The arrangement of apparatus by Buckley and Brookes is shown in Fig. 201, which is a
reproduction of Fig. 1 of their paper.[19]   In this case the Lummer-
Brodhun cube *LB* is placed outside the spectrometer but is
imaged by the lens L_3 in the plane of L_4, giving a field of type II-b.
Sectors of fixed aperture are placed at D_1 and D_2 as shown, giving
discontinuous variations in brightness as in the previous
apparatus.

Continuous variations in brightness are secured by varying
the voltage on lamp A_1.   Calibration of the scale is carried out
by means of the Wien equation:

$$J_\lambda{}^s d\lambda = RC_1\lambda^{-5}e^{-\frac{c_2}{\lambda T_c}}d\lambda \tag{75}$$

The symbols have the usual significance.   From this it is shown
that

$$\log\left(\frac{J_\lambda{}^s}{J_\lambda{}^{s_1}}\right) = -\left(\frac{c_2}{\lambda}\right)\left(\frac{1}{T_c} - \frac{1}{T_{c_1}}\right) = \log\left(\frac{J_\lambda{}^v}{J_\lambda{}^{v_1}}\right) \tag{76}$$

where S_1 and T_{c_1} refer to the temperatures at the standard voltage, V_1, and S and T_c refer to any other voltage, V.   If
$-\log (J_\lambda{}^v/J_\lambda{}^{v_1})$ is designated as $D_\lambda{}^v$, then

$$D_\lambda{}^v = \left(\frac{c_2}{\lambda}\right)\left(\frac{1}{T_c} - \frac{1}{T_{c_1}}\right) \tag{77}$$

and for any other wavelength λ' it follows that

$$D_{\lambda'}{}^v = \left(\frac{\lambda}{\lambda'}\right)D_\lambda{}^v \tag{78}$$

Hence the relation between $D_\lambda{}^v$ and voltage can be computed
for all wavelengths after it has been determined at some one wavelength.   At that one wavelength it is experimentally determined
by means of the sectors.

In measuring transmissions, the sample is placed at F.   Frosted
glass is placed at O_1 and O_2, immediately in front of the gas-filled
projection lamps A_1 and A_2.   At P is a prism which may be
inserted to ascertain whether the introduction of the sample F
has caused any important deviation of the beam.   The image of
O_2 is formed on a screen about 10 ft. away and is magnified about
20 times.   If, because of nonparallelism of the surfaces of F,

the image is deviated, it may be brought back to its original position by movement of the lens L_2, in its own plane. Errors due to multiple reflections between LB and F are eliminated by inclining LB sufficiently to throw the image of O_2 about 5 mm off the slit C.

FACTORS AFFECTING THE RELIABILITY OF SPECTROPHOTOMETRIC DATA

Illumination and Reference Standards.   The use of the substitution method in spectrophotometry may be considered an absolute necessity for accurate work.   In this method, the path of the light without and within the instrument should be effectively identical for the sample being measured and for the standard with which it is compared.   As already illustrated in the various types of instrument, this may be accomplished either by having the light from the sample and standard brought successively into one-half of the photometric field, the two light beams being evaluated in turn by means of the light in the comparison beam, or by having the light beams from the sample and standard compared after simultaneously traversing different paths leading to the two parts of the photometric field and then again compared after interchanging them.

1. *For Transmission Measurements.*   In measuring the transmission of a transparent nondiffusing sample such as a glass filter, the standard is merely the "blank" beam.*   The important thing to consider in this case is whether or not the unavoidable change in optical path caused by introduction of the sample into the beam has effectively changed the standard; in other words, whether the effective illuminant has been varied in any respect by insertion of the sample being measured.   Such variation may occur by change of optical distance in a diverging beam, by displacement of a focused image of a nonuniformly bright illuminant (or by any change in the used area of such illuminant), or by multiple reflections between the surfaces of the sample and the optical parts of the apparatus.

---

* In case the transmittancy of a solution is to be measured, a cell containing the solvent is placed in the blank beam to compensate for losses by reflection and absorption of the solvent and end plates, this cell being similar in all respects to that containing the solution.

One should also consider whether the average distance traversed by the used portion of the beam through the sample is significantly greater than the thickness of the sample, and whether the variations of transmission with changes in temperature, which occur at certain wavelengths for nearly all materials, owing to variations in room temperature or to heating of the sample in the beam, are of importance in any particular instance.

Methods for eliminating errors from certain of these causes have been noted in connection with some of the instruments described. It is not attempted here to discuss the various other ways by which such errors may be avoided. It is sufficient to say that accurate results cannot be claimed unless these factors have been properly considered.

Since nearly all materials whose spectral transmission is desired are transparent, nondiffusing substances, such as glass filters or dye solutions, the angular distribution of the incident illumination is relatively unimportant, provided it properly fills the photometric field. The sample is placed at right angles to the unidirectional beam and the same values are obtained as if the sample were diffusely illuminated. If, however, the sample scatters the incident light to any important extent, as does, for example, a photographic film or opalescent glass, the type of illumination and direction of transmitted light become as significant as the corresponding quantities in apparent-reflectance measurements.

2. *For Apparent-reflectance Measurements.* The accurate measurement of the absolute reflectance of diffusing materials is very difficult. Furthermore, it is often the apparent reflectance* rather than the reflectance which is of interest and importance. This is nearly always true in colorimetric specifications. Practically all spectrophotometers are designed to measure the spectral apparent reflectance of diffusing materials relative to that of some other material, designated as the reference standard, whose reflection characteristics are considered known, or at least reproducible. Magnesium carbonate and magnesium oxide have both been widely used for this purpose. The use of the former should

---

* Luminous apparent reflectance is the reflectance which a sample appears to have in any specified direction. More exactly, it is the luminous reflectance which a perfectly diffusing surface would need to have in order to yield the same brightness under the same observing conditions.

be discouraged, however, since it is now known to be subject to variations in reflectance amounting to several per cent.

The advantages of an MgO surface as a reference standard when properly prepared, are as follows:[20]

a. It is nearly as good a diffuser as any other surface.

b. Its light reflectance of about 0.97 is nearly as high as that of any other surface.

c. The reflectance varies with wavelength in the visible spectrum by less than 1 per cent.

d. Its reflectance is nearly, if not perfectly, constant with time.

e. The apparent reflectance for 45-deg. incidence and normal viewing or vice versa is 1.00.

The disadvantage of MgO is its fragility. If desired, therefore, a working standard of porcelain, milk glass, or other suitable material may be used; this may then be calibrated in terms of MgO and checked as often as desired.

Various types of illumination for apparent-reflectance measurements have been illustrated in the instruments described. It should be remembered, however, that no one particular condition of illumination and viewing will give complete information regarding the reflection of diffusing materials. Such information can be obtained only by measuring the apparent reflectance at several angles of view from 0 to 90 deg. and for several angles of unidirectional illumination from 0 to 180 deg. in the plane of view and from 0 to 90 deg. in a plane at right angles to the plane of view. If the surface has structural regularities, it must also be rotated from 0 to 90 deg. in its own plane.*

If one is limited to a single set of conditions, it is a matter of choice which to adopt. Two sets of conditions are worthy of special notice:

A. Diffuse illumination, perpendicular viewing. This is illustrated in Figs. 192, 194, and 197. One may distinguish between illumination which is in effect completely diffused, *i.e.*, of equal intensity from all directions over the solid angle 2π, Fig. 192, and illumination which only approximates this condition, Figs. 194 and 197, the approximation depending on the

---

* Apparatus enabling such universal measurements to be made, in addition to measurements at various angles of view with completely diffused illumination, for both apparent reflectance and transmission either as a function of wavelength or as averaged with respect to the total luminous effect, has been constructed at the Bureau of Standards and is described in a paper by H. J. McNicholas.[21]

reflectance and diffusion of the sphere wall.   The features of completely diffused illumination and normal viewing are:

a. The reflected light is unpolarized, unless the sample has certain types of structural regularity.

b. The apparent reflectance obtained is numerically equal to the reflectance with unidirectional illumination at 90 deg.

c. The specular component of the reflected light is included.

d. The sample is uniformly illuminated.

B. Unidirectional illumination at 45 deg., angle of view 90 deg.   This set of conditions was recommended by the International Commission on Illumination in 1931.[22]   The following points may be noted with reference to this method of illuminating and viewing:

a. The apparent reflectance obtained is numerically equal to that obtained with illumination at 90 and 45 deg. viewing.   This latter condition, however, gives a greater brightness to the reflecting material; a uniform brightness is also more readily obtainable in the latter case.

b. The reflected light is, in general, partially polarized.

c. The specular component of the reflected light is excluded.

For either set of conditions, it is essential that the sample and standard receive identical illumination.   It has been pointed out[23] that this condition is not fulfilled if the sample and standard are alternately placed in position at the opening of a diffuse-illumination device; in this case, because of multiple reflections, the sample and standard are not subjected to identical illumination, even if identically placed, unless they are of equal reflectance.   The error is small unless the sample and standard differ considerably.   The proper condition is to have both sample and standard illuminated throughout the measurements, as illustrated in Figs. 192, 194, and 197.

In case the reflected light is partially polarized, the plane of polarization should be so oriented as to be at 45 deg. to the plane of polarization of the dispersing prism or other polarizing parts of the apparatus.   The polarized component is then transmitted as if unpolarized and no error results.

3. *For Relative-energy Measurements.*   The standard in this case is usually an incandescent lamp of known relative spectral-energy distribution.   Over the range covered by visual measurements, this standard can be most accurately established by way of its color temperature.   If the color temperature of the lamp is accurately known, its spectral-energy distribution may be obtained from various published tables of spectral-energy distribution derived on the basis of the Planck equation.[24]

Such relative-energy measurements are now rarely attempted on incandescent illuminants in the visible spectrum, because of the easy and accurate means of deriving such values *via* color temperature. In case, however, the energy distribution in other types of illuminants, *e.g.*, fluorescent spectra, is desired, such a standard becomes necessary.

Table 25. Filters for Elimination of Stray Light in Spectrophotometry

Source	Wavelengths to be used with, mμ	Filter
Incan. Hg* He	460 and below 404.7, 435.8 447.1	Corning 585 (3 mm) or Jena BG 3 (1 mm), plus Corning 428 (3 mm) or Jena BG 14 (2 mm)
Incan. He	460–500 471.3	Corning Signal Blue (75%)
Hg	491.6	Wratten 75
Incan. He	640–680 667.8	Corning Signal Red (100%) or Jena RG 2 (2 mm)
Incan.	680–720	Jena RG 5 (2 mm)
Incan.	720 and above	Jena RG 8 (2 mm)

* If the transmissions of the sample at 404.7 and 435.8 mμ are widely different, it is best to use a violet filter such as Corning 597 (2 mm), plus Corning 428 (3 mm) or Jena BG 14 (2 mm), at 404.7 mμ.

Wavelength Calibration. A thorough calibration or check of the wavelength scale of the spectrophotometer should always be made, regardless of whether or not the instrument reads directly in wavelength. Such calibration can be made by means of the mercury* and helium lamps with such additional wavelengths as may seem necessary or desirable. Furthermore, constant check should be kept on the calibration, particularly if any but the best bilateral slits are used. It is good practice to make such check every time one uses the instrument or changes the slit widths, unless experience has shown that the stability is such as to make this unnecessary.

* See p. 79.

Stray Light. Stray light may introduce serious errors in spectrophotometric measurements if not eliminated, not only in the end regions of the visible spectrum but also in regions of low transmission for certain samples which transmit freely in adjacent regions. This should be eliminated so far as possible by keeping all optical surfaces carefully cleaned and by the use of optical filters in the regions of low brightness.

The proper type of filter to use is one which transmits freely in the wavelength region where measurements are being made and absorbs strongly in all spectral regions of higher brightness. A set of two or three each for the blue and red ends of the spectrum is desirable, with special filters as needed for special purposes.[25] The list of filters given in Table 25 will be found useful in spectrophotometry.

Slit-width Errors. The theory of slit-width corrections in visual spectrophotometry has been discussed by Hyde,[26] who developed an expression for the luminous intensity of a pure spectrum $\phi(\theta)$, in terms of that of the impure spectrum $F(\theta)$, resulting from the use of finite slit widths, θ being the angle of deviation of the ray considered. The expression is:

$$\phi(\theta) = \frac{1}{A}[F(\theta) - K\Delta^2 F(\theta) + L\Delta^4 F(\theta) + \cdots], \quad (79)$$

in which the values of A, K, and L depend only on the relative values of the collimator and telescope slit widths and $\Delta^2 F(\theta)$ and $\Delta^4 F(\theta)$ are defined as follows:

$$\Delta^2 F(\theta) = F(\theta + c) + F(\theta - c) - 2F(\theta),$$
$$\Delta^4 F(\theta) = \Delta^2 F(\theta + c) + \Delta^2 F(\theta - c) - 2\Delta^2 F(\theta)$$

in which c equals one-half the sum of the collimator and telescope slit widths, expressed in the same units as θ.

Hyde illustrates the application of the formula to the case of spectral-energy distribution measurements, with numerical examples of the magnitudes involved. For spectral-transmission measurements, the above expression may represent the luminous intensities with no sample in the beam. If a sample whose transmission is τ is placed in the beam and $\phi_\tau(\theta)$ and $F_\tau(\theta)$ represent the corresponding luminous intensities, we have

$$\tau = \frac{\phi_\tau(\theta)}{\phi(\theta)} = \frac{F_\tau(\theta) - K\Delta^2 F_\tau(\theta) + L\Delta^4 F_\tau(\theta) + \cdots}{F(\theta) - K\Delta^2 F(\theta) + L\Delta^4 F(\theta) + \cdots} \quad (80)$$

assuming the relative values of the slit widths to be unchanged
in the two cases. For a given sum of collimator and telescope
slit widths, the errors or corrections are least when the two
slit widths are equal. For this case

$$K = \frac{1}{12}$$

and

$$L = \frac{1}{90}$$

The application of the formula is simplified if the Δ^4 terms
are neglected. This is probably justified in most cases, not
only because of the relative magnitudes of K and L, but because
the correction is of necessity, in most cases, of only an approximate nature. This approximation arises, not from inaccuracy
of the formula, but because of uncertainty in the function
assumed in order to evaluate the Δ^2 and Δ^4 terms. The exact
values of $F(\theta)$ and $F_\tau(\theta)$ which should be used in the formula
depend on (1) the observer's luminosity function, (2) the relative-
energy distribution of the source, (3) the dispersion and transmission of the instrument—all as functions of wavelength.
The observer's luminosity is, in general, unknown, and in any
case depends on the size and brightness of the photometric field.
It is customary, therefore, to assume an average luminosity function, and to determine or estimate the other quantities.

If the Δ^4 terms be neglected, the formula becomes

$$\tau = \frac{\phi_\tau(\theta)}{\phi(\theta)} = \frac{F_\tau(\theta) - K\Delta^2 F_\tau(\theta)}{F(\theta) - K\Delta^2 F(\theta)} \tag{81}$$

It may be noted that:

1. The errors or corrections are zero when τ is constant over the range
of wavelengths included by $\theta \pm c$, that is, provided $F_\tau(\theta) = kF(\theta)$ over that
range, k being a constant.

2. They are also zero when c is zero. With incandescent illuminant this
can be attained only in the limiting case of zero slit widths. With homogeneous light, however, as from the Hg or He lamps where only a single line
is transmitted by the slits, c is in effect equal to zero.

3. The errors or corrections are approximately proportional to the square
of the sum of the ocular and telescope slit widths. For, expanding $F(\theta + c)$
and $F(\theta - c)$ by Taylor's theorem, we have

$$\Delta^2 F(\theta) = F''(\theta)c^2,$$

neglecting higher even-power terms.

4. They also, therefore, depend on the curvature of that portion of the spectral luminous-intensity curve included by the slits, and not on the slope.

The importance of the slit-width errors and the need for making corrections depend on the slit widths used and the purpose for which the data are obtained. Because of the labor of making the corrections, it is desirable, if possible, to use such narrow slits that the errors are negligible. It should be noted also that slit-width errors or corrections can be determined experimentally. Since the error is proportional to the square of the slit widths, the measured values of transmission rapidly approach a constant limiting value as c is decreased. Extrapolation to zero width can, therefore, readily be made, provided the slit-width errors are not too small relative to the photometric uncertainty.

Checking the Reliability of the Photometric Scale. Two relations may be accepted almost without question in visual photometry, *viz.*, the inverse-square law and Talbot's law of the rotating sector. The former law is one of the fundamental relations of photometry but is rarely used directly in spectrophotometry. In order that the law be accurately obeyed, the illuminant cannot be operated too close to the diffusing surface. With ordinary illuminants, the necessity of using a diffusing screen is apt to result in a brightness of the field of the spectrophotometer too low for general utility, although the method affords a valuable means of checking the photometric scale in the brighter parts of the spectrum. The law applies strictly to a point source. However, if an extended source is used, concentrated essentially in a plane at right angles to the direction of the beam, and the minimum distance used is 15 times the diameter of the source, the errors in the inverse-square law should not exceed 0.1 per cent.

Talbot's law states that when a beam of light is periodically interrupted, as by a rotating sectored disk of aperture α deg., at a frequency great enough to eliminate flicker, the eye integrates the transmitted light in such a way that its apparent intensity is equal to $\alpha/360$ of the original intensity. Provided the angular aperture is accurately known, the relation is perhaps the most reliable of any available for maintaining or checking the accuracy of the photometric scale. The method is particularly suitable for checking the reliability of polarization instruments as illustrated in Fig. 192 or for extending the scale to low values of transmission while maintaining its reliability, as illustrated in Figs. 192, 200, and 201. In all these cases rotating sectors of fixed aperture are used, which may be accurately calibrated mechanically. Rotating sectors of variable aperture should be checked for accuracy, the same as polarization devices, optical wedges, etc.

It should be emphasized, however, that the reliability of the photometric scale is only one of several factors affecting the accuracy of spectrophotometric measurements; the others have been noted above. All the factors must be considered in order to be certain that accuracy is obtained. A closing check on the reliability of spectrophotometric data may be secured by making the same measurements on different apparatus or by checking the transmission of filters of accurately known transmission.[27] Agreement of results will usually indicate reliability. Measurements on a solution at different thicknesses will also assist in detecting errors, the negative logarithm of the transmittancy being accurately proportional to the thickness.

Precision of Measurement. While precision of setting or reproducibility of results is no guarantee of reliability, it is a matter of considerable importance. The eye is capable of remarkable precision when the proper equipment and technique are employed and can maintain this precision without undue strain for considerable lengths of time when properly used. The following factors contribute notably to the precision of spectrophotometric measurements: (1) Comfort of the observer, (2) ease of manipulation of the photometric device, (3) large and uniform photometric field, (4) relatively high field brightness,* (5) fineness of dividing lines, and (6) freedom from stray light. If these conditions are properly satisfied, average deviations from the mean of only a fraction of 1 per cent are readily obtainable.

---

* Brightness can rarely be obtained too high in spectrophotometry. Room illumination, extraneous light, etc., also affect the precision of measurement. In general, the room illumination should be low, but the observer's eyes should be totally shielded from all other light only when working at very low brightnesses of photometric field.

Chap. XI]

REFERENCES

353

References

1. K. S. GIBSON, *Jour. Optical Soc. Am. and Rev. Sci. Inst.*, **10**, 169–241 (1925). See also report of progress committee on radiometry and photometry, *Jour. Optical Soc. Am. and Rev. Sci. Inst.*, **11**, 359–361 (1925).

2. F. F. MARTENS and F. GRÜNBAUM, Über eine Neukonstruktion des Königschen Spektralphotometers, *Ann. Physik*, **12**, 984–1003 (1903). See also Schmidt and Haensch, Catalog II, "Spektralphotometer," pp. 13–21, October, 1930.

3. H. J. McNICHOLAS, Equipment for routine spectral transmission and reflection measurements, *Bur. Standards Jour. Research*, **1**, 793–857 (1928).

4. K. S. GIBSON, Spectrophotometry at the Bureau of Standards, *Jour. Optical Soc. Am.*, **21**, 564–587 (1931).

5. I. G. PRIEST, *et al.*, Color and Spectral Composition of Certain High-intensity Searchlight Arcs, *Bur. Standards Tech. Paper* 168, 1920.

6. SCHMIDT and HAENSCH, Catalog II, pp. 13–21, October, 1930.

7. Akatos, Inc., Descriptive circular entitled "Spectrophotometers According to Koenig-Martens and Koenig-Bechstein."

8. BAUSCH and LOMB, Advertising booklet entitled "Microscopes and other Scientific Instruments," pp. 232–245, 1929.

9. GAERTNER, Bull. No. 126, entitled "Optical Instruments of Recent Design."

10. J. H. DOWELL, A New Polarizing System for Spectrophotometers, *Jour. Sci. Inst.*, **8**, 382–384 (1931). A New Industrial and Research Spectrophotometer, *Jour. Sci. Inst.*, **10**, 153–156 (1933). See also Hilger Publication No. 156/3, "Outfits for Absorption Spectrophotometry," pp. 26–29, 1933.

11. HILGER, Section H, entitled "Spectrophotometers, Colorimeters and Apparatus for Sensitometry," p. H5, August, 1932.

12. This is a reproduction of Fig. 1 from a paper by C. W. Keuffel, A Direct Reading Spectrophotometer, *Jour. Optical Soc. Am. and Rev. Sci. Inst.*, **11**, 403–410 (1925).

13. O. LUMMER and E. BRODHUN, Photometrische Untersuchungen, V, Ueber ein neues Spektralphotometer, *Zeitschr. Instrumentenk.*, **12**, 132–139 (1892). See also Schmidt and Haensch Catalog II, Spektralphotometer, p. 5, October, 1930.

14. Reference 1.

15. E. P. HYDE, Slit-width corrections in spectrophotometry and a new form of variable sectored disk, *Astrophys. Jour.*, **35**, 237–267 (1912).

16. BRODHUN, E., Messbare Lichtschächung durch rotierende Prismen und ruhenden Sektor, *Zeitschr. Instrumentenk.*, **27**, 8–18 (1907). See also Schmidt & Haensch Catalog III, Rotierende Sektoren und Sektorenmesseinrichtungen, p. 4, June, 1929.

17. F. L. DUNN, A Cylindrical Rotating Sector Photometer, *Rev. Sci. Inst.*, **2**, 807–809 (1931).

18. J. GUILD, An Equipment for Visual Spectrophotometry, *Trans. Optical Soc.*, **26**, 74–94 (1924–1925).

19. H. BUCKLEY and F. L. C. BROOKES, A new type of spectrophotometer, *Jour. Sci. Inst.*, **7**, 305–317 (1930).

20. Preparation and colorimetric properties of a magnesium-oxide reflectance standard, *Bur. Standards Letter Circ.* LC 395, Dec. 9, 1933. References to the authorities for the advantages here given may be found in the circular.

21. Equipment for measuring the reflective and transmissive properties of diffusing media, *Jour. Research Natl. Bur. Standards*, **13**, 211 (1934).

22. Commission Internationale de l'Eclairage, *Compt. Rend. des Seances*, p. 23, 1931.

23. A. C. HARDY and O. W. PINEO, The errors due to the finite size of holes and sample in integrating spheres, *Jour. Optical Soc. Am.*, **21**, 502–506 (1931).

24. M. K. FREHAFER and C. L. SNOW, *Bur. Standards Misc. Pub.* 56, 1925. J. F. SKOGLAND, *Bur. Standards Misc. Pub.* 86, 1929. R. DAVIS and K. S. GIBSON, *Bur. Standards Misc. Pub.* 114, Table 2, 1931.

25. K. S. GIBSON, Spectrophotometry at the Bureau of Standards, *Jour. Optical Soc. Am.*, **21**, 570, Table 2, (1931).

26. See reference 15. NICHOLS and MERRITT, *Phys. Rev.*, **30**, 328 (1910).

27. For example, see *Jour. Optical Soc. Am.*, **24**, 58 (1934).

CHAPTER XII

OPTICAL AND RADIATION PYROMETRY

W. E. Forsythe*

When measuring ordinary temperatures, the measuring instrument is generally placed in very close contact with the body whose temperature is desired. However, if the temperature of the source is continually raised, a point is soon reached where no known substance will, in general, remain constant in any of its temperature-measuring properties if placed in direct contact with the source. Also, it is occasionally necessary to measure the temperature of a source that is so small or so situated that it is very difficult to bring the measuring instrument into direct contact with the source. When these conditions exist, advantage is taken of the well-known fact that all bodies, when at sufficiently high temperatures, send out measurable amounts of radiant energy that have been found to be related to the temperature. The only body for which the relation between the intensity of its radiant energy and the temperature is theoretically known is the blackbody. Using these known relations,[†] the temperature of a blackbody can be determined by measuring its radiant flux for any wavelength interval or for the entire spectrum. First, methods of determining temperature by measuring the intensity of the radiant flux for a certain wavelength interval within the visible spectrum will be considered, and then methods depending upon measurement of the total energy will be taken up.

The temperatures of very hot bodies have probably always been judged by eye observations of the color or brightness. With practice, one can estimate probably within 50 to 100°C. of the correct value; however, if judgment is left to the eye alone,[‡]

---

* Physicist, Incandescent Lamp Department, General Electric Company, Cleveland, Ohio.

† See p. 2.
‡ See p. 389.

very much larger errors are sometimes made, owing to the use that has been made of the eye just previous to the time of estimating.   To secure accurate measurements with the eye, a comparison source is necessary.

Optical Pyrometers.   The introduction of a comparison source as an aid in measuring the radiant energy is the first step toward an optical pyrometer, which consists of a comparison source and some convenient arrangement for matching this source, either in brightness or in color, against the source studied.   However,

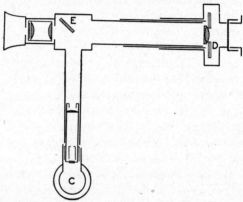

Fig. 202.— Arrangements used in one form of Le Châtelier optical pyrometer.

most pyrometers are based upon brightness measurements, rather than color measurements.

Optical pyrometers are divided into three classes, the division being due either to the method of introducing the comparison source or to the method of making the brightness comparison between this and the source being studied.   One class has its comparison source arranged as shown in Fig. 202.   The image of this comparison source is reflected into the eyepiece by a mirror or prism located at the focus of the objective lens.   Brightness matches are made either by varying the brightness of the comparison source or by varying the brightness of the image of the source studied.

The polarization type of pyrometer has an image of the source studied and of the comparison source which are observed side by side through the same eyepiece, with the light from the two sources polarized in planes at right angles to each other, and the balance made by rotating a nicol in the eyepiece. By operating the comparison source at a constant temperature, the instrument may be made direct-reading by having a scale attached to the rotating nicol.

The two forms just described are troublesome to use because both require a rather large source for observation and, in general, it is not possible to see clearly the source being studied.

The Disappearing-filament Optical Pyrometer. The third class, called the disappearing-filament type, has the appearance of a telescope, but it differs from a telescope in that it contains, for use as a comparison source, a lamp filament, called the pyrometer filament, which is located at the focus of the objective lens. This filament is in series with a small battery, a resistance, and an ammeter. To measure the temperature of any hot body with this pyrometer, the instrument is first sighted upon the hot body, which is done as easily and in much the same manner as the focusing of an opera glass. When looked at, the hot object is seen with the pyrometer filament crossing it at a selected point, and the temperature is measured by matching the filament in brightness with the image of the source, by increasing or diminishing the current through the filament.

There are two types of disappearing-filament optical pyrometers. In the first, the photometric balance between the pyrometer filament and the image of the source is made by varying the current through the pyrometer filament and then obtaining the temperature from the previously measured relation between current and temperature. In the second,[1] the pyrometer filament is kept at a constant current and thus at a constant brightness, and balances are made by rotating a wedge-shaped circular absorbing screen between the pyrometer lamp and the objective lens, thus varying the apparent brightness of the image of the source studied. The advantage of this form is that it can be made direct-reading, having a scale attached to the frame that carries the specially made absorbing screen. A diagram of the disappearing-filament optical pyrometer is shown in Fig. 203.

Advantages of the Disappearing-filament Optical Pyrometer. The disappearing-filament pyrometer possesses several advantages over other forms. In the first place, the observer is able to see the object whose temperature is being measured directly through the pyrometer, the same as through a telescope. It is hard to overestimate this advantage. Often it is desirable to measure the temperature of a particular point of an extended body, as for instance, a mass of molten iron in the furnace or a particular spot on an ingot that is being rolled. This can be easily done with this pyrometer, while it is very difficult with most other forms. Another advantage that is to be considered is the fact that this form of pyrometer is almost free from any error due to polarization. Any effect due to this cause would be negligible in almost the worst case possible.

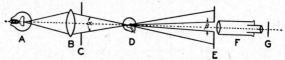

Fig. 203.—Arrangement of disappearing-filament optical pyrometer. *A*, background; *B*, objective lens; *C*, entrance cone diaphragm; *D*, pyrometer filament; *E*, eyepiece diaphragm; *F*, eyepiece; *G*, monochromatic filter. For the setup as usually used, the dimensions are as follows: $AB = 40$ cm; $CD = 55$ cm; $DE = 60$ cm. Diameter of opening in diaphragm at C and E are respectively 20 and 9 mm.

Monochromatic Screen for Optical Pyrometer. Temperatures can be measured with an optical pyrometer using the total visible spectrum, but if this is done, errors are apt to be introduced, and observers may differ widely in their readings, owing to the color difference between the comparison source and the source studied. This difficulty can be overcome and a much more accurate brightness match made by using a so-called monochromatic screen in the eyepiece of the pyrometer.

Advantages of Red Screens. For the most part, red glass screens have been used as pyrometer monochromatic screens, rather than blue screens, or those having a transmission band near the central part of the visible spectrum, for the following reasons:

1. At low temperatures, the red radiation first becomes visible and thus readings may be made at a somewhat lower temperature with the red glass.
2. The color change for a change in wavelength is much less in the red part of the spectrum than in the green, which makes the red the better part of the spectrum for this work.
3. Better monochromatism can be obtained in glass of this color.
4. By using a red screen when measuring a temperature so high that a rotating sector or absorbing glass is necessary, the transmission of the sector or absorbing glass that must be used to reach a particular temperature is greater for the longer wavelength than it is for the shorter wavelength.

Colored glass to be suitable for a monochromatic screen must have a rather narrow transmission band, in order that there will not be enough color difference between the source studied and the comparison source to prevent accurate comparisons from being made. As there may be more than 1000°C. difference in temperature between the sources compared, this is very important.

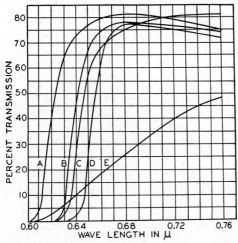

FIG. 204.—Spectral transmission of various red glasses. Curve *C* for Jena red No. 4512, 2.93 mm thick. Curve *E* for Jena red No. 2745, 3.2 mm thick. Curve *A* for Corning high-transmission red marked 150 per cent, 5 mm thick. Curve *B* for Corning high-transmission red, marked 50 per cent, 5 mm thick. Curve *D* for Corning high-transmission red, marked 28 per cent, 6 mm thick.

In Fig. 204 are shown the spectral transmissions of several red glasses that are nearly enough monochromatic for use under various conditions. The glass having the spectral transmission shown by curve *A* does very well for a commercial pyrometer for low-temperature ranges, because the amount of light transmitted is so great. The glass having the transmission shown by curve *E* was formerly used for this purpose. As the effective wavelength (see below) for this glass varies about twice as much as for the other glasses, it is not so satisfactory. The glasses having the transmission shown by curves *B*, *C*, and *D* are suitable for the most accurate work.

It is not absolute measurements of brightness that are made with the optical pyrometer, but rather comparisons of brightness, i.e., the brightness of the unknown source is compared with that of a standard blackbody at a particular temperature. If the Wien equation (Eq. 4) is used to calculate this relative brightness, but one constant, c_2, is required. The value of c_2 that fits best all the different experimental data* is $14,320\mu$ deg. The value generally accepted for the melting point of gold is 1336°K, which is the value found by Day and Sosman. This value for the gold point, together with the above value of c_2, leads to 1828°K as the palladium point.[2]

Effective Wavelength of a Monochromatic Screen.[3] While it is necessary to use a colored screen in the eyepiece of the pyrometer to overcome certain color differences, an optical pyrometer can be so calibrated and so used as to make unnecessary a knowledge of the extent to which the screen is monochromatic. To do this requires for calibration a blackbody furnace or other source that can be operated at various known temperatures up to the highest temperature for which the pyrometer is to be used. Since the wavelength enters in the Wien equation if it is used to calculate the extension of the temperature scale either above or below that of the standard furnace by the use of rotating sector disks or absorbing glass, i.e., to find the temperature of a blackbody having a brightness of, say, ten times (assuming a sector or absorbing glass that transmits one-tenth of the radiation emitted) that of a blackbody whose temperature can be measured directly, a knowledge of what wavelength to use, i.e., the effective wavelength of the screen, is necessary. The effective wavelength also must be known if the pyrometer is used to measure the temperature of non-blackbodies.

In using the pyrometer, it is the integral luminous intensities, through the monochromatic screen, of the source studied (at one temperature), and of the pyrometer filament (at a lower temperature) that are compared. For this reason the effective wavelength of the screen, for a certain temperature interval, has been defined as the wavelength, for the definite temperature interval for a blackbody, for which the ratio of radiation intensities equals the ratio of the integral intensities through the screen used.

Knowing the spectral transmission of the glass, it is possible to calculate the effective wavelength λ_e for any temperature interval by means of the following equation:

* See p. 3.

$$\frac{\int_0^\infty J(\lambda T_1)K_\lambda \tau_R d\lambda}{\int_0^\infty J(\lambda T_2)K_\lambda \tau_R d\lambda} = \left(\frac{J(\lambda T_1)}{J(\lambda T_2)}\right)_{\lambda_e} \tag{82}$$

where $J(\lambda T)d\lambda$ is the radiant intensity, as given by the Wien equation, for the wavelength interval from λ to $\lambda + d\lambda$; τ_R is the spectral transmission of the red glass; K_λ is the spectral luminosity and thus $\int J(\lambda T_1)K_\lambda \tau_R d\lambda$ the luminous intensity from the

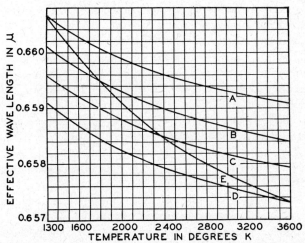

Fig. 205.—Effective wavelengths for Corning red glass. Spectral transmission shown by curve B, Fig. 204. Curve A, effective wavelengths from 1300° to other temperatures. Curve B, effective wavelengths from 1800° to other temperatures. Curve C, effective wavelengths from 2400° to other temperatures. Curve D, effective wavelengths from 3600° to other temperatures. Curve E, limiting effective wavelength.

source at temperature T_1 that is transmitted by the red screen. These integrals can be computed by the step-by-step method with sufficient accuracy for this purpose. Using Eq. (82), the effective wavelength was calculated for the red glass having the spectral transmission shown by curve B, Fig. 204, for a number of temperature intervals and plotted, as shown in Fig. 205. By connecting the points where the curve for the effective wavelength from any particular temperature crosses the same temperature ordinate, a curve is obtained (E, Fig. 205) that gives the limiting effective wavelength for a particular temperature.

To show how these curves may be used, the effective wavelength for two or three temperature intervals will be found.   The effective wavelength between 1800 and 2900°K is given by the ordinate of the point where the 1800°K curve crosses the 2900°K ordinate, *i.e.*, it is 0.6587μ. For the range between 2100 and 2900°K, the effective wavelength is likewise given by the point where the 2100°K curve would cross the 2900°K ordinate. The 2100°K curve is not drawn but will have to be imagined as being parallel to the 1800°K, one point of its position being determined by where the curve E crosses the 2100°K ordinate. The effective wavelength for this interval is 0.6584μ. It can be seen from the figure that the effective wavelength for any temperature interval is given quite closely by the mean of the limiting effective wavelength for the two temperatures.

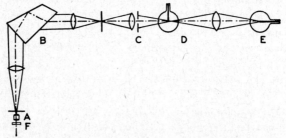

Fig. 206.—Diagrammatic sketch of spectral pyrometer.

Spectral Pyrometer. A monochromator may be used as the means for obtaining the monochromatic radiation for observing the pyrometer filament. This results in what has been called the spectral[4] pyrometer. A diagram of one form of spectral pyrometer is shown in Fig. 206. If a suitable monochromator is used, any wavelength interval within the visible spectrum may be used. This form of pyrometer has one serious disadvantage in that for a narrow wavelength interval but a small amount of energy is transmitted. Thus what may be gained in spectral purity is lost in not having sufficient energy to make satisfactory brightness matches.

A pyrometer of this type may be used as a spectrophotometer. In this case the pyrometer filament is used as the comparison source, and the calibration consists in finding the relation between the current through the filament and relative brightness for different wavelength intervals. Then the relative brightness of any two sources whose images can be in turn focused upon the slit of the spectrometer may be measured. If the source is one whose image cannot be made to cover the slit of the spectrometer, its relative spectral distribution may be measured by reflecting its radiation from a magnesium block placed in the position ordinarily occupied by the source, and comparing this reflected radiation with that from a standard source. Methods of measuring transmission and reflection are obvious.

Use of an Optical Pyrometer. It often happens that when it is necessary to measure the temperatures of a hot radiating body with an optical pyrometer, the operator does not know just how to proceed. Although optical pyrometers can be purchased ready for use, calibration and all, if it is necessary to construct one, it will usually be much easier to build one of the disappearing-filament type. All that is required for this is an objective lens about 3 cm in diameter and about 25 cm focal length, a piece of red glass, a long-focus eyepiece, a pyrometer lamp, and for operation an ammeter and a battery.

An ordinary spectacle lens of the right focal length can be used for the objective lens, and two such lenses of the proper focal length will do for the eyepiece. For ordinary work it is not necessary to have achromatic lenses since a red glass is used in the eyepiece. The optical parts may all be mounted on some sort of an optical bench or, if they are to be used permanently, it is well to have them mounted inside of a tube after the manner of a telescope. The pyrometer lamp is to be so mounted with respect to the objective lens that an image of the source being investigated can be brought to a focus in the plane of the filament, and this image and the pyrometer filament both observed through the eyepiece. When using this instrument, the different parts are so adjusted that the images of both the source being investigated and the pyrometer filament are as well defined as possible. The particular way in which the pyrometer is built depends upon the purpose for which it is intended. If it is desired to measure the temperature of a large source, it will not be necessary to have very large magnification. The distances between the pyrometer lamp and the eyepiece depend upon the focal length of the lens in the eyepiece F. The main requirement is for the image of the source in the plane of the pyrometer filament to be much larger than the pyrometer filament, since it has been found by experiment that accurate matches cannot be made unless the background image is somewhat larger than the pyrometer filament.

The furnace or object whose temperature is desired is to be observed through the pyrometer, the same as any object is observed with an opera glass, and then the current through the pyrometer filament varied until the filament disappears against the image of the source. The temperature is read from the current-calibration curve of the pyrometer filament.

Pyrometer Filaments. Some care is required in the selection of the pyrometer filament. Carbon filaments are quite satisfactory for low temperatures, but they will not have a very long life if operated at a high temperature. Tungsten pyrometer filaments are just as good as carbon filaments and have a long life if not operated at a brightness above that necessary to match a blackbody at the temperature of melting palladium (1828°K). They are often constructed with a small bend at the exact point where the filament is to be observed. A small pointer is sometimes used to help locate the exact spot. The 2½-mil (0.063-mm) filaments require about 0.46 amp. to apparently match in brightness the blackbody at the temperature of melting palladium.

Measuring the Current through the Pyrometer Filament. For the highest accuracy an ammeter is not accurate enough for measuring the current through the pyrometer filament. Some form of potentiometer must be used. If the same potentiometer is used to measure the current through the lamp being studied and the pyrometer, a great deal of time is wasted in changing the potentiometer for each reading. A good method, which is at the same time quite accurate, is to use the deflection potentiometer principle. The regular Leeds and Northrup potentiometer lends itself quite readily to such adaptation.[5] By connecting a millivoltmeter or a galvanometer of the proper sensitivity in series with the standard resistance and between the binding post marked *Br* and a traveling plug inserted in the proper place on the dial, pyrometer currents can be read to one part in three or four thousand very easily. The readings can thus be made very rapidly, and at the end of the set these same readings can be checked on the potentiometer. This makes the current readings practically independent of the constancy of any deflection instrument. With a switch in this millivoltmeter line, the potentiometer is left free to check any other current, such as the one through the lamp that is being investigated.

Calibration of Optical Pyrometers.   Despite all that has been written about the calibration of an optical pyrometer, a question is often asked concerning the starting point for the calibration of the pyrometer.   To make a completely independent calibration of any pyrometer would be a great undertaking.   Fortunately, it is not necessary or desirable that each one should make an absolutely independent calibration.   If one has to calibrate an ordinary mercury thermometer at about 100°C, it would be calibrated by immersing the thermometer in steam.   If a higher point is wanted, some material with a melting or boiling point in the proper region might be used, and the calibration made at the melting or boiling point as the case might be.   The temperature of boiling water is defined as 100°C, but the temperature of the other points in this region are used with just as little question and with just about as much confidence as this one.   To probably a lesser extent, the same condition exists at high temperatures. The melting point of gold or of palladium is constant and well known.   It only remains to bring the standard radiator, *i.e.*, the blackbody, to a number of definite temperatures, and from these to calibrate the pyrometer.   In this case, the pyrometer filament is matched in brightness with the image of the blackbody across which it is seen through the eyepiece of the pyrometer.

Calibrating an Optical Pyrometer from a Source at One Standard Temperature.   The standard radiator at a standard temperature, that is, the gold point or the palladium point, gives one point on the calibration.   The blackbody may be set at other temperatures for further calibration points, or the entire calibration of the pyrometer can be obtained from the blackbody at the one temperature if the proper equipment is available.[6]   Another point on the calibration may be obtained by taking readings of the current through the pyrometer filament for an apparent-brightness match with a rotating sector, or absorbing glass of known transmission, between the pyrometer lamp and the standard blackbody.   This will give a measure, in terms of the pyrometer current, of a brightness that is some known fraction of that of the standard radiator at the standard temperature.   If monochromatic radiation is used, it is easy to calculate the temperature T_2 of the blackbody corresponding to this current through the pyrometer filament, *i.e.*, to this measured brightness, from T_1, the standard temperature, by the following formula derived from the Wien equation:

$$\frac{1}{T_1} - \frac{1}{T_2} = \frac{\lambda \cdot \log \tau}{c_2 \log \mathsf{e}} \tag{83}$$

where τ is the transmission of the sector, and λ is the wavelength used. If the measurements are made with a red glass in the eyepiece, the temperature that corresponds to this fraction of the brightness of the standard blackbody can be calculated just as before, except that in this case the effective wavelength of the red glass for the temperature interval is to be used. The use of other sector or absorbing glasses in a similar manner will give other points of the calibration.

When a blackbody furnace is used as a standard of radiation for calibration of an optical pyrometer, it is held at the temperature either of melting gold or of melting palladium. In order to be sure that the furnace is at the temperature desired, a sample of gold or palladium, mounted between platinum wires supported by two refractory tubes with the circuit completed through a battery and bell or other indicating instrument, is melted in the furnace. It is necessary to mount the specimen in such a manner that the central part of the sample cannot touch either of these two tubes, as it has sometimes been found that if a single tube is used, the melted metal will touch and cling to the end of the tube so that the electric circuit is not broken at the instant of melting, and thus a high value is obtained. With the central part of the sample free, it is assumed that the circuit is broken at the instant of melting. When a melt is obtained, the furnace is held at this temperature, using as an indicator the e.m.f. of the thermocouple, and then a number of readings made with the optical pyrometer sighted upon the blackbody. Another melt is then obtained and the process repeated. This procedure is necessary because it has been found that the e.m.f. of a platinum-rhodium thermocouple is apt to change when used at high temperatures, unless the most exceptional precautions to eliminate impurities in its manufacture and to prevent contamination during use have been taken.

Extending Temperature Scale.   The filament of the pyrometer lamp should not be heated to too high a temperature if it is to hold its calibration for any length of time.   A safe temperature for a tungsten filament is somewhere in the neighborhood of 2000°K.   Since it is often necessary to measure temperatures much higher than this, some means must be provided for this purpose.   The observed brightness of the furnace at a high temperature can be reduced by the use of a rotating sector or absorbing glass of known transmission.   In this case, the temperature of the furnace is to be calculated from the temperature corresponding to the current through the pyrometer filament for a brightness match with the furnace through the sector or absorbing screen or sector, and the transmission of the sector or absorbing glass used, by means of Eq. (83), except in this case for τ, use the reciprocal of the transmission of the sector or absorbing glass, and then T_2 will come out greater than T_1.   A convenient method is to work out such extrapolated temperatures for the various sectors and absorbing glasses that are to be used, and plot the extrapolated temperatures against the temperatures as determined from the pyrometer reading.   Such curves can then be used with any pyrometer using the same red glass, provided the same sectors or absorbing glasses are used.

Error of the Wien Equation.   The Wien equation is generally used to calculate temperatures from brightness measurements. This equation does not fit the experimental evidence except for small values of the product λT.*   Table 26 has been prepared to show just what errors result from the use of this equation rather than the more exact Planck form.   These results were obtained by calculating the higher temperature from 1828°K, using a wavelength of $\lambda = 0.665\mu$.

TABLE 26.   Corrections to Be Added to Temperatures Obtained from the Wien Equation, Starting at 1828°K, to Reduce Them to What Would Be Obtained from the Planck Equation ($\lambda = 0.665\mu$)

Temperature, °K	Corrections to Temperature, °K
2000	− 0.01
2600	− 0.05
3000	− 0.3
3600	− 1.5
5000	−15.6

* See p. 7.

From Table 26 it can be seen that the Wien equation is quite satisfactory for $\lambda = 0.665\mu$ and for temperatures up to about 3600°K, since the error obtained by its use is less than the experimental error.

Standard Lamp for Calibrating Optical Pyrometers. It is very troublesome to operate a blackbody every time it is necessary to calibrate an optical pyrometer. Much time can be saved if a tungsten lamp with a filament of a suitable size is standardized so as to have the same brightness, as observed with the optical pyrometer, as the blackbody furnace for a particular temperature. The lamp may also be standardized for other temperatures and thus, by its use, the pyrometer can be calibrated very easily.

For the highest accuracy, the tungsten lamp that is to be used for calibration purposes should be standardized with an optical pyrometer, using a red glass that is the same as that on the pyrometer to be compared, or corrections should be made for the difference. If the effective wavelengths are known, this correction can easily be made by the method outlined below. For practical purposes, however, if similar red glasses are used, the error will be quite small.

Tungsten filaments have been found to depart very markedly from the Lambert cosine law[7] in their radiation. To avoid error due to this cause, care must always be taken to determine the temperature of circular filaments by measuring the brightness of the central part of the filament. For this reason, the pyrometer filament should always be parallel to the background filament. This, of course, requires that the pyrometer filament be much smaller than the image of the background filament.

The tungsten lamp with a wire or a ribbon filament that is used as a secondary standard for calibrating an optical pyrometer may be calibrated; *i.e.*, the relation between the current through the filament and its temperature given so that the entire calibration of the pyrometer can be checked by the use of the secondary standard, not only for the low points, but even for the extended scale, if the extended scale does not go beyond the safe temperature of the operation of a tungsten filament lamp (*i.e.*, about 2500°K for a gas-filled lamp). Chaney[8] and his coworkers of the National Carbon Company have shown that the positive crater of the arc between certain well-prepared carbons, properly operated, is so constant in its brightness temperature, which they give as 3814°K, that it can be used as a secondary standard for this high temperature region.

Absorbing Screens for Optical Pyrometry. A sector that has been very carefully calibrated, if used properly, is the best means that can be used for cutting down the observed radiant intensity of a source that is being studied. In a research or a standardizing laboratory, the rotating sector is thus a valuable instrument. For commercial work, however, where a portable pyrometer is desired, a rotating sector adds to its size and makes necessary another source of power to drive the sector, so, for a commercial

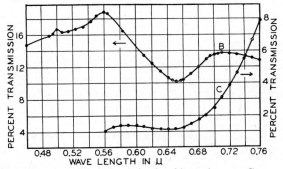

Fig. 207.—Spectral transmission of absorbing glasses. Curve *B*, Jena absorbing glass, 1.5 mm thick. Curve *C*, Noviweld obtained from Corning Glass Works; shade about 6.

pyrometer, absorbing glasses are generally used, and when properly calibrated and properly used, they are very satisfactory.

The main requirement, when it is necessary to use absorbing screens to reduce the apparent brightness of the source studied, is to have a screen that approximates a neutral-tint screen sufficiently well to enable comparisons in brightness to be made by different observers, with very nearly the same results. The degree to which it is necessary for the absorbing screen to have a spectral transmission independent of the wavelength depends on the so-called monochromatic glass used in the eyepiece. It is quite evident that if this eyepiece glass is absolutely monochromatic, any absorbing glass will answer.

In Fig. 207 are shown the spectral transmissions of a piece of Noviweld (curve *C*) and a piece of Jena absorbing glass (curve *B*). Either of these glasses is nearly enough neutral tint for use with the red glasses having transmission curves shown by

B, C, and D in Fig. 204.   The Noviweld absorbing glass is made in different shades with transmissions, when used in connection with red glass, ranging from less than 1 per cent to several per cent.

With a red glass in the eyepiece, by total transmission of a screen for a particular temperature is meant the ratio of the brightness of the blackbody at this temperature observed through both the red glass and the black glass, to the brightness of the same source observed through the red glass alone.   Without a red glass, using the entire visible spectrum, it is generally very hard to make such measurements, owing to the color differences introduced by even the best absorbing glasses; with a good red glass in the eyepiece, such transmission measurements can be made easily.

The total transmission of the absorbing glass, when used with a red glass, can be calculated for any blackbody distribution, *i.e.*, any temperature, by the following formula:

$$\tau_B = \frac{\int_0^\infty J_\lambda K_\lambda \tau_R' \tau_B' d\lambda}{\int_0^\infty J_\lambda K_\lambda \tau_R' d\lambda} \tag{84}$$

where $J_\lambda d\lambda$ is the radiant intensity as given by the Wien equation for interval λ to $\lambda + d\lambda$, K_λ is the spectral luminosity, and τ_R' and τ_B' are the spectral transmission of red and absorbing glasses, respectively.   It is very evident that if the spectral transmission of the absorbing glass is different for different wavelengths, the total transmission will be a function of the temperature of the source under investigation.

In Fig. 208 is shown, as a function of the temperature of the source, the total transmission for red light, of the absorbing glasses having the spectral transmission given by curves B and C in Fig. 207, as calculated using Eq. (84).

When the brightness of a hot body is measured with an optical pyrometer, using an absorbing glass, the temperature T_2 must be calculated, using Eq. (83), from the transmission of the absorbing glass, and T_1, the temperature corresponding to the pyrometer current when no absorbing glass is used.   Now, since the transmission of the absorbing glass, as given by Eq. (84), is the same as that obtained experimentally by comparing its transmission with that of a sector, the same effective wavelength of the red glass is to be used with both the absorbing glass and a sector having the same transmission.   Thus, to calculate the extrapolated brightness temperature of a source whose brightness temperature is measured, using an absorbing glass, it is necessary to know the transmission of the glass as a function of the temperature of the source studied, and also the ordinary effective wavelength for the red glass used.   In calculating the extrapolated temperature, using an absorbing screen, it is necessary to know this temperature approximately, in order to find the effective wavelength for the interval.   The calculation is, therefore, one

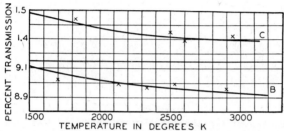

Fig. 208.—Total transmission of absorbing glasses, as a function of temperature of source when used with red glass No. 4512—5.8 mm thick.   B, one piece Jena absorbing glass; C, Noviweld glass from Corning Glass Works.   Curves drawn through points calculated from equation.

of successive approximation.   When a so-called neutral-tint glass is used, additional care is required, because both the effective wavelength of the red glass and the transmission of the absorbing screen depend on the temperature reached.

Absorbing Screen for Very High Temperatures.   For special work, it is sometimes necessary to extend the calibration of an optical pyrometer, so that temperatures[9] up to about 7000°K can be measured.   This can be done by using two absorbing glasses, of the proper transmission, between the pyrometer lamp and the source being investigated.   The spectral transmissions of two such glasses are shown by curves A and B, Fig. 209, and that of the combination is shown by curve C in the same figure. Curve C was obtained from the product of the spectral transmissions of the two glasses at the different wavelengths.

The reason for using two absorbing glasses is that the spectral transmission of each of these glasses alone is readily measured, while a single absorbing glass with a transmission as small as that of the combination of the two would be very difficult to measure but can be calculated from the transmissions of the two glasses,* since, for any narrow spectral interval, the transmission

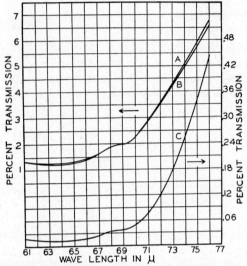

Fig. 209.—Spectral transmission of two absorbing screens (curves *A* and *B*) and the spectral transmission of the two together (curve *C*).

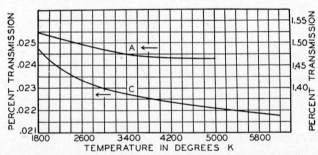

Fig. 210.—Total transmission for red radiation of the absorbing screen whose spectral transmission is shown by curve *A*, Fig. 209, and of two absorbing glasses whose spectral transmission is shown by curve *C*, Fig. 209.

of the two glasses together is given by the product of the separate transmissions for the same interval. The total transmissions of these absorbing glasses for red radiation were calculated from

* This method neglects the small error in transmission due to interreflection of the two filters[10] which would cause an error of only a fraction of a degree even at 5000°K.

their spectral transmissions by Eq. (84), for various temperatures of incident radiation, and are shown in Fig. 210.   From the values of the total transmissions thus obtained, the extrapolated temperatures for one glass and for the combination of the two were calculated by means of Eq. (83) and are shown in Table 27. It will be seen that when the two glasses are used together, the temperatures may be measured up to about 7000°K.

TABLE 27.   EXTRAPOLATED TEMPERATURES USING RED GLASS FOR ONE ABSORBING GLASS AND FOR TWO ABSORBING GLASSES HAVING THE TRANSMISSIONS SHOWN IN FIGS. 209 AND 210

$c_2 = 14{,}320\mu$ deg.

Initial temperature, °K	Transmission of one absorbing glass	Extrapolated temperature for one absorbing glass, °K	Transmission of two absorbing glasses	Extrapolated temperature for two absorbing glasses, °K
1200			0.000238	2,226
1300			0.000233	2,599
1400	0.0149	1,922	0.000230	3,035
1500	0.0148	2,116	0.000227	3,553
1600	0.0147	2,322	0.000224	4,177
1700	0.0147	2,540	0.000221	4,945
1800	0.0146	2,771	0.000218	5,910
1900	0.0146	3,014	0.000215	7,174

Attempts have been made to obtain an absorbing screen that is strictly neutral tint, or even one that has such a transmission as to correct for the change in effective wavelength of the red glass used.   Such a glass would probably be all right, but it is not necessary.   What is wanted is a glass that will permit comparisons of brightness to be made by different observers with practically the same result.   If a good red glass is used, suitable absorbing glasses can easily be found.   Many attempts have been made to obtain absolutely monochromatic screens for optical pyrometry.   This may be satisfactory for some purposes, but it is not necessary in general, and such screens have the disadvantage of not transmitting enough light to permit brightness comparisons at low temperatures.   A good red glass can easily be obtained that transmits enough light to permit brightness comparison at low temperatures and, at the same time, is sufficiently monochromatic to enable different observers to obtain the same results, even under the unfavorable conditions existing when the comparison source and the source studied are quite different in temperature. In addition to this, if the effective wavelength of the red glass is known, all results can be readily reduced to the condition for a common wavelength.

Effect of Change in Temperature of Absorbing Glass on Its Transmission. As the spectral transmissions of some colored glasses show a marked change, with change in their temperatures, it was thought worth while to investigate the transmissions of the absorbing glasses as a function of their temperatures.[11] Accordingly, a heater was built and so mounted that different absorbing glasses could be heated in position to a temperature of about 200°C. Their transmissions were then measured as recorded in Table 28. These transmissions correspond to a color temperature of the source of 2380°K. The Jena glass has the spectral transmission shown by curve B, Fig. 207. The Noviweld is a piece of shade 5, which was obtained somewhat later than that used in the preceding work. These two pieces of Noviweld probably have somewhat the same spectral transmission. The Jena absorbing glass shows but a very small

TABLE 28. TRANSMISSION OF ABSORBING GLASSES AT DIFFERENT
TEMPERATURES

Temperature, °C.	Noviweld absorbing glass, per cent	Jena absorbing glass, per cent
20	1.70	8.96
102	1.55	8.90
200	1.39	8.87

change in transmission, due to a change in its temperature. Since the spectral transmission of colored glass changes when heated as though the transmission curve were shifted to longer wavelength, this is what would be expected from the shape of the spectral-transmission curve.

The change in transmission of the Jena glass, due to a change in its temperature, is so small as to be negligible for any ordinary temperature change. The change in the transmission of the Noviweld filter, however, is enough to cause a small error, for the temperature changes met with in practice. For a glass of this kind calibrated at a temperature of 20°C and used at a temperature of 30°C, in extrapolating from 1800 to 2400°K and 3000°K, the errors would be, respectively, +7.5°K and +11.5°K.

Dependence of Measured and Calculated Temperature on Various Conditions. The brightness of a surface observed through a telescope is independent of its distance,[12] unless too large a magnification is used. An optical pyrometer is generally calibrated with about the same magnification as it is used, so that no error is introduced due to the distance of the source studied.

a. Brightness. A very great advantage of the optical pyrometer in measuring temperature is due to the relation between a change in the brightness and the corresponding change in temperature. At 1000°K for red radiation ($\lambda = 0.665\mu$) the brightness varies about 22 times as fast as the temperature. At 2000°K for red radiation the ratio is about 11.

b. Clean Optical Parts. The first thing to keep in mind is that the optical pyrometer is a calibrated instrument and must be handled as such. All the optical parts of the instrument should be kept clean. The actual error due to a change in the transmission of an objective lens due to an accumulation of dirt is not very great. An error of 15° at 1500°K would be caused by allowing the lens to become so covered with dirt that its transmission would be reduced to 85 per cent of its value when clean. Errors much larger than this, however, are possible if the lenses are allowed to become dirty. If the lenses and pyrometer lamp bulb are allowed to become dirty, it interferes with the clearness of the images, and thus lessens the accuracy of the setting. They should be kept clean, but in cleaning them care is required, or scratches will be produced which will again interfere with definition. Also, if a glass or other window is used, a correction to the temperature is necessary for it.

c. Comparison Source. Great care must be taken not to change the comparison source in any way. In some pyrometers even the position of the comparison lamp must not be changed. In the disappearing-filament type, small changes in the position of the part of the filament under observation will cause no appreciable error. In no case must the filament be overheated, since this may greatly change its characteristics. The pyrometer lamp of tungsten, if not used at a temperature higher than 1828°K, will have a very long life. The lamps have been aged for a considerable time at a temperature much higher than this, so a current somewhat above that for which it is calibrated will not change its calibration. A good plan is to allow no current higher than that for which it has been calibrated to pass through the filament.

Position of Rotating Sector. If the rotating sector is used to cut down the apparent intensity of the background, care must be taken as to the location of the sector.[13] There is a marked difference in the results of temperature measurements, depending on whether the sector is located near the objective lens or as near as possible to the pyrometer lamp. There is also a difference depending on the relative position of the openings in the sector and the source, provided the source is a lamp filament. If a sector of small transmission is mounted near the lens and so placed that the openings of the sector are parallel to the axis of the background filament when the sector is passing across the center of the lens, the definition will be very bad, while, if the openings of the sector are turned through 90 deg., so that they are perpendicular to the axis of the filament, the definition will be quite good, but not so good as if the sector is located near the pyrometer lamp. When the rotating sector is located near the pyrometer lamp, the definition is good, and practically independent of the position of the opening of the sector. If a very large source is used, no such effect is noted. Using a pyrometer calibrated against such a large background, and thus independent of the position of the sector, to measure the brightness temperature of a small tungsten filament, large variations in temperature are found when different sectors are located near the objective lens. No such differences are found when the sector is located near the pyrometer filament.

In Table 29 are given results showing the effect of the position of the sector. A 15-mil (0.381-mm) tungsten lamp operated at a brightness temperature of about 2275°K was used as a background, and readings were made on the current through a 2½-mil tungsten pyrometer filament, for an apparent-brightness match with a sector having two 1-deg. openings. From the table, it can be seen that the position of a sector of this size can cause an error of about 14°K for this condition, if care is not taken as to its location. When a sector is used, it should be rotated so fast that no flicker is noticeable. Not only is an error apt to be made if the sector is not rotating fast enough, but the flicker is bothersome in making accurate brightness comparisons.

TABLE 29.   ERRORS IN TEMPERATURE MEASUREMENTS DUE TO IMPROPER LOCATION OF SECTOR

Position of 2-deg. sector	Near lens		Near pyrometer lamp	
	Opening of sector parallel to background filament	Opening of sector perpendicular to background filament	Opening of sector parallel to background filament	Opening of sector perpendicular to background filament
Current, in amperes, through pyrometer filament for brightness match........	0.3332	0.3354	0.3357	0.3357
Apparent relative brightness...................	0.9390	0.9950	1.0000	1.0000
Temperature of background for these readings, °K...	2,263	2,275	2,277	2,277

Errors Due to Various Causes.   If an optical pyrometer with too short a pyrometer filament (*i.e.*, less than about 2 cm) is used to measure temperatures lower than about 1200°K, an error is apt to be introduced, if the ambient temperature is much different in use than when the pyrometer was calibrated.[14]   In Table 30 is given the variation in extrapolated temperature due to a variation in initial temperature, in effective wavelength, in transmission of absorbing glass or transmission of sector, and in current through the pyrometer filament. First is given the change in the temperature due to 1 per cent variation of each, and then some other possible variation.   An inspection of the table will show that, in extrapolated temperatures, quite an error is allowed in the effective wavelength or the transmission of the sector or of the absorbing glass, without any great error in the final results.   Any error, however, in calibrating at the initial temperature will cause a much larger error in the final result.

General Notes.   If an optical pyrometer, as shown in Fig. 203, is so constructed as to transmit sufficient light to enable temperatures to be measured as low as 1000°K, this pyrometer will transmit too much light for comfort at high temperatures. The diaphragm before the eyepiece telescope at E can be constructed as shown, so as to have several openings of various sizes. For a low temperature, the larger opening is to be used, thus transmitting more light, while for a higher temperature, a smaller opening should be used. In this manner, the same instrument can be used over a wide range without discomfort.

Table 30. Changes in Temperature of 2400°, and 3000°K Extrapolated from 1800°K as Initial Temperature, Using the Wien Equation, Due to Various Changes

Variation leading to error	Percentage change			Actual change, °K		
	1,800	2,400	3,000	1,800	2,400	3,000
Change of 1 per cent initial temperature..........................	1.0	1.30	1.70	18.0	32.0	50.0
Change of 3°K in initial temperature..	...	....	....	3.0	5.0	8.0
Using a wavelength, 1 per cent in error	...	0.30	0.70	....	8.0	20.0
0.001μ error in wavelength..........	...	0.05	0.10	....	1.2	3.0
If in extrapolating the λ_e of red glass between 1300 and 1800°K is used (see Fig. 205)....................	...	0.10	0.30	....	2.4	7.5
Calibrating pyrometer filament against tungsten lamp as background that was standardized with a red glass different from one used in pyrometer being calibrated. Suppose λ_e to change from 0.665μ to 0.650μ......	...	....	....	3.5		
Error of 1 per cent in value used for transmission of sector or absorbing glass............................	...	0.26	0.32	....	6.2	9.6
Variation of 1 per cent in current through 2½-mil pyrometer filament	0.5	0.70	0.80	9.0	16.0	25.0

If too large an opening[15] is used before the telescope eyepiece, the pyrometer filament will not disappear against the image of the background, but there will be dark streaks along the edges of the pyrometer filament. If these dark streaks are too prominent, it is impossible to make consistent settings. The resolving power of whatever eyepiece is used should be so adjusted that the pyrometer filament disappears as a whole, i.e., such that one does not see either dark or bright streaks along the edge of the pyrometer filament. If, for any reason, it is necessary to use an eyepiece of high resolving power, good disappearance can be obtained by increasing the size of the cone of rays that reach the pyrometer filament from the objective lens. If this is pushed too far, an objective lens with a very large aperture is required. If the light is too intense for comfort, it can be cut down by using one or more additional red glasses before the eyepiece. If two red glasses are used in the eyepiece, the addition of a third red glass will reduce the apparent intensity of the image by about 50 per cent. If more light is desired for sources at lower temperatures, it is often quite a help to remove one of the two red glasses that are being used. If two red glasses are being used and one of them is removed, the brightness of the image observed will appear about twice what it did with two red glasses. If no sector or absorbing glass is used with the pyrometer, there will be very little effect on temperature measurements if the number of red glasses in the eyepiece is changed. If a sector or absorbing glass is used, corrections will have to be made for the change in effective wavelength for the number of red glasses used.

Observations on Nonblack Sources. Optical pyrometers are generally used to measure the temperature of furnaces where approximately blackbody conditions exist. However, it is often convenient to study non-blackbodies with an optical pyrometer, and to assign a temperature to a brightness of a non-blackbody, as if it were a blackbody. It has already been pointed out* that such temperatures are lower than the true temperatures and that they are called brightness temperatures. Thus, when one says that a non-blackbody has a brightness temperature of 1500°K for $\lambda = 0.665\mu$, one means that it has the same brightness as a blackbody at 1500°K for this wavelength interval. The difference between the true temperature and the temperature thus obtained varies from a few degrees, for such a substance as untreated carbon, to more than 200°C for such a metal as polished platinum at its melting point.

The Emissivity of Non-Blackbodies. The ratio of the brightness of a non-blackbody to that of a blackbody at the same temperature is called the emissivity. The spectral emissivity may

* See p. 23.

vary with the wavelength and with the temperature. Thus, the brightness temperature will in general depend upon the wavelength used.

The relation between brightness temperature and true temperatures from the Wien equation is

$$\frac{1}{T} - \frac{1}{S_\lambda} = \frac{\lambda \log e_\lambda}{c_2 \log \mathbf{e}} \qquad (85)$$

where T is the true temperature, S_λ the brightness temperature, and e_λ the emissivity for wavelength λ.

As examples of emissivity, the following may be mentioned: For platinum, the emissivity for the red ($\lambda = 0.665\mu$) varies from 0.36 for a temperature of 1000°K to 0.32 for a temperature of 1400°K. For tungsten, the variation for the red ($\lambda = 0.665\mu$) is from 0.46 for $T = 1200$°K to 0.42 for $T = 2800$°K. For the blue ($\lambda = 0.465\mu$) for tungsten, the change is from 0.49 for $T = 1200$°K to 0.45 for $T = 2800$°K. The emissivity of carbon for the red ($\lambda = 0.665\mu$) varies from 0.86 for $T = 1200$°K to 0.79 for $T = 2200$°K. Iron oxide has a very high emissivity, being about 95 per cent for the red radiation for $T = 1400$°K. The values of brightness temperature obtained by observations on heated iron oxide with an optical pyrometer are very nearly equal to the true temperature.

In Table 31 are given the values that must be added to different brightness temperatures for different values of the emissivity in order to obtain the true temperature.

Wavelength to Which Brightness Temperature Should Be Ascribed. If a screen that is absolutely monochromatic is used before the eyepiece, it is at once evident to what wavelength the temperature of a non-blackbody thus measured should be ascribed. However, if a red glass is used, such as those having the transmission shown in Fig. 204, some consideration is necessary.[16]

When the blackbody-brightness temperature of a source is determined with an optical pyrometer with a so-called monochromatic screen before the eyepiece, what is really measured is the brightness of the source through the screen. The value of the brightness thus obtained would correspond to a certain temperature T if it were obtained from measurements of a black-

body.   Therefore, the temperature of the source is to be called
a brightness temperature S, where $S = T$.

The brightness temperature S must be ascribed to a wavelength such that the energy emitted by a blackbody per unit
area at temperature $T(=S)$, for this wavelength will equal that
emitted per unit area by the source for the same wavelength.
Thus, there are two sources with different spectral distributions
that have the same brightness when observed through the red
screen, a blackbody at temperature T, and the source being
studied, which is at a brightness temperature S.   Call the color
temperature* of the source studied T_c.   As these two distributions are different, and yet the sources have the same brightness,
the curves representing these distributions must cross if they are
plotted with energy emitted per unit area against wavelength.

TABLE 31.   CORRECTIONS TO ADD TO BRIGHTNESS TEMPERATURE READINGS
FOR DIFFERENT EMISSIVITY, $\lambda = 0.665\mu$

Emis-sivity	Pyrometer readings, degrees Kelvin of														
	1,000	1,100	1,200	1,300	1,400	1,500	1,600	1,700	1,800	2,000	2,200	2,400	2,600	2,800	3,000	3,600
0.10	119	146	176	209	246	286	329	377	429	543	676	827	1,000	1,196	1,416	2,251
0.20	80	98	118	140	163	189	217	247	279	352	433	524	627	740	867	1,325
0.30	59	72	86	102	119	137	157	178	201	251	308	371	442	519	604	907
0.40	44	54	64	76	89	102	117	132	149	186	227	272	323	379	439	651
0.50	33	40	48	57	66	76	87	98	110	137	167	201	237	277	320	472
0.60	24	29	35	41	48	55	63	71	80	99	121	145	170	199	229	336
0.70	17	20	24	29	33	38	43	49	55	68	83	99	117	136	157	228
0.80	10	13	15	18	21	24	27	30	34	42	51	61	72	84	96	139
0.85	7	9	11	13	15	17	19	22	25	31	37	44	52	60	70	96
0.90	5	6	7	8	10	11	13	14	16	20	24	28	33	39	45	65
1.00	0	0	0	0	0	0	0	0	0	0	0	0	0	0	0	0

The values given in this table also give the correction for a window having the transmission given in column 1
for different temperatures of the sources when this window is used between the source and the pyrometer.

If the source is considered, it will be seen from the definition
of color temperature that its distribution of energy corresponds
to that of a blackbody at T_c, the difference being that each
ordinate of the curve representing the blackbody distribution
at temperature T_c bears a constant ratio K to the corresponding
ordinate for the source studied.   Thus the actual energy distribution of the source being investigated is given by $J(\lambda T_c)/K$.

* See p. 23.

As stated, this curve and the one representing the distribution of a blackbody at the temperature T will cross at the wavelength where $J(\lambda T_c)/K = J(\lambda T)$. As each ordinate of the curve representing the distribution of energy from the source studied is a certain fraction $(1/K)$ of that for a blackbody at temperature T_c, the brightness will be reduced the same amount. Thus, if B_s is the brightness of the source studied,

$$B_{T_c} = KB_s \qquad \text{and} \qquad \frac{B_T}{B_{T_c}} = \frac{B_T}{KB_s} = \left[\frac{J(\lambda T)}{J(\lambda T_c)} \right]_{\lambda_e} \qquad (86)$$

or

$$\frac{B_T}{B_s} = 1 = \left[\frac{J(\lambda T)}{\dfrac{J(\lambda T_c)}{K}} \right]_{\lambda_e} \qquad (87)$$

Thus $J(\lambda T)$ and $J(\lambda T_c)/K$ are equal for the wavelength λ_e, in other words, the curves representing these two distributions cross at this point. From this it follows that the brightness temperature S is to be ascribed to the effective wavelength for the screen used for the temperature interval of a blackbody from $T(= S)$ to T_c.

Corrections of Brightness Temperatures to a Constant Effective Wavelength. As the brightness temperatures of a source are measured using a particular screen before the eyepiece, there will be a variation in the wavelength to which these temperatures are to be ascribed. Sometimes it is desirable to know the brightness temperature over quite a range of temperatures for the same wavelength. If the color temperature of the source is known, the brightness temperature can be calculated for any wavelength when it is known for one wavelength. Thus for a source at a color temperature T_c, using the Wien equation and the conditions that hold for color match, the following relation between two brightness temperatures (S_1 and S_2) for two wavelengths (λ_1 and λ_2) can be derived.

$$\frac{1}{S_2} = \frac{\lambda_2}{\lambda_1} \left[\frac{1}{S_1} - \frac{1}{T_c} \right] + \frac{1}{T_c} \qquad (88)$$

If a double thickness (6.8 mm) of the red glass known as Jena Rotfilter No. 4512 (spectral transmission shown by curve C, Fig. 204) is used before the eyepiece of the pyrometer, this correction, when applied to the brightness temperature of tungsten, will be small. The effective wavelength of this red glass changes from 0.6657μ, for the range between brightness and color temperature at a brightness temperature of 1600°K, to 0.6626μ, for this range for a brightness temperature of 3000°K. If the brightness temperatures are corrected to a wavelength 0.6657μ, this correction will amount to about -2°K at a brightness temperature of 3000°K; for most work when using this screen, this correction will be negligible.

Objections have often been made to the use of red-glass screens on the ground that, as the range of wavelength transmitted was so large, there was no method of knowing to what wavelength the resulting temperature was to be assigned. If the effective wavelength of the red glass used is known for different temperature ranges, the results can be treated just as definitely as if an absolutely monochromatic screen were used; in addition, the red glass has the added advantage of transmitting enough light to enable very accurate brightness comparisons to be made.

TOTAL-RADIATION PYROMETRY

Total-radiation pyrometry is based upon the Stefan-Boltzmann law. Thus temperatures are measured by measuring the intensity of the radiation for all wavelengths. Usually the energy radiated by the source is focused in some manner upon one junction of a small thermocouple. The temperature to which this junction rises is approximately proportional to the rate at which energy falls upon it, which in turn, by the Stefan-Boltzmann law, is proportional to the fourth power of the absolute temperature of the source, assuming, of course, that the source gives blackbody radiation. The resulting e.m.f. of the thermocouple is measured by an appropriate galvanometer or other measuring instrument as described in Chap. X. Several methods[17] have been developed for focusing the radiation onto the thermopile so that the response of the instrument is independent of its distance from the source whose temperature is being measured.

Figure 211 shows the principle of the Thwing pyrometer. The radiation from the furnace enters the diaphragm A and falls upon the hollow conical mirror K, which by multiple reflection along the side of the mirror is finally concentrated upon the hot

junction of the thermocouple located at C as shown. Except
for incidental errors, which will be considered later, the reading of
the instrument is independent of the sighting distance, provided
the diameter of the source is sufficient to fill the cone of rays
defined by the geometrical design of the receiving tube as shown
in Fig. 212.

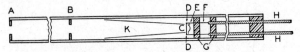

Fig. 211.—Diagram of Thwing total-radiation pyrometer.

The amount of radiation falling upon an element D of the
conical mirror is proportional to the solid angle FDA', which is
independent of the distance from the point D to the source; this
is true of every point on the base of the cone DD'. Hence, the
total energy entering the cone is independent of the distance from
the pyrometer to the source, provided the source is of sufficient
size. The minimum size of source for any distance is determined
by the lines $A''D'$ and $A'D$. Thus, for the distance BA the
diameter of the source must be at least $A'A''$. The Thwing
instrument is so constructed that the source must have a diameter
at least one-eighth of the distance from the source to the receiving
tube; thus, at 8 ft. (2.4 m) from a furnace the opening into the
furnace must be 1 ft. (0.3 m) in diameter. For permanent
installations, the tube is ventilated and has several extra dia-

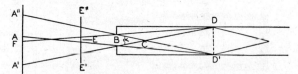

Fig. 212.—Diagram of cone type of total-radiation pyrometer.

phragms to prevent local heating of the instrument and reradiation to the couple.

In another form of pyrometer called the Féry radiation
pyrometer (Fig. 213) the radiation is focused upon the thermocouple by a concave mirror. This form of pyrometer has an
observation eyepiece so that the observer can see when the radiation from the source is properly focused upon the thermocouple.

The readings with a Féry pyrometer, when properly focused, and neglecting secondary errors, are independent of the sighting distance, as is the case with the fixed-focus radiation pyrometer. Figure 214 shows a schematic diagram of a fixed-focus total-

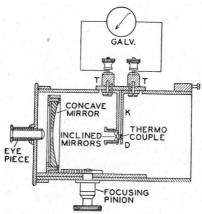

FIG. 213.—Féry radiation pyrometer.

radiation pyrometer using a quartz lens as the focusing device. The advantage of this instrument is that it is totally enclosed, which reduces very markedly errors due to dust and smoke. Any thermopile or other radiation-measuring device may be used as a total-radiation pyrometer provided consideration is taken of

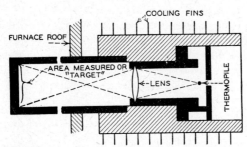

FIG. 214.—Schematic diagram of Thermotube; by Leeds and Northrup The target area comes up to furnace temperature; dotted lines indicate way in which quartz lens focuses target's heat onto thermopile.

the fraction of radiation from the source that falls upon the thermocouple when the unknown is measured as compared with the amount of radiation that falls upon the thermocouple when it is calibrated. This means either some fixed focusing device as already described or that the pyrometer should be used under the same conditions as to distance and area of blackbody as it was calibrated or corrections made for the difference.

The use of total-radiation pyrometers is subject to all the errors that one meets in measuring radiation. They are thus affected by stray radiation, by dust and smoke, and by water vapor or carbon dioxide in the line of sight, and also by the accumulation of dirt on the optical parts. One important advantage in this type of pyrometer is that it is easy to make direct-reading, and when once installed it requires but little attention except as noted. The use of this type of pyrometer assumes blackbody conditions in the furnace and if these do not exist, corrections are necessary. Since all non-blackbodies radiate less energy at any temperature than the blackbody at the same temperature, temperatures of non-blackbodies measured by a total-radiation pyrometer will be less than the true temperature and are called radiation temperatures.[18]

From the theoretical bases underlying total-radiation pyrometry (Stefan-Boltzmann law) the measured flux is related to the temperature as follows:

$$\Phi = A\sigma T^4.$$

For a non-blackbody the radiant-flux density Φ_n may be represented by a similar equation

$$\Phi_n = A e_t \sigma T^4 \tag{89}$$

where e_t represents the total emissivity. This equation serves, in fact, as the defining equation for this quantity. As is indicated elsewhere, e_t may, and usually will, vary with the temperature and the material studied. We may also write

$$\Phi_n = A\sigma T_R{}^4 \tag{90}$$

an equation similar to Eq. (1). T_R, called the radiation temperature, is less than the true temperature T. From Eqs. (89) and (90) there follows:

$$T_R = \sqrt[4]{e_t}\, T. \tag{91}$$

Evidently this relation may be used to determine e_t, the total emissivity when T and T_R are known or, if the emissivity is known, this equation can be used to find the relation between true temperature T and radiation temperature T_R. The total emissivity of substances varies over a wide range, as for instance, e_t is about 5 per cent for polished silver at 1000°K, 10 per cent for polished platinum at 1000°K, about 11 per cent for polished tungsten at 1000°K, about 30 per cent for tungsten at 2500°K, and about 85 per cent for iron oxide at 1000°K.   Thus some care must be taken to see that blackbody conditions are provided when any total-radiation pyrometer is used, or corrections must be made for the total emissivity of the source studied.

PHOTOELECTRIC-TUBE PYROMETERS

Just recently there appeared a pyrometer where the detecting instrument is a photoelectric tube.   These instruments are readily made recording and, although they do not measure the total radiation, they can be calibrated to give true temperature in much the same way that an optical pyrometer using monochromatic screens is calibrated, except that in this case the sensitivity of the photoelectric tube replaces the sensitivity of the eye in the calculation.   Here again care must be exercised if the furnace whose temperature is measured is not a blackbody, since the calculation assumes blackbody conditions.   If these do not exist, corrections should be made.   The corrections for either a total-radiation pyrometer or a pyrometer using a photoelectric tube as the detecting device can easily be calculated for non-blackbody conditions provided the spectral emissivity of the source over the range covered by the instrument is known.   This is done using the same equation that is used for calculating the transmission of a neutral-tint screen for optical pyrometers.*

Measuring Color Temperature.   An optical pyrometer may be so constructed that it can be used to measure the color temperature† of the source studied but, in general, color temperatures are measured with regular photometric equipment.   Most observers claim that more accurate results can be obtained by the use of the contrast field‡ than with the equality-of-brightness field. To measure color temperature requires a double setting since accurate color matches cannot be made unless there is at the same time a brightness match as observed in the photometer.   In general the color match is obtained by varying the voltage that

* Equation (84).
† See p. 23.
‡ See p. 390.

is supplied to the comparison lamp and the brightness match obtained by moving either the photometer head or one of the lamps. By this method quite accurate color match can be made between the source studied and a standard lamp that has been standardized by comparison with a blackbody. For sources giving blackbody radiation the color temperature is the true temperature, but for non-blackbodies corrections to the color temperature are necessary to obtain true temperature. From the color temperature of such sources whose radiant energy can be color-matched with that of a blackbody—and this includes most temperature radiators—very accurate spectral distributions can be obtained by calculation with the Wien equation using for the temperature the color temperature obtained.

References

1. Foote and Fairchild, Pyrometer Symposium, *A.I.M.M.E.*, p. 331, 1920.
2. E. P. Hyde and W. E. Forsythe, *Astrophys. Jour.*, **61**, 244 (1920).
   Fairchild, Hoover, and Peters, *Bur. Standards Jour. Res.*, **2**, 931 (1929).
   G. K. Burgess, *Bur. Standards Jour. Res.*, **1**, 640 (1929).
3. E. P. Hyde, F. E. Cady, and W. E. Forsythe, *Astrophys. Jour.*, **42**, 294 (1915).
4. Henning, *Zeitschr. Inst.*, **30**, 61 (1910).
   Mendenhall, *Phys. Rev.*, **33**, 74 (1911).
   Forsythe, *Astrophys. Jour.*, **49**, 238 (1919).
5. A. G. Worthing and W. E. Forsythe, *Jour. Optical Soc. Am.*, **10**, 601 (1925).
6. C. E. Mendenhall, *Phys. Rev.*, **33**, 74 (1911).
7. A. G. Worthing, *Astrophys. Jour.*, **36**, 345 (1912).
8. N. K. Chaney, V. C. Hamister, and S. W. Glass, *Trans. Electrochem. Soc.*, **67**, 107 (1935).
9. Forsythe, *Jour. Optical Soc. Am.*, **10**, 19 (1925).
10. Benford, *Jour. Optical Soc. Am.*, **25**, 136 (1935).
11. Forsythe, *Trans. Faraday Soc.*, **15**, 21 (1920).
12. A. Schuster and J. W. Nicholson, "Introduction to Theory of Optics," p. 154.
13. Hyde, Cady, and Forsythe, *Astrophys. Jour.*, **42**, 302 (1915).
14. Forsythe and Worthing, *Astrophys. Jour.*, **61**, 179 (1925).
15. Worthing and Forsythe, *Phys. Rev.*, **4**, 163 (1914).
    Fairchild and Hoover, *Jour. Optical Soc. Am.*, **7**, 543 (1923).
16. Forsythe, *Gen. Elec. Rev.*, **26**, 830 (1923).
17. Foote and Fairchild, Pyrometer Symposium, *A.I.M.M.E.*, p. 341, 1920.
18. A. G. Worthing, Pyrometer Symposium, *A.I.M.M.E.*, p. 373, 1920.

CHAPTER XIII

PHOTOMETRY

W. E. Forsythe* and Herbert E. Ives†

Photometry is that part of radiometry which deals with the measurement of light, and light has been defined[1] as "radiant energy evaluated according to its capacity to produce visual sensation." This presupposes the eye as the measuring device, thus again bringing in the use of a selective receiver. Many experiments[2] have been made to determine the relative response of the average eye to radiation of different wavelengths until finally the work of Gibson and Tyndall[3] at the National Bureau of Standards gave results that were considered sufficiently satisfactory so that weighted average values‡ of their results and certain other measurements were adopted by the International Commission on Illumination as the international luminosity curve.[4] The eye is not at all an accurate instrument for the absolute measurement of light, but it is able to detect very slight differences in the brightness of two adjacent surfaces when they are identical in color. While differences in brightness of two adjacent surfaces can be detected even with a color difference, the accuracy of such detection decreases markedly with an increase in the color difference. Many devices[5] have been used to bring the two surfaces that are illuminated by the two light sources being studied into the field of view for comparison, but here only the two methods that are almost universally used in visual direct comparison photometry will be considered.

The Photometer Cube. Lummer and Brodhun,[6] in about 1888, brought out their two-part cube and their contrast cube, and these two types of photometer cubes have been used in almost all the tests since that time and are now used as part of the stand-

---

* *Physicist, Incandescent Lamp Department, General Electric Company, Cleveland, Ohio.*

† *Physicist, Bell Telephone Laboratories.*

‡ Table 33, col. 3, p. 411.

ard equality-of-brightness and contrast photometer in almost all laboratories. These two devices are shown diagrammatically in Fig. 215 and Fig. 216.

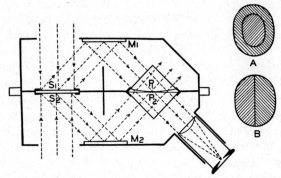

Fig. 215.—Lummer-Brodhun equality-of-brightness photometer. Two types of field shown at *A* and *B*.

The cube of the equality-of-brightness photometer is so made (Fig. 215) that the field of view is generally divided into two parts which may consist of halves of pairs of quarters or of a central spot surrounded by an annulus. One part of the field of view is illuminated by the light from the standard source, and the

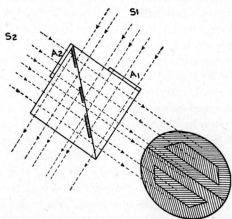

Fig. 216.—Diagram of Lummer-Brodhun contrast photometer cube.

second part by the light from the comparison source. The contrast photometer cube divides the field into two halves and, as shown in Fig. 216, the center of each half is a trapezoid which is illuminated by light from the opposite source from the main part of this side, with the light intensity for the trapezoids reduced by absorbing screens. At the position of balance, these two trapezoids are supposed to "stand out" with equal prominence. This "contrast" is claimed by workers in this field to be a help in making a balance when these two parts of the field differ in color.

The field of the photometer is viewed with an eyepiece having a visual angle of 8 to 10 deg. Some work[7] has been done with a smaller angle, *i.e*, about 2 deg. With an approximate color match, the balance is but little affected by the visual angle, but, when comparing two light sources of widely different color, the readings obtained depend upon the visual angle used in observing this field. The visual angle most used in photometry is that of the standard Lummer-Brodhun photometer (8 to 10 deg.), and this had come to be the recognized practice in the field of photometry until the recent introduction of lamps with highly colored light output. The resulting problem in heterochromatic photometry led photometrists to adopt the 2-deg. field as standard. The photometer cube should be so adjusted that the line of separation of the two parts of the field disappears when the two parts of the field are equal in brightness.

It requires some experience to learn to use and make accurate brightness matches of the two parts of the field of the equality-of-brightness photometer, or accurate settings for equal contrast of the trapezoids with the contrast photometer; however, with a little practice readings, to well within 1 per cent, can be made with the use of either type of photometer cube.

The two sources whose horizontal intensities are to be compared are generally so mounted, on the opposite ends of an optical bench, with the photometer head between them, that either source or the photometer sight box may be moved. For the most accurate work a very rigid bench (Fig. 217) and supports are necessary so that either lamp in its holder or the photometer head can be moved along the bench and kept in the same relative position with respect to the other.[8] Screens and diaphragms should be placed along the photometer bench and back of the lamps, so arranged that no light can reach the photometer screen except directly from the lamp being measured. These screens should be covered with some such material as black velvet so

that they will reflect a negligible amount of light into the field
of view.

The relative intensities of the two light sources are calculated
from their distances from the photometer screen of the sight
box for the condition of balance of the two parts of the screen
by using the inverse-square law. This means that provision
must be made for accurately measuring the distance between
either lamp and the screen of the photometer head.

A comparison source is generally used and first its intensity
compared with that of the standard lamp and then with that of
the unknown lamp. The unknown should be in exactly the same

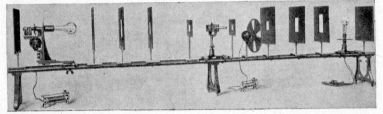

Fig. 217.—Photometer bench (Leeds and Northrup Company).

position, if possible, as the standard lamp had been. Sometimes
the comparison-lamp holder is fastened to the sight-box carriage
so that they move together. This makes the calculation easier
since the distance between the comparison lamp and the photometer screen is constant and drops out. When comparing the
intensity of two lamps that are of such different magnitudes
that the distances available are not sufficient to get a brightness
match, calibrated sector disks or calibrated neutral-tint screens
are used between the more intense light source and the photometer
head. Suitable neutral-tint screens for accurate work are hard
to find, so sector disks are generally used. With a set of disks
ranging in transmission from 2 to 75 per cent, the intensity of most
sources can be measured with a bench about 3 m long.

To make sure that the inverse-square law is obeyed a light
source should be at least 10 to 15 times its largest dimension
from the photometer head[9] (Table 32). For most sources a
distance of 100 cm is quite satisfactory considering both the
dimensions of the lamp and the accuracy of reading the scale.

When measuring the light output of incandescent lamps the
applied voltage or current should be very carefully measured

since in general the light output varies faster than the voltage or current. For most accurate work a potentiometer is generally used. For the many other precautions necessary one should consult an extended book[10] on this subject.

TABLE 32.   APPARENT CANDLEPOWER OF DISK OR LINE SOURCE AT VARIOUS DISTANCES

d/L	Candlepower, per cent	
	Line	Disk
5	99.31	99.0
10	99.83	99.74
12	99.88	99.83
15	99.94	99.90
20	99.98	99.95

d = distance.
L = length or diameter of (disk) source.

The Unit of Luminous Intensity. The standard of light intensity, like most physical standards, had to be selected. Various flame sources have been used from time to time as the standard of luminous intensity, but about the time the carbon lamp became fixed in the art it was found that the flame standards of intensity were not so constant in their light output as the sources being measured. This resulted in the setting up of the international candle[11] which is maintained by a number of carefully selected and carefully compared carbon lamps kept at the various national laboratories. As thus defined the international candle corresponds to a color temperature of about 2080°K.

The International Candle. The unit of luminous intensity or candlepower is thus the international candle, which can only be defined as a certain fraction of the light output in a definite direction of the groups of carbon lamps maintained at the different standardization laboratories. This standard is not reproducible, which makes it unsatisfactory as a physical standard. It was suggested by Waidner and Burgess[12] that 1 cm² of blackbody at the freezing point of platinum be adopted as the standard of intensity. The experimental work[13] of setting up this standard has been practically completed so that now it may be said that the standard of intensity can be checked by any laboratory that wants to go to the trouble to make the necessary experiments.

The candlepower of a lamp may be measured in a very definite direction such as the horizontal candlepower or the mean spherical candlepower may be measured. Means are provided for rotating vacuum lamps to get the mean horizontal candlepower. The mean spherical candlepower can be determined by integration from candlepower readings taken at different directions with or without a mirror for reflecting the light onto the photometer screen. When making the integration to determine the mean spherical candlepower from readings taken at different directions around the lamp, consideration must be taken of the areas within the different zones.[14] This is fully outlined in the more extensive books on photometry.

The Lumen. Luminous flux is defined as radiant flux* evaluated according to its ability to produce visual sensation. The unit of luminous flux, which is the lumen, is the flux emitted per unit solid angle by a source whose average candlepower throughout the solid angle is 1.

Heterochromatic Photometry. The international candle is defined in terms of a specific illuminant, which, while representative in color of the majority of light sources of commercial importance at the time of its establishment, is considerably different in color from many light sources which have been more recently produced, and from light sources which may be of importance in experimental work. The methods of direct visual photometry, which depend upon obtaining an exact brightness match in the photometric field, become increasingly difficult when the two portions of the field differ in color. When a color difference exists in the photometric field, the judgment of equality of brightness becomes a function of the illumination (Purkinje and allied effects), the size of the photometric field, the photometric method employed, and the physiological and psychological characteristics of the observers. There is, strictly speaking, no unique answer to the question of how relatively bright are two fields of different color. A practical answer can be given only on a statistical basis, and upon the adoption of certain conventions of measurement.

* See p. 4.

A large amount of research has been done to establish conditions, methods and conventions for the measurement of lights
of different color.   Among these may be mentioned as most
prominent: first, the use of the Lummer-Brodhun equality-
of-brightness photometer with definite field size,* or their contrast photometer, with a large number of observers, and with few
steps, of color difference or with many steps, each so small that
the difficulty of making a judgment is minimized; second,
methods dependent on receivers or filters calibrated spectro-
photometrically in terms of the I.C.I. standard observer; and
third, the flicker photometer.

Flicker Photometer.   The flicker photometer is an instrument
in which the two halves of the photometric field are presented
to the observer[15] in rapid and constant succession.†   Photometric
balance is indicated by the setting which gives a minimum of
flicker, and for the greatest sensitiveness a speed should be
selected such that flicker is visible for very small displacements
from the position of balance.   With a color difference the necessary speed, which is ordinarily of the order of ten alternations per
second, is higher the greater the color difference.   The peculiar
applicability of the flicker photometer to measurements with a
color difference is due to the fact that there occurs a fusion of the
colors before the flicker caused by difference of brightness
disappears.   Many different forms of flicker photometer have
been devised which are described in the books and papers cited.
With this device, it is possible to make reasonably definite and
precise photometric settings for color differences which are
practically impossible of estimation by a steady equality-of-
brightness setting.   Neither method escaped the difficulties
due to variations in the size of the photometric field, illumination, or characteristics of the observers.   With a small size of the
photometric field and a relatively high field brightness, the results
obtained by a large number of observers using the two methods,

* The standard field size is now 2 deg.

† It is essential in a flicker photometer that the transition from one field
to the other be made without any spurious variation of the light such as the
dark or illuminated edge of the sector disk used in primitive forms of the
device introduced.   Such edges themselves cause a considerable flicker
which materially diminishes the sensitiveness.   A polarization instrument
in which the alternation of fields is made absolutely uniformly is described
by Ives.[16]

viz., step-by-step and flicker methods, tend to approximate each other. Both methods are suited only for a standardizing laboratory where observers of normal vision can be selected, and are best used for the calibration of secondary standards of different colors, or of color filters which can be used with standard lamps to eliminate the color difference.

Ordinarily the most practical method of photometry where a color difference exists is to use color filters, *e.g.*, bluish glasses which placed over a carbon lamp will make the color of the resulting light that of a tungsten lamp.* Such glasses must, however, be so calibrated that the results obtained by their use conform to the conditions and conventions generally agreed upon. A preferred method for determining the transmission of color filters is to calculate this by the use of spectrophotometric transmission curves of the filters, and the spectral luminosity. The luminosity factor itself has been determined, by agreement, for a set of conditions of field brightness, size, and selection of normal observers. Hence, by the use of this function with the spectrophotometric transmission, the calibration of the screens corresponds to the results of direct measurements under the chosen conditions.

The formula for obtaining the transmission of a color filter in this way is as follows:

$$\tau = \frac{\int J_\lambda K_\lambda \tau_\lambda d\lambda}{\int J_\lambda K_\lambda d\lambda} \tag{92}$$

where J_λ is the spectral radiant intensity, K_λ the spectral luminosity, and τ_λ the transmission of the filter for wavelength λ. For the luminosity function,† the values adopted by the International Commission for Illumination[18] should be used.

The use of filters for equalizing the color difference of the light from sources whose intensities are to be measured assumes an exact match in color and spectral composition. This is seldom obtained, especially with gaseous-discharge lamps, so again care must be taken in selecting the observers. The color match will

---

* Care[17] must be taken that the filter is not placed so close to the photometer as to cause an error by the light reflected back from it. Also, it should not be put so near the comparison lamp that its temperature is changed, as its transmission is apt to change with its temperature.

† Table 33, col. 3, p. 411.

often be observed to fail as the eye is moved in and out from the photometer head, thus changing the size of field. To insure the highest accuracy in the use of filters for this purpose, the approximate conditions[2] of field size and field brightness which were used for establishing the luminosity function should be used, and the characteristics of the observers' eyes should be determined by adequate[19] test.

A very attractive solution of the photometric problem with a color difference consists in embodying the luminosity function in some physical measuring device, such as a thermocouple, which may be used for direct measurement of illuminants, or to calibrate filters. This will be discussed under physical photometers.

Candlepower Standards for Sources at High Temperatures. When the photometrists at the National Bureau of Standards found it necessary to measure the light output of the tungsten lamp, which is about 400°K higher in color temperature than the standard carbon lamp, they obtained a blue glass[20] which, when used between the carbon-lamp standards and the photometer, gave a very good color match with light from the tungsten lamp used on the other side of the photometer. By the use of these blue glasses, where transmissions were determined by a chosen procedure, tungsten-lamp horizontal-candlepower standards of intensity rated at $1\frac{1}{4}$ watts per mean horizontal candle were established in terms of the carbon standards.

Again the value of the intensity of the light from the incandescent lamps in use was no more than settled when another change was necessary owing to the introduction of the gas-filled tungsten lamps which operated at a much higher temperature than the vacuum tungsten lamps. Thus another correction due to color difference was necessary. This time another factor was introduced.

Mean Spherical Candlepower or Lumen Standards. Up to about 1913, the filament of the incandescent lamp was mounted in such a form that there was a fairly constant relation between the mean spherical candlepower and the mean horizontal candlepower. This ratio, for both the carbon lamp and the early straight-filament vacuum tungsten lamp was about 79 per cent. Sometime about 1914 when the gas-filled incandescent lamp was introduced, the form of the filament was changed and not kept the same in all lamps so that a constant relation between mean spherical candlepower and mean horizontal candlepower no longer held. Another difficulty was introduced since it did not seem possible to rotate the gas-filled lamp in order to obtain the mean horizontal candlepower. The reason the lamp could not be rotated was because rotation disturbed the gas currents within the lamp and caused a different distribution of the temperature of the different parts of the filament and thus changed its intensity. Some work was done at the National Bureau of Standards[21] that showed that a speed of rotation could be found that would not change the light output of the lamp, but this method never came into general use. At about this same time it was decided to give the output of incandescent lamps in lumens rather than in mean horizontal candles and so the best solution for these difficulties seemed to be to use the Ulbricht sphere and measure the mean spherical output of the incandescent lamp.

At the National Bureau of Standards[22] 500-watt gas-filled incandescent-lamp mean spherical standards were set up about 1917. First, mean spherical standards corresponding in color to the vacuum-tungsten-lamp standard rated at $1\frac{1}{4}$ watts per mean horizontal candle were set up by measuring the intensity in different planes around the lamp and obtaining the mean spherical intensity by integration. The intensity ratio of the vacuum-lamp standard to the 500-watt gas-filled standard was measured, using a number of experienced observers whose eyes had been tested by the Ives[19] method, and overcoming the color difference by the use of a flicker photometer. To make sure that the sphere integrated in the same way the output of the two lamps differing in color, the 500-watt standards were measured at two voltages on the bar photometer and in the sphere, and it was found, as one would assume, that the measured total output varied in the same ratio as the horizontal intensity. The lower voltage was such that a color match was obtained with the vacuum standards, and the other voltage corresponded to that necessary for about 15 lumens per watt.

Twelve years later, in 1929, the mean spherical candlepower of these 500-watt lamps was rechecked by an entirely new set of measurements.[22] This time the color difference between the $1\frac{1}{4}$-watt horizontal standards and the gas-filled standards was equalized by the use of a blue-glass filter. The average value obtained in this measurement of the six 500-watt gas-filled mean spherical standards agreed to within about 0.25 per cent with the previous values.

There were three chances for error between the carbon standards and the gas-filled-lamp lumen standard, two due to color difference, and the third due to passing from the mean horizontal intensity to the mean spherical intensity; but this last test seems to show that the spherical standards maintained at Washington are quite accurate.

The mean spherical candlepower may be determined either by measuring (1) the candlepower in various azimuths or zones and integrating, considering, of course, the size and position of the various zones; (2) by computing from the mean horizontal candlepower using the reduction factor; or (3) by a single measurement using a properly equipped Ulbricht sphere. Formerly, mean spherical candlepower values were obtained by methods (1) and (2), but today, except for very special cases, the Ulbricht sphere is employed whenever the mean spherical candlepower is measured.

ULBRICHT SPHERE

The Ulbricht sphere, Fig. 218, has thus come into use as a result of the necessity for an integrating instrument for measuring the output of gas-filled tungsten lamps. It consists of a large hollow sphere coated on the inside with white paint or other material of as nearly perfect diffusing power as possible and having at one point a window of translucent glass set into it. The lamp to be measured is placed inside of the sphere, and between it and the window is placed a screen so that the direct rays from the lamp do not strike the window. From theoretical consideration it can be shown that the brightness of the window is directly proportional to the mean spherical candlepower of the lamp, provided the sphere and the paint satisfy the following conditions:

The paint on the inside of the sphere must have a matte surface and be as nearly nonselective as possible so that the light from the lamp will not be changed too much by repeated reflections. It should have a high reflection factor because in this case certain errors due to objects within the sphere and the fact that the paint may not have a matte surface are partially corrected.

Obviously the paint should be of such character that it will not change very rapidly with time. The theory applies rigorously to a perfectly diffusing and empty sphere, neither of which is realized in practice. However, it has been shown that large spheres, *i.e.*, large as compared to the lamp being measured, give quite accurately the mean spherical candlepower if the method of

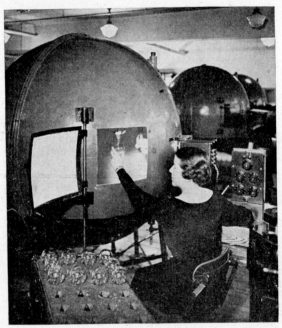

Fig. 218.—Ulbricht sphere.

substitution is used. If the lamp being measured differs markedly from the standard lamp, arrangements should be made to have both of them in the sphere at the time the measurements are made.

The translucent glass for the window should be very carefully selected since it is apt to change markedly the color of the light that it transmits and thus introduce an error.

Any type of photometer may be used to measure the brightness of the sphere window, but in most lamp factories the output of the sphere is measured with a physical photometer using a photoelectric tube as the detecting device. Figure 219 shows some of the equipment that goes with this sphere. The equipment is for controlling and measuring the voltage and current applied to the lamp and the voltage applied to the photoelectric tube and the amplifying device used to measure the phototube output for the condition of balance.

Practical operating conditions[23] have been worked out for the sphere, so that very accurate measurements can be made on the lumen output of different-sized lamps in terms of the spherical standards that have been set up.

Fig. 219.—Some equipment used with photoelectric photometry in connection with the Ulbricht sphere.

Several methods have been described for measuring the reflecting factor of the paint used on the sphere. Taylor,[24] in 1916, in a Bureau of Standards paper, and Benford,[17] in 1935, outlined methods for measuring this reflection factor. Also using a spectrophotometer, the spectral character of the light from the sphere window can be compared with that from the lamp alone, and from these measurements the relative integrating factor for light sources of different colors can be computed.

Measuring the light output of highly colored light sources, such as the sodium and the mercury arc, introduced further complications and differences.

The output of the sodium arc was measured, using a yellow screen* with the proper spectral transmission in front of the comparison lamp, operated at about the color temperature of the 500-watt standard lamp, so that a reasonably good color match was obtained with the light from the sodium lamp that is transmitted through the window of the sphere.

The light from the high-pressure mercury arc comes from a number of lines in the yellow, green, and blue parts of the spectrum. The yellow and green lines furnish the major portion of the light, while the lines toward the blue end of the spectrum contribute only a small amount of light but enough to affect the color. While photometric comparisons can be made directly between a 500-watt incandescent-lamp standard and a high-pressure mercury arc, no very accurate results can be obtained with this color difference.

Here again filters were selected and the photometric comparison made with as good a color match as possible.

Physical Photometry. Owing to the many difficulties in visual photometry, such as the uncertainty of measurements when large color differences are encountered, the variation of the readings of the same individual from day to day, errors due to eye fatigue, etc., there has been a desire for a long time to set up some sort of a physical photometer so that the equating or measuring of the intensities of light sources could be made without depending upon the eye to make the final judgment.

To set up a physical photometer that will work under all conditions requires an energy-measuring device that will weight radiation wavelength by wavelength just the same as the average eye does under various conditions of exposure to radiation of different intensity. Owing to the variation of the eye sensibility[25] when the intensity of radiation is low, such a device for all ranges of intensity is practically impossible. For intensities above a certain low value the relative sensibility of the eye for radiation of different wavelengths is found to be approximately of constant value. Since the wavelength calibration curve of the eye, for high values of intensity, is known, it ought to be possible to set up an energy-measuring device in connection with a filter so that the combination would have a response curve of practically the same shape as the average luminosity curve.

* Obtained from the Corning Glass Works.

The first suggestion of a workable physical photometer found in literature was by Féry[26] about 1908. This physicist suggested the use of an energy-measuring device, such as a thermocouple back of a filter, with a spectral transmission curve as nearly as possible the same shape as the curve that represents the luminosity function. Féry and his coworkers set up a physical photometer of this type and made some measurements of certain light sources, but this type of physical photometer was not thoroughly tested until 1915 when Ives and Kingsbury[27] prepared a filter consisting of a solution with the proper transmission and backed this up with a thermocouple as their measuring device. With this instrument, they measured the efficiency of a number of light sources and showed that it was possible to make a physical photometer along this line. This type of physical photometer has one big disadvantage in that the amount of energy to be measured is very small, making necessary a highly sensitive galvanometer and a delicate thermopile, which restricts its use to the standardizing laboratory.

The Phototube Physical Photometer. About 15 years ago work was started on the problem of using the photoelectric tube as a measuring device for photometers. At first it was thought that a photoelectric tube could be made with a wavelength-sensitivity curve similar to that of the luminosity function so that measurements could be made with the tube that would agree with those made by the average eye. If an attempt were made to measure the light intensity for the entire range of light used, including not only incandescent lamps and natural sources, which range in color temperature from about 1800 to 6000°K or even higher, but also such sources as the gaseous- and vapor-discharge tubes, the wavelength-sensitivity curve of the tube and the luminosity function would have to be very nearly the same. However, if only the light outputs of incandescent lamps are to be measured, the range in color temperature is much smaller, *i.e.*, from about 2270 to about 3000°K, or somewhat higher if some of the high-intensity lamps for special purposes are included, and thus a much less close agreement is necessary.

Tubes with a wavelength-sensitivity curve sufficiently similar from tube to tube and sufficiently constant for this purpose have not yet been developed. However, photometers have been developed using the photoelectric tube as the measuring device.

Several methods[28] have been suggested and used in this type of physical photometry. Since it was not found possible to obtain a photoelectric tube that could be used as a measuring device over the entire range of color temperature necessary for incandescent lamps, standards were obtained for about all the different types of incandescent lamps to be measured and comparisons made of intensity of the light output for practically one color. This put the burden of furnishing the standards upon the standardization laboratories.

For some time now, practically all the measurements of the light output of incandescent lamps made in the laboratories of the incandescent-lamp factories in this country have been made with photoelectric-tube photometers attached to Ulbricht spheres. By the use of this type of physical photometer, three very great advantages were obtained for the industrial laboratories. First, the measurement of the output of the incandescent lamps did not depend upon a selected group of trained observers; second, an increased accuracy in the relative measurements for any one type of lamp; and third, increased speed of operation. With this limited physical photometer an operator at the sphere can compare any one type of incandescent lamp with the proper standard as accurately as, or in many instances more accurately than, was possible in the standardization laboratories by eye observation.

Gradually as better phototubes were developed, it was found that by selecting the tubes the range of color temperature of the lamps for which the response was linear was widened. At first, it did not seem that a color screen used with the tube would be of any special advantage as the wavelength sensitivity of the tube did not extend far enough to the red end of the spectrum. However, a caesium vacuum tube was developed with a wavelength sensibility that extended to longer wavelengths than the red end of the visible spectrum. One laboratory started using a green filter with the tubes and very greatly extended the range of color temperature over which accurate readings could be made with a single photoelectric tube and a single standard lamp.

It was found recently[29] that a phototube could be selected which when used with an available green filter had a wavelength response of such character that if it were calibrated with light from a source at a color temperature of 2700°K (about the

color temperature of the 40-watt gas-filled lamp), it would read
the light output of lamps up to a color temperature of 2970°K
(the color temperature of the 500-watt gas-filled lamp) with an
error of only about 1 per cent.   This offered very great promise
for the usefulness of these types of photoelectric tubes with the
green screen for the measurement of the light output of incandescent lamps.

A New Measuring Device for Photometry.   The dry-disk
photo-e.m.f.[30] cell which, unlike a photoelectric tube, requires
no external source of e.m.f., seems to be one of the most convenient devices ever offered for the measurement of light output.
This cell consists essentially of a thin
metallic disk on which is a film of lead
oxide, selenium oxide, or some other
similar substance to serve as the light-
sensitive material.   The metal disk forms
the positive terminal, and a metal col-
lector ring in contact with the light-
sensitive surface forms the negative
terminal.   A picture of one of these
cells is shown in Fig. 220.   The current
output of such cells varies with the
illumination, and a properly made cell
connected to a galvanometer or micro-
ammeter of the proper resistance has been found to give an
approximately linear relation between illumination and current
output for a wide range of illumination.   Several of these cells
from various manufacturers have been studied and some of their
characteristics measured.   In general, the wavelength-response
curve* of this type of cell is somewhat broader than the luminosity
curve.   Nearly all that have been measured, however, have a
wavelength response that could be corrected with a filter to agree
very accurately in shape with the luminosity-function curve.
Some cells that have been corrected with filters so that their
response agrees reasonably well with that of the average eye give
results that agree within about 1 per cent, even when measuring
the light output of a high-intensity mercury lamp with the cell
calibrated by the light from a 100-watt incandescent standard.
Even the uncorrected cell will read the relative output of various

FIG. 220.—Photo-e.m.f.
cell   (Weston   photronic
cell).

* See Fig. 153.

incandescent lamps with but a small error (2 or 3 per cent) and will read the output of such colored lamps as the high-intensity mercury-arc or the sodium lamp with an error of only

a few per cent (6 to 10 per cent). An error of 20 to 40 per cent may be introduced, if an attempt is made to measure daylight illumination with a cell (without filter) that has been calibrated, using a gas-filled tungsten lamp as the standard. These new light-sensitive cells have been used extensively as the detecting element of foot-candle or light meters. It has been found possible to make light

FIG. 221.—Foot-candle meter with photo-e.m.f. cell as sensitive element.

meters that can be used to measure the illumination in various places such as offices, factories, etc., and although some are small enough to carry in one's pocket, they maintain their calibration very well. A picture of one such light meter is shown in Fig. 221.

References

1. I.E.S. Nomenclature and Standards Report, 1932. *Trans. I.E.S.*, **28**, 263 (1933).
2. IVES, *Phil. Mag.*, **24**, 149, 853 (1912). COBLENTZ and EMERSON, *Bur. Standards Sci. Paper*, 303 (1917); NUTTING, *Trans. I.E.S.*, **9**, 633 (1914). GIBSON and TYNDALL, *Bur. Standards Bull.*, **19**, 131 (1923).
3. *Bur. Standards Sci. Papers*, **5** (1923).
4. *Report I.C.I.*, 1924.
5. WALSH, "Photometry," p. 146.
6. LUMMER and BRODHUN, *Zeitschr. Instrumentenk.*, **9**, 23 (1889).
7. CRITTENDEN and RICHTMYER, *Bur. Standards Bull.*, **14**, 87 (1918). IVES, *Phil. Mag.*, **24**, 824 (1912).
8. HYDE and CADY, *Abst. Bull. Nela Research Lab.*, **1**, 192 (1913).
9. WALSH, *Light and Lighting*, **29**, 76 (1936).
10. WALSH, J. W. T., "Photometry."
11. HYDE, *Trans. I.E.S.*, **2**, 426 (1907); *Bur. Standards Bull.*, **3**, 65 (1907).
12. *Elec. World*, **52**, 625 (1908).
13. WENSEL and coworkers, *Bur. Standards Jour. Research*, **6**, 1103 (1931).
14. WICKENDEN, "Illumination and Photometry," p. 37.
15. IVES, *Phil. Mag.*, **24**, 149, 352, 744, 853 (1912).
    TAYLOR, *Jour. Optical Soc. Am.*, **13**, 193 (1926).
    WALSH, "Photometry," p. 260.
    FERREE and RAND, *Psychol. Rev.*, **22**, 110 (1915).

16. Ives, *Phil. Mag.*, **33**, 360 (1917).
17. Benford, *Gen. Elec. Rev.*, **37**, 342, (1934).
18. Gibson, *Com. Int. Poids et Mesures*, Procès-verbaux des Séances, **14**, 323 (1933).
19. Ives and Kingsbury, *Trans. I.E.S.*, **10**, 203 (1915).
20. Middlekauff and Skogland, *Bur. Standards Bull.*, **12**, 591 (1916).
21. *Bur. Standards Bull.*, **12**, 257 (1915).
22. Teele, *Trans. I.E.S.*, **25**, 78 (1930).
23. Rosa and Taylor, *Trans. I.E.S.*, **11**, 543 (1916).
24. Taylor, *Trans. I.E.S.*, **11**, 466 (1916).
25. Nutting, *Trans. I.E.S.*, **9**, 633 (1914).
26. *Jour. Phys. Radium*, **7**, 632 (1908).
27. *Phys. Rev.*, **6**, 319 (1915).
28. Sharp, *et al.*, *Trans. I.E.S.*, **21**, 117 (1926); *Trans. I.E.S.*, **23**, 428 (1928); Deshler and Schroeder, *Trans. I.E.S.*, **23**, 391 (1928).
29. Forsythe, *Trans. I.E.S.*, **31**, 181 (1936).
30. Bartlett, C. H., *Rev. Sci. Inst.*, **3**, 543 (1932).

CHAPTER XIV

SPECIAL PROBLEMS

Some problems in radiant-energy measurements require very special procedures and often special apparatus. A good method for describing such methods and procedures is to outline some of the problems and describe one or more of the methods that have been used in making the measurements. Some such problems are the study and the use of selective receivers, the evaluation of various sorts of stimuli, color and brightness, the erythemal effect of radiation, the luminosity of radiation, measurements of spectral radiation of heavenly bodies, and the solar constant.

EVALUATION OF DATA OBTAINED WITH NONHOMOGENEOUS RADIATION

B. T. Barnes*

Nonselective Receiver. If one has a source emitting radiation of various wavelengths, the radiant flux density received at a certain point can be ascertained with a single reading, if the measuring instrument is nonselective over a wavelength range which includes all the radiation from the source. Instruments with blackened receivers measuring the heating effect of the radiation, such as thermopiles, bolometers, and vane radiometers, are ordinarily sufficiently nonselective throughout the ultraviolet, visible, and near infrared portions of the spectrum† so that they may be used for measuring the total radiation from suitable sources, or the fraction of this radiation transmitted by, or reflected from, a given object.

Selective Receiver. If the available nonselective receivers are not sufficiently sensitive or are unsuitable for some other reason, a selective receiver such as a photoelectric tube may sometimes yield the desired information. For example, if the

---

* *Physicist, Incandescent Lamp Department, General Electric Company, Cleveland, Ohio.*

† See p. 211.

spectral distribution of the radiation from a source, and the spectral sensitivity of the receiver are both known, the intensity of the total radiation can be obtained in absolute value. With a selective receiver, the transmission of a neutral filter or the reflectivity of a nonselective surface can be measured directly, but the transmission or reflection of selective substances is obtainable only by measuring the spectral distribution of the radiation from the source and the spectral transmission or reflection values over the required wavelength range, and computing the integral transmission or reflection. Thus the fraction of the radiant flux from a given source transmitted by a given substance is

$$\tau = \frac{\int \Phi_\lambda \tau_\lambda d\lambda}{\int \Phi_\lambda d\lambda} \tag{93}$$

where $\Phi_\lambda d\lambda$ is the radiant flux of wavelengths between λ and $\lambda + d\lambda$ received from the source when the filter is not present, and τ_λ is the fraction of the flux of wavelength λ transmitted by the filter.

Evaluating Stimuli.   If one wishes to know the luminous effect of radiation, measurements are often made visually by matching the intensity of the light with that from a calibrated comparison source, by subjective photometry. The intensity of light may also be measured very simply by using a calibrated receiver whose spectral sensitivity is approximately the same as that of the average eye.*   Unless one of these methods is used, the radiation must be separated into its component wavelengths, the intensity for each wavelength measured, and the luminous flux calculated by means of the equation

$$F = C \int_0^\infty \Phi_\lambda K_\lambda d\lambda$$

where F is the luminous flux, $\Phi_\lambda d\lambda$ the radiant flux of wavelengths between λ and $\lambda + d\lambda$, K_λ the relative luminosity, for the average eye, of the radiation of wavelength λ, and C is the constant for converting energy-flux units of the wavelength of maximum visibility to luminous-flux units

(1 watt of radiation of $\lambda5550A = 621$ lumens).

* See Table 33, col. 3, p. 411.

With any other excitation process, a similar procedure is followed in evaluating the effective radiation received direct from the source or through a filter or from a reflector. One needs only put the relative sensitivity S_λ of the receiver which is being excited in place of the relative eye sensitivity K_λ, introduce the proper constant to convert to the stimulus unit which one wishes to use, and integrate over the entire range of effective wavelengths, in order to obtain the intensity of the stimulus for the particular excitation process being considered. This procedure is used in evaluating the effectiveness of a source in producing erythema, in blackening a photographic plate, in producing photoelectrons, and in other excitation processes. However, one must be very careful in applying the results of such a computation if there is not a one-to-one correspondence between energy received and effect produced. For example, if one had a source giving just enough ultraviolet radiation to kill bacteria with a certain fairly long exposure, another source giving one-tenth as much effective radiation might not be one-tenth as effective. In fact, it might have no effect at all, even if the bacteria were exposed to it continuously throughout their lives. In this case, a rating of the two sources on the basis of their effective radiation means simply that if, without changing the spectral distribution of the radiated energy, the intensity from the weak source were increased tenfold or that from the strong source reduced by a factor of 10, they would have the same effect.

Color and Brightness. By mixing red, green, and blue light of suitable character in the correct proportions, white light or light of almost any given color can be produced. This fact is used as the basis of most systems of color specification: colored light is defined by the amounts of each of three primary stimuli which, when mixed, will match it. In the system adopted by the International Commission on Illumination in 1931, the primaries are called the x, y, and z stimuli.* Table 33 gives the relative amounts of these stimuli required to match light of various wavelengths in an equal-energy spectrum (equal amounts of energy flux per unit wavelength interval throughout spectrum).

---

* This has the advantage over the designations "red," "green," and "blue" in that the latter are calculated to suggest physical constituents rather than psychological components.

The $\bar{y}$ coefficients in the table below are the I.C.I. standard luminosity coefficients. This makes it possible to obtain the brightness and color specifications of light by using three sets of

TABLE 33.   RELATIVE AMOUNTS OF PRIMARY STIMULI REQUIRED TO MATCH LIGHT OF WAVELENGTH λ IN AN EQUAL-ENERGY SPECTRUM, FOR 1931 I.C.I. STANDARD OBSERVER

Wave-length, A	Distribution coefficients for equal-energy stimulus			Wave-length, A	Distribution coefficients for equal-energy stimulus		
	$\bar{x}$	$\bar{y}$	$\bar{z}$		$\bar{x}$	$\bar{y}$	$\bar{z}$
3800	0.0014	0.0000	0.0065	5800	0.9163	0.8700	0.0017
3900	0.0042	0.0001	0.0201	5900	1.0263	0.7570	0.0011
4000	0.0143	0.0004	0.0679	6000	1.0622	0.6310	0.0008
4100	0.0435	0.0012	0.2074	6100	1.0026	0.5030	0.0003
4200	0.1344	0.0040	0.6456	6200	0.8544	0.3810	0.0002
4300	0.2839	0.0116	1.3856	6300	0.6424	0.2650	0.0000
4400	0.3483	0.0230	1.7471	6400	0.4479	0.1750	0.0000
4500	0.3362	0.0380	1.7721	6500	0.2835	0.1070	0.0000
4600	0.2908	0.0600	1.6692	6600	0.1649	0.0610	0.0000
4700	0.1954	0.0910	1.2876	6700	0.0874	0.0320	0.0000
4800	0.0956	0.1390	0.8130	6800	0.0468	0.0170	0.0000
4900	0.0320	0.2080	0.4652	6900	0.0227	0.0082	0.0000
5000	0.0049	0.3230	0.2720	7000	0.0114	0.0041	0.0000
5100	0.0093	0.5030	0.1582	7100	0.0058	0.0021	0.0000
5200	0.0633	0.7100	0.0782	7200	0.0029	0.0010	0.0000
5300	0.1655	0.8620	0.0422	7300	0.0014	0.0005	0.0000
5400	0.2904	0.9540	0.0203	7400	0.0007	0.0003	0.0000
5500	0.4334	0.9950	0.0087	7500	0.0003	0.0001	0.0000
5600	0.5945	0.9950	0.0039	7600	0.0002	0.0001	0.0000
5700	0.7621	0.9520	0.0021	7700	0.0001	0.0000	0.0000
5800	0.9163	0.8700	0.0017	7800	0.0000	0.0000	0.0000

coefficients instead of four.   If the radiant flux* $\Phi_\lambda\Delta\lambda$ of wavelength between λ and λ + Δλ is multiplied by $\bar{x}$, $\bar{y}$, and $\bar{z}$, respectively, and each of these products summated over the entire visible spectrum, these sums give the amounts of the primary stimuli required to match the light in question.   The luminous flux is $C\Sigma\bar{y}\Phi_\lambda\Delta\lambda$, the constant C being 621 lumens per watt, if $\Phi_\lambda\Delta\lambda$ is expressed in terms of watts and the result is to be in lumens.   The color† of the light is specified by the numbers

* See p. 4.
† Strictly speaking *chromaticity*.

x, y, and z, defined by the equations

$$x = \frac{\Sigma \bar{x} \Phi_\lambda \Delta \lambda}{\Sigma (\bar{x} + \bar{y} + \bar{z}) \Phi_\lambda \Delta \lambda} \tag{94}$$

etc.   Since $x + y + z = 1$, any two of them determine the third. Colors may conveniently be represented by plotting y against x; Figure 222 gives such a plot[1] for the spectrum (homogeneous radiation), for the daylight and sunlight substitutes specified by the I.C.I. in 1931, for light from tungsten at 2848°K and for

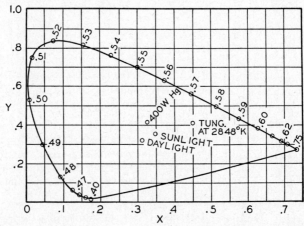

Fig. 222.—Diagram giving x-y coordinates (1931 I.C.I. color-specification system) for I.C.I. sunlight and daylight substitutes, for light from tungsten at a color temperature of 2848°K, and for light from a 400-watt high-intensity mercury lamp. Points for pure spectrum light of various wavelengths (indicated in microns) are shown on curve.

light from a mercury arc operating at about atmospheric pressure. The coordinates for light of every color fall within the region bounded by the spectrum locus and the line joining its ends. Light whose x and y values are within the range 0.33 ± 0.02 may be considered as white. The greater the departure from this range, the greater the degree of coloration. In any one direction from the region of pure whites, all the colors are of the same hue, the change being first to a pale tint, then to a stronger color. If a certain particular white is selected as a reference standard and a straight line drawn on the (x, y) plot (Fig. 222) from the point representing this white to a point representing a spectrum color (homogeneous radiation), then any intermediate color C on this line can be matched by combining the white light with the homogeneous (spectrum) light. The wavelength of the latter is called the dominant wavelength of C; the fraction of the total brightness supplied by the homogeneous radiation, when the latter is mixed with the white light to match C, is called the colorimetric purity of the color C.

The purity p of a color with coordinates x and y is given by the formulas:[1]

$$p = \frac{(y - fy_w)}{y}; \qquad f = \frac{(x - X)}{(x_w - X)} \qquad (95)$$

or

$$f = \frac{(y - Y)}{(y_w - Y)}$$

where x_w, y_w, and X, Y are the respective coordinates of the white light and the homogeneous (spectrum) radiation which can be mixed to match the given color. Two formulas for f are given because the first gives greater accuracy if the line from the point x, y to the white point makes an angle of less than 45 deg. with the x-axis, the second formula being superior if the angle is greater than 45 deg.

Light of nonspectral colors (purples, etc.) has coordinates falling in the region on the (x, y) plot between the whites and the straight line joining the ends of the spectrum locus. By adding homogeneous (spectrum) light of the appropriate color to light of a nonspectral color, any selected white light can be matched. The wavelength of the homogeneous light required for this match is obtained by drawing a straight line from the point representing the nonspectral color through the white point to the spectrum locus. This wavelength is called the dominant wavelength of the nonspectral color, but light of this wavelength is conspicuous by its deficiency. This fact is denoted by assigning to the nonspectral color a negative purity whose magnitude is the ratio of the brightness of the homogeneous light to that of the nonspectral light in the mixture matching the white light.

Erythemal Effectiveness. Sources of ultraviolet radiation are frequently rated in terms of their effectiveness for producing a slight reddening of untanned human skin of average sensitiveness. Figure 223 gives the relative effectiveness of radiation of different wavelengths for producing a "minimum perceptible erythema."[2] For intense reddening, the relative-effectiveness curve is quite different[3]: the radiant flux of wavelengths less than 2900A becomes much less effective than that of greater wavelengths, because the latter penetrates more deeply and hence is able to produce more severe "burns." Thus the curve of Fig. 223 applies only to the average untanned individual exposed just enough that a slight reddening is observable 12 to 24 hr. after the exposure. This requires[4] about 0.05 joule of radiation of λ2967A per cm², or correspondingly greater amounts of radiation of other wavelengths. The required energy is independent of

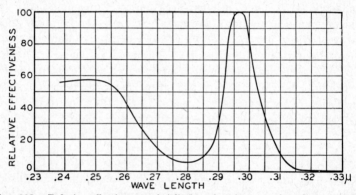

FIG. 223.—Relative effectiveness of radiation of various wavelengths in producing a "minimum perceptible erythema."

the length of exposure, provided the latter does not exceed an hour or two.

The name E-viton has been suggested[5] for a unit of radiant flux weighted according to its effectiveness for producing a "minimum perceptible erythema." The stimulus S in E-vitons is given by

$$S = 0.001 \Sigma S_\lambda \Phi_\lambda \Delta\lambda,$$

where the flux $\Phi_\lambda \Delta\lambda$ is in microwatts, and S_λ is the relative sensitivity of untanned skin as given in Fig. 223 ($S_\lambda = 100$ for λ2967A). For flux density, the name finsen for a viton per square foot was suggested. Exposure per square foot could be expressed in finsen-hours and total exposure in viton-hours.

Transmission vs. Thickness. When monochromatic radiation passes through a uniform material, the fraction absorbed in traversing a given thickness remains constant. With non-homogeneous radiation, the fraction absorbed in a given thickness keeps decreasing as the radiation goes through the material (unless the absorption coefficient is the same for radiation of all wavelengths present). This is due to the change in spectral distribution produced by the absorption. Since the relative magnitude of the change depends on both the original spectral distribution and the spectral transmission of the material being traversed, it is ordinarily not possible to derive a formula expressing the relationship between the fraction of nonhomogeneous radiation of a given spectral distribution transmitted and the thickness of the material traversed. Instead, the radiation must be treated as a mixture of a number of essentially monochromatic components: the transmission is computed for each component and the resultant total transmission obtained by a summation procedure, as indicated on page 409. The transmission τ_λ for radiation of wavelength λ varies with the thickness d of homogeneous material traversed according to the relation

$$\frac{\tau_\lambda}{(1 - r_\lambda)} = e^{-\alpha_\lambda d}$$

where α_λ is the absorption coefficient of the material for radiation of wavelength λ, and r_λ is the fraction reflected for this wavelength. The exponential variation of transmittance with thickness often makes transmission vs. wavelength curves for two markedly different thicknesses entirely unlike each other. For example, if a filter 0.5 mm thick, absorbing 50 per cent of the radiation of a certain wavelength, is replaced by a filter 4 mm thick, only about one-third of one per cent of this radiation is transmitted. If the thin filter transmitted radiation of certain wavelengths without absorption, the thick one will also. In such a case, increasing the thickness narrows the transmission band. Conversely, a transmission band is widened if the thickness is decreased (except in the theoretical case of abrupt transition from maximum to zero transmission). For example, if a corex D bulb 1 mm thick, absorbing 95 per cent of radiation of wavelength 2537A, is blown out into a "bubble" window only 0.1 mm thick, it will absorb only 26 per cent of the radiation of this wavelength. Such a procedure extends the range of effective transmission considerably, if the log transmission-vs.-wavelength curve is not too steep in the region of low transmissions. For example, a transmission of 1×10^{-8} per cent is increased to 10 per cent by reducing the thickness by a factor of 10.

THE LUMINOSITY OF RADIANT ENERGY

W. E. FORSYTHE*

Any photometric measurement depends upon eye observation and, as the eye is a very selective receiver for radiant flux of different wavelengths, a calibration of the eye with respect to its reaction to radiation of different wavelengths is often necessary. The eye responds to a very narrow band of radiant flux, i.e., between about 4000 and 7600A, and in this range the relative sensibility of the eye varies by a factor of about 1,000, being very small at either wavelength limit and reaching a maximum at about the center, i.e., about $\lambda = 5550$A.

Numerous investigations have been made to determine this eye calibration, i.e., the relation between luminous flux and radiant flux in the different parts of the spectrum, called the luminosity of radiant flux. By definition, these three quantities are related as follows:

$$K_\lambda = \frac{F_\lambda}{C\Phi_\lambda} \tag{96}$$

where K_λ = spectral luminosity.
  F_λ = spectral luminous flux.
  Φ_λ = spectral radiant flux.
  C = a constant, 621 lumens per watt.

To obtain the luminosity factor, it is necessary to measure both the luminous flux and the radiant flux. Measurement of the radiant flux is a straightforward measurement and requires, of course, all the care previously outlined for such measurements. In this case, however, extreme care must be exercised to eliminate the stray radiation. This is because the relative sensitivity of the eye varies so much from one part of the spectrum to another that an amount of stray radiation that would be entirely negligible from a radiation-measuring standpoint might introduce a very serious error into the luminosity, since the stray radiation may

* Physicist, Incandescent Lamp Department, General Electric Company, Cleveland, Ohio.

be of such a wavelength as to give more than a thousand times the luminosity of the same amount of radiation at the wavelength considered. The measurement of the luminous flux is probably the more difficult because it contains the human element, *i.e.*, a comparison by means of the human eye. Since the measurements of the relative luminosity can be made directly or indirectly only by some photometric method, any peculiarity of the method is very apt to be intimately connected with the form of the spectral-luminosity curve obtained.

For such photometric measurements, either the equality-of-brightness method (simultaneous comparison) or the flicker method (alternate comparison) are used. The equality-of-brightness method is the older, and for lights of the same quality of color (hue and saturation) it is capable of greater precision than the other. The precision of measurement by the equality-of-brightness method, however, decreases as the difference in the color quality of the two lights increases, and for most inexperienced observers, the attempt to photometer lights of widely different quality—*e.g.*, white with red, green, or blue—is subject to enormous uncertainty if it is not altogether impossible. On the other hand, the precision by the flicker method is but little affected by differences in quality of color, and almost any observer with but little training can make and repeat with good precision such photometric settings with a flicker photometer.

By means of the flicker photometer, several reliable investigations of the luminosity of radiation have been made.[6] Using the flicker photometer the luminosity for different wavelength intervals can be measured in terms of a selected intensity quite readily and with a fair consistency even by inexperienced observers. Ives,[6] who was the first to make an extensive investigation of luminosity by the flicker method, prefaced his measurements by a study of the effect of the field size and brightness upon the results obtained by the two methods. He came to the conclusion that a field size of approximately 2 deg. and a brightness of approximately 2.5 millilamberts were the essential conditions which brought the two methods into agreement. The 2-deg. field recommended by Ives is considerably smaller than the usual Lummer-Brodhun field so widely used. The luminosity obtained under these conditions of field size and brightness can not be employed legitimately in computations based upon photometric data obtained with larger fields and fields of different brightness.

Since it is so difficult to make photometric measurements with a large color difference, the cascade or step-by-step method[7] has been suggested as a method for eliminating the necessity of making such measurements in this kind of work.

The step-by-step method of measuring luminosity is so called from the fact that the luminosity for a particular wavelength is measured in terms of the luminosity at a slightly different wavelength, this latter relative to that at a third wavelength, and so on throughout the spectrum. The size of step between wavelengths is so chosen that little or no hue difference is perceptible between any two wavelengths being compared. With these successive ratios of spectral luminous flux and the corresponding radiant-flux measurements, it is then possible to compute the relative-luminosity curve for the region of the spectrum studied. Reduction of this curve to an equal energy basis gives the spectral-luminosity curve as usual.

This method is related to the method of measuring the lumen output of a high-temperature incandescent lamp in terms of that of a lamp at lower temperature by first reading the output of the high-temperature lamp at such a voltage that its light output differs but a small amount in color from the standard, and the light output at a higher voltage in terms of that at the first voltage, and so on, making as many steps as may seem necessary to make the large color step. While this method does not eliminate errors in photometry due to color differences, it makes it possible for the untrained observer to make a photometric determination with a color difference that many think impossible to make by direct comparison. If the same size of field and the same field brightness are used with this method and with the flicker method, the results should agree, according to the findings of Ives.[6]

At first it might seem that the step-by-step method of determining the eye calibration would require a prohibitive number of photometric settings, but it is possible to take readings at a comparatively few wavelengths, plot a curve, and obtain the values of the ratios of luminosity from this curve.

In a determination of the luminosity function[8] made at the National Bureau of Standards in 1923, the step-by-step method was used with approximately the field and brightness conditions suggested by Ives.[6]   Great care was taken to avoid such errors as it was possible to foresee, and corrections were made for unavoidable errors.   The step, *i.e.*, the wavelength difference between the compared radiation, was selected to give as small a color difference as possible and still not make it necessary to take too many readings.   The apparatus was kept set up at the Bureau for some time and the luminosity factors measured for many experienced observers as they happened to come to Washington.   In all, the spectral-luminosity curve of 52 observers was determined and these 52 should be given more weight than is usual since many of them were selected because of their experience in this kind of work.   The results obtained were in close agreement with the flicker-photometer data obtained by Ives[6] and by Coblentz[6] and others, and seemed so satisfactory that results based upon them have been adopted as the standard luminosity curve by the I.E.S.[9] in this country and by the I.C.I.[10] as the international luminosity curve.   The final result of the average luminosity curve is given in column 3 of Table 33, page 411.

SPECTRAL-ENERGY MEASUREMENTS OF HEAVENLY BODIES

C. G. Abbot*

Knowledge, independent or confirmatory, regarding the physics of the heavenly bodies involves determinations of their spectral intensities.   Unfortunately only one of them, the sun, is intense enough and near enough to make it easy to conduct the necessary measurements with considerable detail.   Hence spectroradiometric devices, though generally associated with powerful telescopes, fall far short of giving the information which is desired.   Measurements must be conducted beneath the atmosphere which is a turbid selectively absorbing screen, subject to large and rapid fluctuations of transparency and of optical homogeneity.

Many important celestial light sources are so faint that only rough separations of their radiation into several wide spectral ranges are practicable.   Such imperfect discriminations are often accomplished by the insertion of absorbing screens.   These

* *Secretary, Smithsonian Institution.*

devices, though intensity-saving, are disappointingly indefinite discriminators in many instances. The spectroscope, whether prismatic or, what is still more prodigal, the diffraction grating instrument, depletes the intensity enormously, and besides is unequally depleting for different wavelengths. The Christiansen filter* seems to offer several advantages for this class of investigation.

The preceding summary indicates some of the difficulties which attend spectral radiometry of the celestial bodies. As a supplementary indication of one phase of these difficulties, one may recall that none of the brightest stars send to the earth more than 1×10^{-10} as much radiation as the sun.[11]

Methods of Solar Spectral Radiometry. With abundant intensity available, it is not necessary to concentrate the solar beam with a telescope unless the study of the rays from detailed localities on the solar surface is desired. Accordingly for many purposes a coelostat for reflecting the solar beam to the spectro-radiometer is sufficient. As the beam is of practically unlimited cross section, one may use a tall slit and prism or grating, concentrating the rays to slightly more or slightly less than the height of the linear receiver by means of a concave mirror or cylindric lens. The bolometer, with its natural linear form, has been most used in solar-energy measurements. Diagrams and descriptions of the spectrobolometric apparatus used for solar research and the means used to determine its selective transmission are given in the *Annals of the Smithsonian Astrophysical Observatory.*[12]

In the study of the distribution of solar radiation of specific wavelengths along the diameter of the solar disk, a long-focus tower telescope was substituted for the coelostat to feed the spectrobolometer. The solar image being allowed to drift by the earth's diurnal motion across the slit of the spectrobolometer, every part of the solar image observed experienced in the telescope exactly the same treatment as every other.[13]

Methods of Stellar Spectral Radiometry. The stars are all so faint that only since the 100-in. telescope of Mount Wilson Observatory has been available could there be a promising study of stellar spectra by radiometric methods. Hence until recently the attempts to determine stellar spectral-energy distribution were made through visual and photographic spectral photometry.

* See p. 104.

Energy spectra of the sun and nine bright stars were observed in 1923 with the spectroradiometer employing star images of 250-ft. focus from the 100-in. reflector of Mount Wilson and using as a measuring device a radiometer with the two vanes, 1.5 by 0.5 mm, separated by 2.5 mm, provided by the late Dr. Nichols and his colleague, Dr. Tear.   The observations extended between

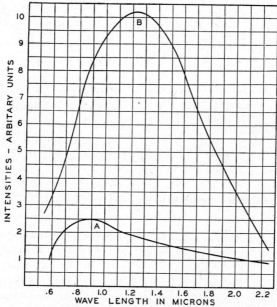

Fig. 224.—Spectral distribution of the radiant energy of two stars outside the atmosphere. $A = \alpha$ Orionis, $B = \beta$ Pegasi.

wavelengths 0.437 and 2.224μ.   This work was extended[11] in 1928 with better apparatus to 18 stars (Fig. 224).   It was possible to eliminate atmospheric and optical selective depletions by using the known solar spectrum as a comparison type.

Radiometric Stellar Observations with Absorption Cells. Extensive investigations of total radiation, and of radiation transmitted by water cells, and by similar devices for cutting off certain parts of the spectrum, have been made by Coblentz[15] and by Pettit and Nicholson,[16] using thermopiles of very sensitive construction.[17]   These investigations have dealt with stars to about the tenth magnitude, and with detailed examinations of the radiation of the moon and the planets.

The thermopiles recently employed by Pettit and Nicholson have junctions of pure bismuth with the alloy of bismuth with 5 per cent tin. Exceedingly fine wires are drawn out in glass tubes, the glass being dissolved off with hydrofluoric acid.[18] Enlarged areas for receiving star images may be made either by flattening tiny globules of solder between glass plates, or by attaching copper receivers with solder or white lead. The receivers are blackened with a suspension of lampblack and platinum black in alcohol and turpentine. The authors state that in one of their receivers the mass to be heated by the star is 0.035 mg. They compute that 1 mm deflection of their galvanometer indicates a rise of temperature of 33×10^{-6}°C. Betelgeuse (α Orionis) gives 500 mm deflection for total radiation as collected in the 40-ft. focus of the 100-in. reflector on Mount Wilson. They are accustomed to record the deflections of their moving-coil galvanometer by photography, and so quiet is the trace that deflections of 0.1 mm are readable.

Stellar Investigations with the Photoelectric Tube. As stellar photometers, photoelectric tubes lend themselves to more accurate measurements than photographic or visual photometry can readily supply, the simplicity and tirelessness of their electrical records being much in their favor. They are especially useful for the study of the curves of variation of intensity of the several types of variable stars.

The photoelectric tube, owing to the large area of its receiving surface, is used with out-of-focus star images. Bad "seeing," therefore, does not produce bad observations. Stebbins states that with his best tubes the limit of observable deflections corresponds to a current of about 10^{-15} amp. The probable error of one normal magnitude he states as about 0.0036 magnitude. Employed with the 40-in. refractor of the Yerkes Observatory, the limit of faintness of stars ordinarily observed is about the ninth magnitude. In use with yellow- and blue-color filters of selected transmitting qualities, a program is being carried out at the Yerkes Observatory to determine the color indices of B-type stars. The color index being the difference between the visual and the photographic apparent magnitude of a star gives a clue to the distribution of light in its spectrum. This is cited merely as one example of the various applications of photoelectric stellar photometry.

MEASUREMENT OF THE SOLAR CONSTANT

L. B. ALDRICH*

Solar-constant measurements have been in progress at selected high-altitude stations of the Smithsonian Institution for over 30 years. These stations are chosen as the best available to fulfill the following requirements: (1) a minimum of atmospheric water vapor, dust and other impurities, (2) uniformity of sky conditions, (3) a minimum of wind, and (4) a maximum of days clear enough for observations.

The solar constant is defined as the intensity of the total solar radiation in free space at the earth's mean distance from the sun. It is usually expressed in calories per square centimeter of surface normal to the radiation, per minute of time. The solar constant is not constant[19] but varies irregularly through a range of nearly 3 per cent. The mean value is about 1.94 cal./(cm^2 min.) for the mean earth distance. Because measurements must unavoidably be made near the bottom of the atmosphere, the determination of the solar constant divides into two parts: (1) the exact measurement of the intensity of solar radiation received at the observing station, and (2) the exact estimation of the loss which the radiation suffers in traversing the atmosphere. The first part requires an accurate pyrheliometer. The second part involves exact measurements of atmospheric transmission coefficients in the solar-spectrum range. In addition this includes estimates of the relative transmissibility of the spectral radiation in the optical apparatus, and of the atmospheric transmission of those feeble parts of the solar spectrum lying in the ultraviolet and the infrared beyond the limits of the spectral region usually observed.

The types of pyrheliometer used by the Smithsonian Institution in solar-constant work are the Abbot silver-disk pyrheliometer[20] and a modified form of the Ångström[21] electrically compensated pyrheliometer. The silver-disk instrument is simple, rugged, requires no accessories and is capable of maintaining a constant scale of readings for many years. The Ångström apparatus is also very satisfactory, though it requires a galvanometer and other electrical accessories. It has the advantage of

* *Assistant Director of Astrophysical Observatory, Smithsonian Institution.*

yielding a complete reading in less time than the silver disk. For the determination of the standard pyrheliometric scale, upon which the scale of all secondary instruments such as the silver disk is based, the Smithsonian Institution has developed the improved water-flow blackbody pyrheliometer.[22] The Abbot water-flow pyrheliometer is essentially a hollow blackbody absorber whose walls are continuously bathed in flowing water. Measurement of the rate of water flow, the rise of temperature of the water, and the area of the aperture receiving radiation yields a value of the total radiation in absolute units. Known quantities of heat electrically produced within the hollow chamber are found to be exactly measured by the instrument. The present modified form of the Abbot water-flow pyrheliometer retains the blackbody absorber but, in accordance with the suggestion of V. M. Shulgin, a second identical hollow chamber is placed beside it. The inflowing water divides as it enters, an equal quantity bathing the walls of each hollow chamber. This device entirely eliminates the former troublesome drift. Observations with this improved water-flow instrument are highly satisfactory. We are confident that the results have established the correct scale of pyrheliometry within 1 part in 400. Seventy copies of the silver-disk pyrheliometer have been standardized against the water-flow pyrheliometer at the Smithsonian Institution and furnished at cost to solar-radiation observers in all parts of the world.

The fundamental solar-constant method, worked out by Langley and known as the "long method," involves a series of determinations of the intensity of all parts of the solar spectrum on a day of unchanging clearness, so as to disclose the increase of intensity of spectral radiation which occurs as the sun mounts higher and higher. Langley[23] showed that for a ray of homogeneous wavelength, the intensity is connected with the length of path in the atmosphere by the exponential formula of Bouguer-Lambert:

$$\log J = m \log a + \log J_0 \qquad (97)$$

where J = observed intensity.

$\quad\quad J_0$ = intensity outside the atmosphere.

$\quad\quad a$ = fraction transmitted with vertical sun (the transmission coefficient).

m = air mass or the ratio of the length of path of the radiation in the atmosphere to that obtaining with vertical sun.

The logarithmic form of this equation is that of a straight line. The equation holds strictly only for radiation of homogeneous wavelength. The observations necessary for obtaining the corrections which are applied, as well as errors, uncertainties and limitations of this method are described and discussed in the *Annals of the Astrophysical Observatory*.[24] At increasing altitudes of the sun a series of bolographs, *i.e.*, photographic records of intensity of solar radiation are made with the spectrobolometer. Each bolograph requires 7 min. and yields a record of intensities in the spectral range 0.34 to 2.5μ. From these bolographs at each of 40 selected wavelengths, air masses are plotted against log J and the best straight line drawn to fit the points for each wavelength. The slope of each of these lines is the coefficient of transmission for the given wavelength, and the extrapolation of the line to zero air mass gives the intensity outside the atmosphere for the same wavelength. A summation of the intensities outside the atmosphere, divided by a summation of the intensities at the earth's surface gives a ratio indicating approximately the relative total intensity of the beam outside and inside the earth's atmosphere. Simultaneous observations with a pyrheliometer give the total intensity of the beam inside the atmosphere in absolute units. The pyrheliometer reading multiplied by the above ratio of the total intensity outside and inside the atmosphere gives the solar constant.

Satisfactory observations by the long method of Langley require a uniform atmosphere continuing over a period of several hours. In order to utilize many days when the sky though apparently clear is not uniform, a new and much shorter method was devised. It is based upon the data obtained from a long series of long-method days upon which observations were also made of the brightness of the sky in a limited zone around the sun at certain standard air masses. This brightness is measured by an instrument called the pyranometer, developed by Abbot.[25] From these data the observed atmospheric-transmission coefficients are expressed empirically at 40 wavelengths as functions of the brightness of the sky and of the water-vapor content of the atmosphere as determined spectroscopically. When once the empirical tables for this short method have been prepared for a given station, the observations for a complete solar-constant determination can be made in a few minutes' time. Five independent values can be determined in the time occupied for the observations of a single long method.

References

1. D. B. Judd, *Jour. Optical Soc. Am.*, **23**, 359 (1933); this article gives a table of x, y, z values for spectrum colors, an extensive treatment of the 1931 I.C.I. color specifications, and a brief discussion of color specification in terms of dominant wavelength and colorimetric purity.
2. W. W. Coblentz and R. Stair, *Bur. Standards Jour. Res.*, **12**, 13 (1934).
3. E. Q. Adams, B. T. Barnes, and W. E. Forsythe, *Jour. Optical Soc. Am.*, **21**, 207 (1931).
4. W. W. Coblentz, R. Stair, and J. M. Hogue, *Proc. Nat. Acad. Sci.*, **17**, 401 (1931).
5. M. Luckiesh and L. L. Holladay, *Jour. Optical Soc. Am.*, **21**, 420 (1931).
6. Ives, *Phil. Mag.*, **24**, 149, 853 (1912).
   Coblentz and Emerson, *Bull. Bur. Standards*, **14**, 167 (1917).
   Nutting, *Trans. I.E.S.*, **9**, 633 (1914).
   Reeves, *Trans. I.E.S.*, **13**, 101 (1918).
   So, *Proc. Phys. Math. Soc. Japan*, **2**, 177 (1920).
7. Ives, *Phil. Mag.*, **24**, 1853 (1912).
8. Gibson and Tyndall, *Bur. Standards Sci. Paper*, **19**, 131 (1923).
9. *Trans. I.E.S.*, **28**, 263 (1933).
10. Report I.C.I. Congress, 1924.
11. *Cont. Mt. Wilson Obs.*, **280**, 19 (1924).
12. *Ann. Smithsonian Astrophys. Obs.*, **2**, 23 and Plate VI; **3**, Plate III; **5**, 75, Fig. 9; **5**, 96, Plates VIII–XI.
13. *Ann. Smithsonian Astrophys. Obs.*, **6**, Figs. 22–24 and p. 217; *Smithsonian Misc. Coll.*, **78**, No. 5 (1926).
14. *Astrophys. Jour.*, **69**, 301 (1929).
15. *Astrophys. Jour.*, **63**, 177 (1926).
16. *Astrophys. Jour.*, **71**, 102 (1930).
17. *Astrophys. Jour.*, **68**, 279 (1928); also *Bur. Standards Paper*, Nos. 244, 438, 460.
18. Taylor, *Phys. Rev.*, **23**, 655 (1924).
19. *Smithsonian Misc. Coll.*, **94**, 10 (1935).
    Ann. Astrophys. Obs., **5**, 247 (1932).
20. *Smithsonian Misc. Coll.*, **56**, 19 (1922).
21. *Ann. Physik. Chem.*, **67**, 633 (1899).
22. *Smithsonian Misc. Coll.*, **87**, 15, (1932); 92, No. 13 (1934).
23. *Ann. Astrophys. Obs.*, **2**, 13–17 (1908).
24. *Ann. Astrophys. Obs.*, **2**, 21 (1908).
25. *Smithsonian Misc. Coll.*, **66**, 7, 11 (1916).

INDEX

Date L